Pesticide Chemistry in the 20th Century

Jack R. Plimmer, EDITOR
United States Department of Agriculture

ASSOCIATE EDITORS
Philip C. Kearney
Gustave K. Kohn
Julius J. Menn
Stanley Ries

A symposium sponsored by the

Division of Pesticide Chemistry

at the 171st Meeting of the

American Chemical Society,

New York, N.Y.,

April 6–8, 1976.

ACS SYMPOSIUM SERIES **37**

AMERICAN CHEMICAL SOCIETY

WASHINGTON, D. C.   1977

Library of Congress CIP Data

Pesticide chemistry in the 20th century.
(ACS symposium series; 37 ISSN 0097-6156)

   Includes bibliographical references and index.

   1. Pesticides—Congresses. 2. Agricultural chemistry—
Congresses. 3. Insect hormones—Congresses. 4. Plant
regulators—Congresses.
   I. Plimmer, Jack R., 1927–   II. American Chemi-
cal Society. Division of Pesticide Chemistry. III. Series:
American Chemical Society. ACS symposium series; 37.

SB951.P393   632'.95   76-51748
ISBN 0-8412-0364-4   ACSMC 8 37 1–310

PRINTED IN THE UNITED STATES OF AMERICA

ACS Symposium Series

Robert F. Gould, *Editor*

FOREWORD

The ACS SYMPOSIUM SERIES was founded in 1974 to provide a medium for publishing symposia quickly in book form. The format of the SERIES parallels that of the continuing ADVANCES IN CHEMISTRY SERIES except that in order to save time the papers are not typeset but are reproduced as they are submitted by the authors in camera-ready form. As a further means of saving time, the papers are not edited or reviewed except by the symposium chairman, who becomes editor of the book. Papers published in the ACS SYMPOSIUM SERIES are original contributions not published elsewhere in whole or major part and include reports of research as well as reviews since symposia may embrace both types of presentation.

CONTENTS

PREFACE

The papers in this volume were presented at the Centennial Meeting of the American Chemical Society held in New York in April 1976. They were delivered at the Symposium "Pesticide Chemistry in the Twentieth Century," sponsored by the Division of Pesticide Chemistry. Although the division was not formed until 1969, pesticide chemistry had previously been an enthusiastically supported activity within the Division of Agriculture and Food Chemistry. The symposium title was chosen to provide some discussion of the development of pesticide chemistry, and also because the growth in use of synthetic organic pesticides is a peculiarly twentieth century phenomenon. Thus, three quarters of the way through the present century seemed an opportune time to record something of the past and to speculate as to the future role and direction of pesticide chemistry. Many of those associated with the early growth and development of synthetic organic pesticides are still active and continue to influence their development. The centennial meeting provided the appropriate occasion for authoritative overview and personal expression of scientific philosophy.

Side by side with this growth of knowledge there has been increasing concern that the implications of the large-scale utilization of synthetic chemicals be fully understood. Chemical methods of pest control have conferred such spectacular benefits on agriculture and the health of mankind that it has become difficult to conceive that these benefits could be offset or outweighed by serious disadvantages. Some of these effects are extremely subtle; others, such as the development of pesticide resistance, rapidly become obvious because no further economic benefit is obtained by continued pesticide use.

The extensive use of pesticides has grown out of the experimental and intellectual achievements of nineteenth century organic chemistry. Naturally occurring organic compounds such as nicotine have long been known to possess insecticidal activity, but the large-scale use of synthetic organic compounds for pest control is a twentieth century phenomenon. During the last 25 years we have experienced a phenomenal expansion in the production and use of synthetic organic pesticides, especially by the developed nations of the world. We have also learned to assess the relative risks and benefits that accompany their use. Scientifically, we have learned a great deal; the investigation of the metabolism of pesticides, their modes of action, chemical reactions, analysis, and many similar studies have been productive of excellent research whose relevance extends far beyond its immediate application to pest control. We now look back to pesticide chemistry of the 1940s and 50s as though we were looking back to the days of the covered wagon. Until the end of those decades, gas chromatography was little used, and methods of residue analysis were often difficult and tedious. With the application of gas chromatography has come the potential for rapid and economical measurement of low-level pesticide residues. Our current knowledge of environmental pesticide levels is based on this technique, and it has provided a guide for the investigation of many other environmental contaminants.

Although we have recognized many of the major problems that have been associated with pesticide chemicals in the past, there is the chance that their shadow may extend well into future decades. Science faces the challenge of establishing the effects of pesticides on many different organisms, the nature and extent of pesticide transformations in the environment, and the environmental fate of xenobiotics. The cost of this research may hinder the development of new compounds very different in chemistry or mode of action from those currently on the market, but we recognize its necessity. We are passing through what may be a critical phase in the use and production of chemicals for pest control, and to remedy this problem we must devise and improve techniques by which the toxicology and environmental fate of new chemicals and products can be evaluated rapidly and economically. An additional challenge is to look beyond our present use of pesticide chemicals and discover new modes of action or new ways of employing chemicals to minimize their effects on the environment and on nontarget species.

Since the discovery of hexachlorobenzene by Faraday, more than 150 years have elapsed. The recognition of the insecticidal activity of the organochlorine compounds and the pursuit of new active structures represents one of the triumphs of synthetic organic chemistry. However, the rapid decline in usage of organochlorine insecticides may not be ascribed solely to the recognition of risks associated with their use, but also to the increasing resistance of insect species to these and, indeed, to many other insecticides. These topics are discussed in the opening chapters of this volume and provide a revealing perspective in which developments in the struggle against pests must be viewed.

In this volume discussions of some major groups of pest control chemicals have been included, as well as some closely related topics such as insect and plant growth regulators. The authors are distinguished by their contributions to research and, as the organizer of the symposum, I would like to thank them for their participation; I would also like to thank my associates in this review who have prefaced each section by a brief introduction. The selection of topics may appear capricious, but in such a broad field there is no attempt to claim that such a symposium can present anything other than a few of the highlights.

I would like to acknowledge assistance and cooperation of my colleagues in this enterprise: P. C. Kearney, G. K. Kohn, J. J. Menn, R. D. O'Brien, and S. K. Ries. My grateful thanks is also due to May Inscoe for her assistance in editing and preparing this volume.

U.S. Department of Agriculture   JACK R. PLIMMER
November 1976

Chlorinated Insecticides: Retrospect and Prospect

G. T. BROOKS

Agricultural Research Council, Unit of Invertebrate Chemistry and Physiology, University of Sussex, Brighton, BN1 9QJ, England

The story of the discovery of the chlorinated hydrocarbon derived insecticides is one of outstanding achievement which deserves due recognition. Indeed, the discovery within so few years of DDT, γ-HCH (γ-BHC), the cyclodiene group and toxaphene, chlorinated insecticide types with distinct origins and synthetic principles, is truly remarkable.

The continuing value of DDT and some other chlorinated compounds in Third World crop protection and human health programmes is widely recognised, whilst at the research level, chlorinated insecticides have already helped to elucidate the basic processes of insecticide metabolism which are a critical feature of insecticidal action. Many questions remain outstanding in regard to the mode of interaction of these compounds with insect nerve and its resistance to them; the answers to some of these questions may arise at any time as our knowledge progresses and may contribute to a better understanding of nerve function.

For this Symposium on Pesticide Chemistry in the 20th Century, in the American Bicentennial year, it seemed appropriate to view this immense subject in a historical context, leading up to the present day situation.

Benzene Hexachloride

In one sense, the story of the chlorinated insecticides begins in 1774, since in that year the Swedish apothecary Karl Wilhelm Scheele discovered chlorine. Michael Faraday, who was born in 1791, first assisted Sir Humphry Davy and later succeeded him as Professor of Chemistry at the Royal Institution in London. In the Philosophical Transactions of 1825 Faraday reported that benzene reacted with chlorine in sunlight to give a "solid body" and dense, viscous fluid, which was undoubtedly the first sample of technical BHC. During the next 87 years several investigations established its constitution to be $C_6H_6Cl_6$ and showed that it contained α- and β-isomers and afforded trichlorobenzenes when treated with alkali. In 1912, the Belgian chemist Van der Linden

discovered the δ- and γ- isomers. The latter comprises only 10-
15% of the technical material and has come to be known as lindane,
after its discoverer.

Since Zeidler had synthesised DDT in a purely chemical context in 1874, it is evident that during much of the explosive
European industrial development of the 19th Century, with its
attendant disease toll and demand for increased food production,
two of the most remarkable pest control agents of all time were
already sitting on laboratory shelves!

One hundred and seven years after Faraday's first reported
preparation of BHC, Harry Bender of the Great Western Electro-
Chemical Company in California, was looking for new uses of
chlorine. He added benzene to liquid chlorine in a Dewar flask in
the open air and noticed that part of the product which spilled on
the ground 'attracted and killed flies and bees'. Thus, although
compounds such as p-dichlorobenzene had been used as fumigants
since World War I and BHC is said to have been used in smoke
screens during that war, Bender's observation made in 1932-3 and
referred to only fleetingly in the literature (1), was the first
indication that technical BHC had unusual insecticidal properties.

Unfortunately, the discovery was lost because samples sent to
Berkeley were recrystallised there before being tested; the γ-
isomer was rejected with the mother liquors and no activity was
found. The subsequent development of BHC was bedevilled by this
association of high activity only with the will-o'-the-wisp γ-
isomer and it is evident that only samples containing mainly the
less soluble α- and β- isomers, contaminated with small and
variable amounts of lindane, were tested between 1933 and 1942.

In the early 1930s technical BHC was made at the Alkali
Division of Imperial Chemical Industries in Widnes, as a precursor of trichlorobenzenes useful as non-flammable dielectrics.
Samples of white, crystalline BHC were screened routinely at
ICI's Jealott's Hill laboratory and according to an account by
Dr. C. C. Tanner (2), were found 'not to be strikingly ovicidal or
aphicidal'. Another report (3) suggests that in 1937 the samples
were found to be 'quite active' but the observation was neither
followed up or published.

When ICI's search for Derris substitutes began in 1942, the
samples of BHC were again added to the screening list because
fairly large amounts were available in store from the dielectric
days. They soon proved to be the only materials with worthwhile
activity against turnip flea beetle. Finally, in the summer of
1942, the pure α- and β-isomers, the only compounds believed at
that time to be present in the crude, crystalline BHC, were
individually tested and shown to be inactive. The search for the
active component then began in earnest and this was shown to be
the γ-isomer by Burrage, early in 1943 (4). In France, Dupire
noted the insecticidal activity of technical BHC to clothes moths
in 1940-41 and the material was subsequently evaluated against
agricultural insect pests (5).

DDT

In complete contrast to the chance discovery of lindane, Müller's discovery of the insecticidal activity of DDT in 1939 was the culmination of a more or less rational application of experience and intuition in the development and improvement of existing moth-proofing agents based on chlorinated benzenes.

In effect, DDT evolved from water soluble moth-proofing agents via the benzene soluble moth-proofing agent Eulan BL of I. G. Farbenindustrie (Figure 1) and the sulfone (B, Figure 1) by an application of the now classical notion that toxicant molecules consist of 'toxophores' that are carried to the site of action by appropriate lipophilic structures or functional groups. Eulan BL combines 3,4-dichlorobenzene, a lipophilic respiratory and contact poison, with the more polar sulfonamide moiety. The sulfone (B, Figure 1) is a powerful stomach poison whereas its methane-derived analogue (C), lacking the electronegative - SO_2-group, has neither good stomach poison nor good contact activity. Hence, the idea arose that for contact activity the moiety separating the benzene nuclei had to contain a strongly electronegative, yet preferably lipophilic group and the trichloromethane group of chloroform, a highly lipophilic inhalation narcotic then became an obvious candidate. Thus, the DDT molecule must represent one of the most remarkably successful examples of all time of the fabrication of a new bioactive molecule from simpler structures which have their own apparently distinct biological effects.

ICI Scientists working on lindane received the news of the new Swiss insecticide, but not its structure, around Christmas time in 1943. So similar were the reported insecticidal properties of DDT to those of lindane that there was speculation as to whether the two compounds were variants of the same chemical.

Cyclodiene Insecticides

The double event described above seems remarkable enough, but the discovery of the cyclodienes and toxaphene, two further types of broad spectrum chlorinated insecticides with distinct origins, was already imminent.

The 'indene-derived' group. At the Velsicol Chemical Corporation in Chicago in 1943, Dr. Julius Hyman was seeking new uses for the cyclopentadiene which was a by-product of U.S. synthetic rubber production and was already used by Velsicol for the manufacture of resins and varnishes by the Diels-Alder reaction (6). A literature search revealed Straus's 1930 synthesis of hexachlorocyclopentadiene ('hex') and, since chlorinated dienes are frequently rather inert, Hyman was interested to determine if 'hex' would participate in the Diels-Alder reaction, either with itself or with cyclopentadiene.

Surprisingly, 'hex' readily gave mono- and bis-adducts with

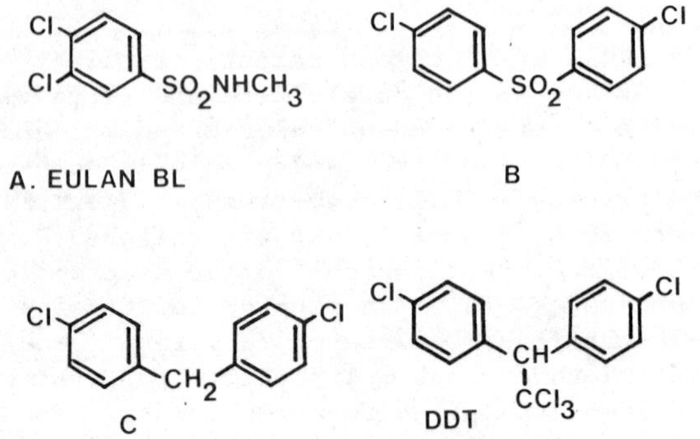

A. EULAN BL   B

C   DDT

Figure 1.   DDT and some structural forerunners mentioned in the text

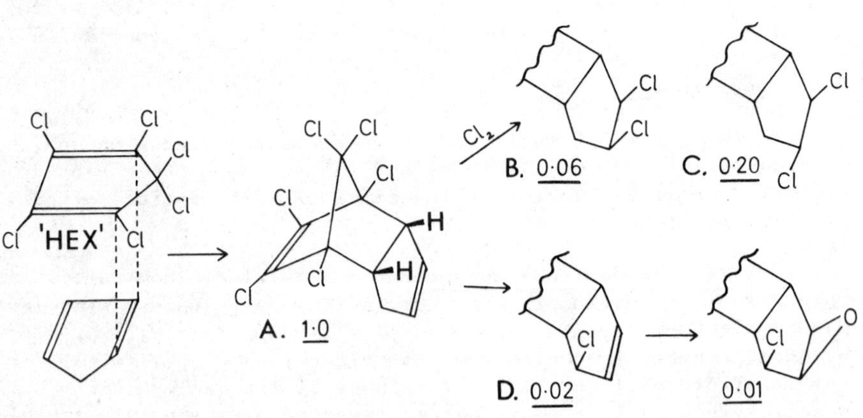

Figure 2.   Synthesis of Chlordene (A), the chlordane isomers (B and C), heptachlor (D),
and heptachlor epoxide (8). Toxicities to houseflies in μg/female (55) are underlined.

cyclopentadiene, and these were quickly tested for insecticidal activity by Professor C. W. Kearns at the University of Illinois - on the ground that every new chlorinated hydrocarbon might be a potential DDT (7). Great excitement attended the finding that the mono-adduct (chlordene) was about one fourth as toxic as DDT, which was newly appearing in the U.S. Chlordene (A, Figure 2) could be made more cheaply than DDT but was unfortunately too volatile to compete with it as a persistent residual insecticide. This problem was overcome by chlorinating the reactive double bond to give chlordane (8) which also was more volatile than DDT but now sufficiently persistent for practical purposes and several times more toxic than DDT to a number of insects (housefly LD50s in μg/female underlined in Figure 2). Chlordane contains 40% or more of the cis and trans- products of double bond chlorination (B and C, Figure 2), about 10% of heptachlor (D), and various other compounds (9). It has found many applications in both public health programmes and agriculture.

R. Riemschneider of the Free University of Berlin was undoubtedly examining the reactions of 'hex' in 1945-46 and published on the insecticidal action of chlordane early in 1947 (10). This is interesting in view of the communication difficulties of the time and may be one example of the frequently observed spontaneous appearance of similar scientific discoveries at nearly the same time in different parts of the world.

The 'naphthalene-derived' group. Sometimes thus called because of their structural origins, the nevertheless non-aromatic compounds, aldrin, dieldrin, isodrin and endrin arose from Hyman's discovery that cyclopentadiene reacts with acetylene to give bicyclo[2.2.1] hepta-2,5-diene (norbornadiene; A, Figure 3) as a stable product previously supposed incapable of existence. It was then logical to test its reaction as a dienophile with 'hex'. This Diels-Alder reaction occurs readily and led to the first preparation of aldrin early in 1948 (HHDN; D, Figure 3). Attempts to reduce the volatility of aldrin without eliminating its insecticidal properties soon led to the discovery of the corresponding epoxide, dieldrin (HEOD; E, Figure 3), by Soloway (6, 11). In Figure 3, housefly LD50s in μg/female are underlined.

If the dienophile (norbornadiene) is chlorinated instead, either via the reaction of 'hex' with vinyl chloride followed by dehydrochlorination, or directly with acetylene, to give 1,2,3,4, 7,7-hexachlorobicyclo[2.2.1] hepta-2,5-diene (hexachloronorbornadiene; B, Figure 3), this compound reacts with cyclopentadiene to give isodrin (C; precursor of the epoxide, endrin) having the opposite (endo-,endo-) stereochemistry to aldrin (and dieldrin), respectively (12). Isodrin has not found commercial use but endrin has been widely used in tropical and sub-tropical agriculture - to control cotton pests, for example.

The 'indene' and 'naphthalene' derived compounds may be

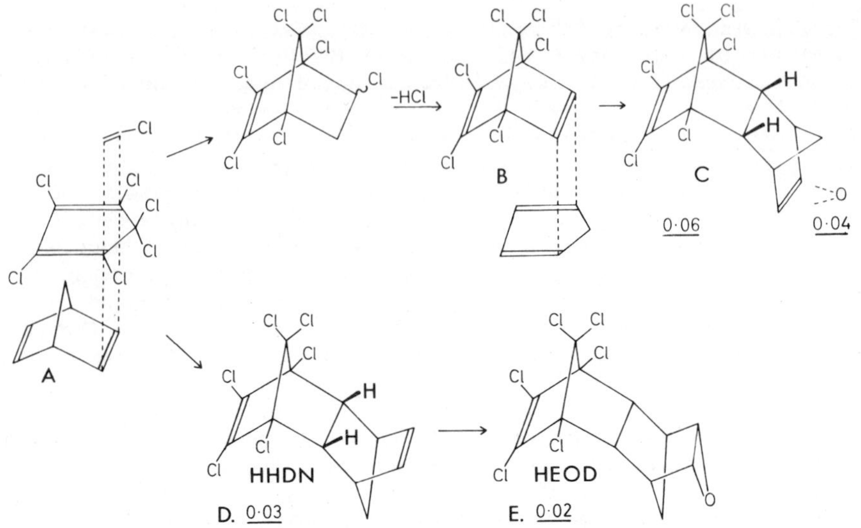

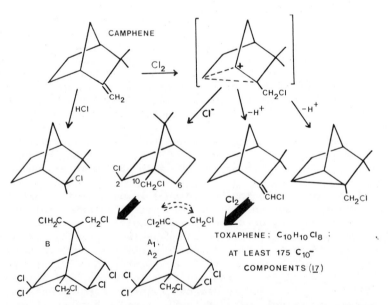

Figure 3. Synthesis of isodrin (C), aldrin (D), and dieldrin (E) (11, 12). Housefly toxicities in μg/female (55) are underlined.

Figure 4. Products (middle row) of camphene chlorination in the dark (15, 16) and toxic compounds (bottom row) recently isolated from toxaphene (17, 18)

regarded as the core discoveries of the cyclodiene series, although another important and widely used cyclodiene, endosulfan, was discovered by Dr. Heinz Frensch and his collaborators at Farbwerke-Hoechst in the mid 1950s (13). Endosulfan is a hydrolysable cyclic sulfite ester derived indifectly from 'hex' and is environmentally much less persistent than most other cyclodienes. Another cyclodiene, isobenzan, had too great a mammalian toxicity to achieve practical use. An obvious point of contrast with the DDT or lindane stories is the number of highly effective insecticides derived from 'hex' that have actually achieved commercial use.

Toxaphene

The dark chlorination of camphene was first reported in 1919 by Langlois, who assigned correct structures to two of the products. In 1944, the Russians Khanenia and Zhuravlev, seeking chemicals to control body-lice, noted that the mild toxicity of terpenes contained in turpentine was greatly enhanced by chlorination. Also, about this time Dr. G. A. Buntin of the Hercules Research Center laboratories in Wilmington was aware of the existence of DDT and was conducting a synthetic programme directed toward household insect control. The first sample of toxaphene was prepared at Hercules and found to be toxic to houseflies in March 1944. Later that year, tests by the USDA showed toxaphene to be toxic to a wide range of cotton insects and pilot scale preparation began at Wilmington in September 1945 (14).

Two independent reports in 1965 (15, 16) established the major products of dark reaction (middle row, Figure 4) first investigated by Langlois, but toxaphene itself is a much more complex product resulting from photochemical chlorination of camphene to a chlorine content of 67-69%, corresponding to an average formula $C_{10}H_{10}Cl_8$. According to recent reports (17, 18), toxaphene contains at least 175 C_{10}-chlorinated hydrocarbons. A recently isolated Cl_7 compound (B, Figure 4) and a mixture of isomeric Cl_8 compounds (A_1 and A_2) comprise 2 and 6% respectively, of this mixture (17). These two isolates are present in relatively large amounts compared with many other components and are considered to contribute significantly to the mammalian toxicity of the commercial product. Although these two isolates are more toxic than the technical mixture (respectively, 6x and 14x more toxic to mice and 2x and 4x more toxic to houseflies), they are likely to be biodegradable, so that a study of their structures in relation to those of other chlorinated polycyclic insecticides is of theoretical interest.

Toxaphene has been very widely used in both agriculture and public health programmes. Since its introduction, one billion lb have been applied to crops and livestock for insect control. It is still used at the rate of 40 million lb annually, mostly combined with methyl parathion for treatment of cotton. It was form-

erly combined with DDT for this purpose and in 1964, toxaphene
and DDT together comprised about 46% of the total pesticides used
in the U.S. The cotton market absorbed half of the total insecticides used and accounted for 70% of the DDT, 69% of the toxaphene and 86% of the endrin employed (19). For comparison, the
corn market absorbed 10% of the total insecticide usage and
accounted for 96% of the aldrin and 84% of the heptachlor used,
an illustration of the different spectra of crop protection
utility for the various chlorinated insecticides.

The Post-War Years

    Recalling that parathion was developed as an insecticide by
Bayer in 1944 and that the Geigy Company were developing the
carbamate anticholinesterases for this purpose in the late 1940s,
we see that the 1950s were entered with (including toxaphene) no
less than four new classes of chlorinated insecticides and two
new classes of anticholinesterase insecticides - a truly unique
situation.
    With this array of insecticidal compounds available and
following the spectacular wartime success of DDT, it seemed that
the total elimination of insect vectors of disease was at hand and
that unheard of benefits to agriculture lay ahead. Nevertheless,
many of the ecological problems that might result from the use of
DDT and other persistent compounds in agriculture were already
recognised and the prospects for DDT in agriculture were viewed
with some caution in 1944. However, it is doubtful whether the
possibility of insect resistance to the new insecticides had been
considered, so the appearance of DDT-resistance in Sweden and
Denmark in 1946, and subsequently in other areas, was a considerable shock to those engaged in insect control. Control
failures were frequently believed to be due to faults in the
technology of DDT application rather than to changes in the
insects themselves; a situation which often led to extra treatments with the toxicant and hence to greater selection pressure
for resistance in the insect populations.
    The onset of DDT-resistance initiated the first investig-
ations in what has come to be known as Insect Toxicology and the
great value of radiotracers for such work soon became apparent.
The 1951 report by Winteringham (20) of the comparative metabolism
of 1,1,1-trichloro-2,2-bis(p-[^{82}Br]phenyl)ethane(^{82}Br-DDT) in
susceptible (S-) and resistant (R-) houseflies must have been one
of the earliest applications of this technique to the metabolic
fate of an organic insecticide in insects. Metabolites were
separated on paper chromatograms which were then analysed radio-
metrically using strip-scanners designed and made in the Slough
laboratory.
    Enzymatic dehydrochlorination proved to be largely respons-
ible for DDT-resistance in some insect strains, as was demonstrated by the fact that DDT-analogues which inhibited the enzyme in

vitro and in vivo could synergise DDT in such strains (21). This observation generated a great interest in synergistic combinations. In addition, the benzylic deuteration of DDT (22, 23) suppressed dehydrochlorination only in certain mosquitoes, whereas a single o-chlorine suppressed it in houseflies (24), thereby demonstrating interspecific differences in the substrate specificity of the enzyme. Kearns and his colleagues concentrated the enzyme from R-houseflies in 1954 and studied it extensively in the late 1950s (25); its natural function is still unknown. It is not present in significant amounts in DDT-S strains of houseflies, although some of these contain an enzyme with different substrate specificity.

Resistance to the cyclodienes was evident by this time and was known to extend to lindane and toxaphene but not to DDT. These cross-resistance patterns were studied by J. R. Busvine at the London School of Hygiene. His partly dieldrin resistant strain of M. domestica vicina from the Sudan became 1000-fold resistant when subjected to intense pressure with dieldrin at Slough.

In 1957 I devised the first syntheses of $[^{14}C]$isodrin and $[^{14}C]$endrin (26). $[^{14}C]$aldrin and $[^{14}C]$dieldrin were later made at the Radiochemical Centre at Amersham, so it was possible to compare the fate of all these compounds in S- and R- houseflies. The well known epoxidation reaction occurred equally well in both strains but there appeared to be no other significant metabolism or any obvious differences to account for the resistance (27). We now know that a single gene on chromosome IV is responsible for dieldrin resistance in houseflies. The mechanism is still obscure, although recent work has shown that houseflies do metabolise small amounts of dieldrin (28).

Before 1960, there was a widespread belief that the cyclodienes were metabolically inert, apart from the epoxidation reaction. By 1955, it was appreciated that mammalian liver converts certain organophosphorus compounds into active anticholinesterases by oxidative reactions and O'Brien (29) showed that these conversions were effected by liver microsomes fortified with NADPH. Drug metabolism studies were about to be accelerated by further important developments; the microsomal mixed function oxidases (MFO) that are involved in drug metabolism in mammals were described in 1956-7, and about the same time, cytochrome P450, the CO-binding pigment responsible for oxygen activation by these enzymes, was discovered in mammalian liver.

A link with chlorinated insecticide (OC) metabolism in insects appeared between 1958 and 1960 when the benzylic hydroxylation of DDT was noticed by Japanese (30) and American insect toxicologists; in 1960 the American group showed that it resulted from MFO attack (31). Also in 1960, Sun and Johnson (32) showed that pyrethrin synergists such as benzodioxole derivatives inhibited the oxidative detoxication of insecticides and at last solved the long-standing mystery of pyrethrin synergism by these

compounds in insects; it now seemed certain that they were MFO
inhibitors in vivo.

At this time I was interested in the natural tolerance of
houseflies to structural analogues of dieldrin and, with Harrison,
I soon showed that whereas tolerance to cyclodienes was often
related to oxidative detoxication and could be reduced or eliminated by benzodioxole synergists, dieldrin-resistance in houseflies did not respond to synergism and was apparently not a consequence of oxidative detoxication (33). Several laboratories
(for their subsequent reviews see 34-36) confirmed the importance
of oxidative biotransformations in insects and in 1964-5, at
Slough, J. W. Ray showed that microsomal preparations from houseflies and other insects contained cytochrome P450 (37). Thus,
the links between insect and mammalian biochemical pharmacology
were finally and firmly established.

Several investigations (38-40) between 1960 and 1965
finally dispelled the myth of dieldrin's metabolic inertness in
mammals and since then numerous laboratories have shown that
cyclodienes conform to the established principles of drug
metabolism (41). Molecular structure has a profound influence on
the exposure of the non-chlorinated portions of these molecules
to enzymatic attack and the low persistence of endrin, as compared to dieldrin, in mammalian tissues appears largely due to
the stereochemical difference (42). The biotransformations of
dieldrin are summarised in Figure 5.

With the application of electron-capture (EC) and micro-
coulometric detection to gas chromatograph effluents from 1960,
the era of the measurement of nothing in everything had arrived
and the environmental controversy was truly on. It was easier to
make an effective EC detector than to interpret the analytical
results correctly and many of the identifications of chlorinated
insecticide (OC) residues made in the early 1960s are undoubtedly suspect, especially since it was found in 1966 that widespread polychlorobiphenyl (PCB) contamination in the bio-sphere
can simulate OC in gas chromatographic analysis.

In the United Kingdom in 1960-1 we had the episodes of bird
poisoning due to seed dressings treated with dieldrin and heptachlor epoxide, and the controversy about the decline of the
peregrine falcon. Government and Industry then agreed to reduce
the use of OCs and environmental levels fell in the mid to late
60s, as indicated by the residue content of human adipose tissue,
mutton fat and shag's eggs. Similar restrictions in central
Europe have also resulted in falls in residue levels and there
appears to have been a situation of decline, or at least stability, in the U.S. since about 1964. Extensive work in the 1960s
on the pharmacokinetics of dieldrin in birds and in mammals,
including man, together with existing data for DDT and other OCs,
led Dr. John Robinson (43) to make the following postulates:-

    1. OC levels in different tissues are functionally
       related.

2. Tissue levels are functionally related to the
    daily intake of OC.
3. Tissue concentrations depend on the time of
    exposure.
4. When exposure ceases tissue levels decline
    exponentially.

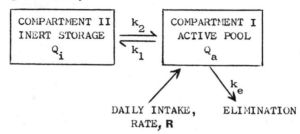

For long term exposures, $Q_a = \frac{R}{k_e}(1-e^{-k_e t})$, where Q_a is the
concentration in the active pool at time t.

Viewing the mammal as a simple, two compartment system of the
mamillary type, the data imply that for a long term ingestion at
constant rate, plateau tissue levels will be attained ($Q_a = \frac{R}{k_e}$, when
$t \to \infty$) that are dictated by the equilibrium between intake
and elimination. This conclusion should be generally applicable
and explains the fall in residue levels observed when exposure is
reduced (66-70).

Besides their biochemistry and toxicology, the environmental
chemistry of OCs has been extensively studied (44, 45). The
photochemistry of the cyclodienes, for example, offers a feast
for the chemist (44), though perhaps a headache for the residue
analyst and toxicologist. The breakdown of terminal residues to
simple molecules capable of entering the natural organic cycles
depends ultimately on microbial activity and anaerobic dechlorination seems an essential preliminary for OC destruction.
Lindane is relatively non-persistent, especially under anaerobic
conditions, and although its more highly chlorinated residues may
present the same problems as those of polychlorophenols, the less
chlorinated residues should follow pathways similar to those
established for the microbial degradation of the chlorinated
phenoxyalkanoic acid herbicides. Recent evidence (46) indicates
that certain microbes can dechlorinate DDT anaerobically, thereby
making available intermediates which may undergo further aerobic
attack, leading in principle to total degradation. The ultimate
fate of the hexachloronorbornene nucleus of cyclodienes is still
uncertain and this question continues to attract attention.

Present Status of Chlorinated Insecticides

In 1963, the President's Advisory Committee on the Use of
Pesticides recommended that the 'elimination of the use of

persistent insecticides should be the goal'. The ensuing skirm-
ish between the administration and the manufacturers has culmin-
ated in the U.S. ban on the use of DDT from 1973 and the more
recent ban on aldrin and dieldrin. Further, the future of
chlordane and related compounds is now uncertain. Clearly, the
bans will have sharply accelerated the decline in home use
already evident in the 1960s and due partly to resistance problems.

Ironically, those pressures of the last 15 years or so have
generated more information about the environmental toxicology of
chlorinated insecticides than we may ever gain about other
classes of pesticides or environmental contaminants. As a side-
benefit, we now know that some xenobiotics may be transferred
into global areas they were never intended to reach and we have
developed the methodology needed to measure these low level con-
taminations. It is also doubtful whether the extensive background contamination by PCB would have come to light so quickly
without the widespread concern about OC.

The annual global use of DDT for disease vector control is
now running at about 66% (40,000 tons) of the 1960 level and is
expected to remain constant for the next decade (47). Major DDT
resistance exists in about 1% of the area treated for malaria
control and although a limited number of organophosphate and
carbamate alternatives are available, their use is so much more
costly that total DDT replacement seems economically impossible.
Many of the less prosperous countries regard DDT as the most
important life-saver known to man. Use of the other OC is more
limited and resistance to them generally more intractable when it
occurs.

Outside the U.S. chlorinated insecticides have accounted for
half of the insecticides used in crop protection (e.g. vegetables,
46%; rice, 57%; other cereals, 85%; cotton, 38%, in 1966). Their
major contribution is undeniable and whilst there has now been
some reduction in public health uses, the crop protection uses in
poorer countries seem likely to decline only slowly. As the rest
of the world slips into ever increasing dependence on North
America for its grain supplies (48) we cannot lightly abandon any
of the well proven means to maintain the food supply, particularly if the alternatives appear safer only because we know less
about them!

Nevertheless, nations with sufficient resources to pioneer
the future must surely do so and the U.S. has long borne such
responsibility. If there is doubt about the long term effects of
chemicals in the environment then it is clearly prudent to restrict their use as far as possible. Restrictions on use also seem
to be the only way to verify experimentally some of the specul-
ations about the long term behaviour of existing residues. If
the reduced use of OC in the U.S. and other advanced countries
can compensate for the continuing need for them elsewhere, then,
hopefully, the overall degree of environmental contamination can

be stabilised or even reduced without greatly upsetting the
status quo regarding world crop protection.

What of the future?

        The chlorinated insecticides will continue to attract
attention because many questions remain outstanding in regard to
their mode of action on living organisms and because some of the
mechanisms of insect resistance to them are not yet understood.
        There is much evidence that poisoning by OC is essentially
reversible and that insect death actually results from persistence in vivo, leading to secondary effects such as dehydration
and starvation. The intoxication of mammals is also reversible
but in severe poisoning death may result from respiratory failure,
which does not occur in insects. This reversibility poses problems if we wish to make the compounds more biodegradable for the
purpose of greater environmental acceptability. Increased biodegradability is likely to increase reversibility and reduce the
efficiency of an insecticide unless we can improve its interaction
with the target itself. During recent years, Holan in Australia
and Metcalf in the U.S. have explored this area for DDT, Nakajima
in Japan for lindane and the author for cyclodienes. From an
analysis of the insect toxicities of a series of DDT-analogues,
Holan (49) concluded that the optimal size of the 'apex' of DDT
(the trichloromethyl group or equivalent) approximates to the
diameter of a hydrated sodium$^+$ and on this basis he modified some
older DDT-analogues and also devised some new biodegradable
structures.
        In Figure 6, methylchlor (A) was once considered as a com-
mercial insecticide and DANP, reported in 1953 (50), was the
first chlorine free isotere of DDT. Biodegradable structures C,
D and E were devised by Holan (49, 51, 52); F and G by Metcalf's
group (53). These molecules are susceptible to attack by MFO at
the positions arrowed, as well as to enzymatic dehydrochlorination in appropriate cases. Housefly toxicities (values relative
to DDT underlined in Figure 6) are increased by co-application
with inhibitors such as the benzodioxole synergists, which block
MFO attack in vivo. It is well known that such attack oxidises
methyl to carboxyl and cleaves simple alkoxy-groups. These are
usually detoxication reactions in target insects but the residual
molecules may yet be fairly stable in the environment. On the
other hand, a molecule such as F (Figure 6) may undergo, besides
MFO attack as arrowed, dehydrochlorination and hydrolysis to yield
two aromatic fragments which are more amenable to microbial attack
than the parent.
        Although lindane is relatively non-persistent, some of its
terminal residues may be highly chlorinated and inimical to nontarget organisms. Consequently, lindane analogues in which
chlorine is replaced by biodegradable groups should be
advantageous from an environmental standpoint, as well as being

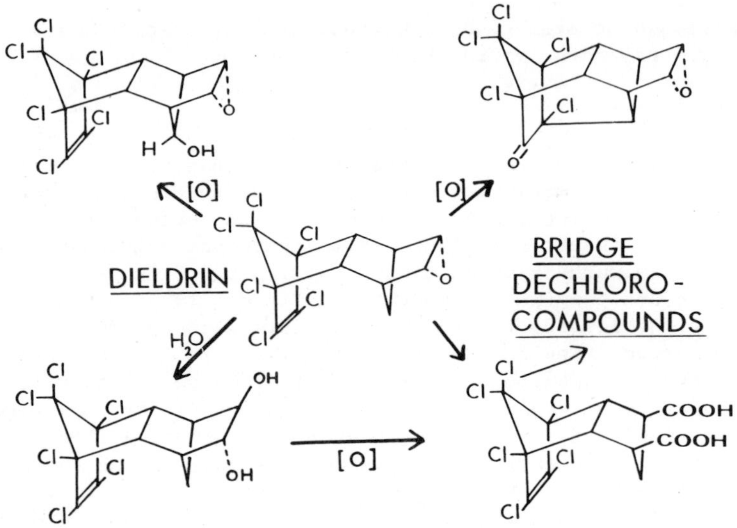

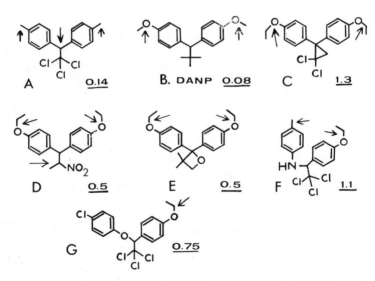

Figure 5. Summary of the biotransformations of dieldrin. These involve hydroxylation, hydration, oxidative dechlorination, and reductive dechlorination (39, 42, 65).

Figure 6. Biodegradable analogues of DDT (49–53). Arrows indicate points of attack by microsomal oxidases. Housefly toxicities relative to DDT (1.0) are underlined.

of theoretical interest.

The Kyoto group recently explored the mode of action of
lindane rather thoroughly and made a number of active analogues
with the same steric configuration as lindane (54). In Figure 7
the mosquito toxicities of these analogues show a decreasing
trend from top left to bottom right of the series shown. However,
the alkyl-, alkoxy- and alkylthio-derivatives are similar to
lindane in their toxicities to mosquitoes, houseflies and the
German cockroach. Synergism by the MFO inhibitor piperonyl
butoxide, especially against houseflies, indicates that these
groups are sites of oxidative attack in vivo. These results show
that provided the aaaeee configuration of lindane is retained,
certain biodegradable groups of similar size may replace chlorine.
The hexamethoxy analogue has a low toxicity, even in the presence
of piperonyl butoxide, so that the replacement process has limits.
The low toxicity of this lipophilic derivative of mucoinositol
(aaaeee) is of interest in relation to the early theory that
lindane is an antagonist of inositol in vivo (4).

In the mid-1960s we showed firstly that the natural tolerance
of houseflies to cyclodienes resulted mainly from oxidative
detoxication (33,55) and secondly that another enzyme system,
epoxide hydrase, converted certain dieldrin analogues into the
corresponding trans-diols, (56,57). Interspecific differences in
ability to attack enzymatically the unchlorinated ring systems of
various analogues, either oxidatively and/or hydratively (if
appropriate) can confer selective toxicity between insect species
and also between insects and mammals (58).

Is it possible that biodegradability of this sort can be
combined with a reduction in chlorine content without loss in
toxicity? Information in the literature suggests that this might
be the case and I have recently explored this possibility. A
little background is necessary at this point. More than 20 years
ago, Busvine (59) drew attention to the cross-resistance between
lindane and the cyclodienes and pointed out that these molecules
had in common a certain pentagonal arrangement of chlorine atoms.
Following this initial observation, it was noticed (60, 61) that
the replacement of the vinylic chlorines of aldrin and dieldrin
by hydrogen increased their toxicities four-fold and that for
aldrin, the bridge chlorine atom anti- to the chlorinated double
bond appeared to be more important for toxicity than the syn-
chlorine atom (61). Also, an aldrin analogue containing only the
1 and 4-chlorines was highly and specifically toxic to the German
cockroach (61).

Soloway (61) suggested that the cyclodienes and lindane have
in common two electronegative centres separated by a similar
distance and pointed out the similarity between the 'profiles' of
these molecules viewed perpendicular to their plane of symmetry.
If one further regards the highly effective and rapidly acting
lindane as a better fit to the same target that is affected by
dieldrin, then the two vinylic chlorines and the syn-Cl of the

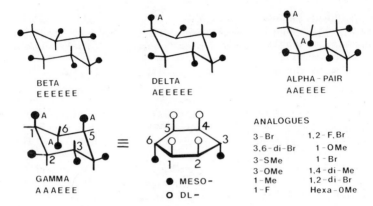

ANALOGUES

3 - Br	1,2 - F, Br
3,6 - di - Br	1 - OMe
3 - SMe	1 - Br
3 - OMe	1,4 - di - Me
1 - Me	1,2 - di - Br
1 - F	Hexa - OMe

● MESO-
○ DL-

Figure 7. Conformations of the BHC (HCH) isomers and recent analogues of the aaaeee *(lindane) structure, some of which have additional biodegradable groups (54)*

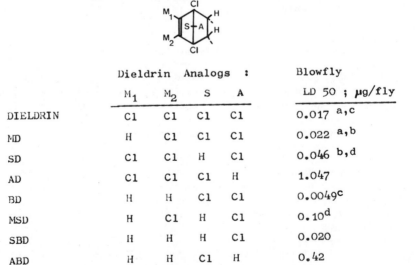

Dieldrin Analogs :

	M_1	M_2	S	A	Blowfly LD 50 ; μg/fly
DIELDRIN	Cl	Cl	Cl	Cl	0.017 [a,c]
MD	H	Cl	Cl	Cl	0.022 [a,b]
SD	Cl	Cl	H	Cl	0.046 [b,d]
AD	Cl	Cl	Cl	H	1.047
BD	H	H	Cl	Cl	0.0049[c]
MSD	H	Cl	H	Cl	0.10[d]
SBD	H	H	H	Cl	0.020
ABD	H	H	Cl	H	0.42

Figure 8. Planar structure of dieldrin and partial structures of some dieldrin analogs (each containing six chlorine atoms) referred to in the text. Table below gives toxicities for dechlorinated derivatives of dieldrin (see key in figure) to adult female blowflies, Calliphora erythrocephala. *Similar superscripts indicate significant difference at 95% probability level (63).*

dieldrin bridge appear superfluous as far as molecular bulk is
concerned (62). Now although replacement of chlorine by hydrogen
may increase metabolic possibilities and also alter electrostatic
interactions with the target, these deductions from models appeared
to accord with the limited toxicity data available.

The above information suggested that, for dieldrin at least,
three specific chlorine atoms might be replaced without loss in
toxicity (62) and confirmatory toxicity data for blowflies
(C. erythrocephala) are shown in Figure 8.

In the molecule SBD, the reduction in toxicity effected by
replacement of the syn-chlorine of dieldrin to give SD appears
to be offset by an increase (compare BD) effected by further
replacement of the vinylic chlorines, so that SBD is similar to
dieldrin in toxicity. In contrast, AD and ABD, which retain the
syn-chlorine, are poor toxicants. In this series there was no
appreciable synergism with the MFO inhibitor sesamex, indicating
that when increased LD50s were seen, these were not the result of
enhanced MFO attack consequent upon the progressive replacement
of chlorine.

The C_{16}-dieldrin analogues ODA and HCE are biodegradable due
to oxidative and/or hydrative attack on their unchlorinated rings
shown in Figure 8. Can chlorine be replaced by hydrogen in such
analogues without serious loss, or perhaps even with an increase
in acute insect toxicity? The products, having lost 1 to 3
chlorine atoms, should be more vulnerable to enzymatic detoxication
in the tissues of higher animals and their terminal residues more
amenable to bacterial degradation. The results for certain dechlorinated analogues of endrin, oxadieldrin, ODA and HCE are
presented elsewhere (63) and preliminary data (unpublished) are
available for derivatives of endosulfan, isobenzan and alodan.
This yet incomplete study shows that in all series for which
information is available, the bridge anti-C1(A) is indeed more
important than the syn-C1 (S) for toxicity, but replacement of the
vinylic chlorines does not necessarily confer the toxicity
increase found in the dieldrin series.

The resemblance between lindane and the cyclodiene structure
is particularly striking if one compares models of lindane and the
photoisomer of the molecule SD (Figure 8), in which the S-chlorine
is replaced by hydrogen and the usual double bond is absent.
There is also some similarity, not very obvious from two
dimensional structures, between models of these molecules and of
the toxic components (Figure 4;A,B) isolated from toxaphene by
Casida's group (17). This is to be expected from insect cross-
resistance patterns and similarities in the poisoning syndrome
produced by the three types of compound.

For cyclohexane derivatives, convulsive activity is
associated, apparently specifically, with a particular molecular
topography that is only achieved with the aaaeee arrangement of
substituents. However, the norbornene and camphene carbon
skeletons apparently permit the attainment of a similar topography,

whilst allowing a greater molecular variety and hence a larger
number of toxic products. With the cyclodienes in particular,
greater structural variation is possible in the non-chlorinated
portion of the molecules and this has resulted in a number of
commercially viable alternatives with different uses. It is con-
ceivable that other carbon skeletons may be used to attain the
same end and Mirex, for example, is derived from the spindle-
shaped fusion product of two cyclopentadiene nuclei.

In conclusion, our knowledge of interspecific differences in
drug metabolism is already being applied to the question of
greater environmental acceptability of chlorinated as well as
other types of insecticides. For example, the simple replacement
of p-chlorines by p-ethoxy-groups in the well known DDT-relative
Prolan gives the biodegradable compound D (Figure 6), which has
low mammalian toxicity and has been shown in extensive field
trials to be effective against a wide range of insect species (64).
At the more fundamental level, mode of action studies with
chlorinated insecticides may yet lead to novel insecticidal
compounds.

We must accept that no device of man will ever be perfect.
Whilst remaining watchful for the inevitable pitfalls, we
should never forget the many positive achievements already
recorded in the field of insect control by chemicals.

Literature Cited

1. Bender, H. U.S. Patent 2,010,841 (1935).
2. Cited in Brooks G.T. 'Chlorinated Insecticides' Vol. I,
        p. 186, CRC Press, Cleveland, 1974.
3. Holmes, E. Agr. Chem. (1951) 6 (12), 31.
4. Slade, R.E. Chem. Ind. (Lond.) (1945) 64, 314.
5. Dupire A., and Raucourt, M. C.R. Acad. Agric. Fr. (1943)
        29, 470.
6. Hyman, J. Private communication.
7. Kearns, C.W., Ingle, L., and Metcalf, R.L. J. Econ. Entomol.
        (1945) 38, 661.
8. Hyman, J. Brit. patent 618,432 (1949).
9. Gab, S., Parlar, H., Cochrane, W.P., Fitzky, H.G., Wendisch,
        D., and Korte, F. Justus Liebigs Ann. Chem. (1976) 1.
10. Riemschneider, R. World Rev. Pest Control (1963) 2, 29.
11. Lidov, R.E., and Soloway, S.B. Brit. patent 692,547 (1953).
12. Bluestone, H. U.S. Patent 2,676,132 (1954).
13. Frensch, H. Med. Chem. (1957) 6, 556.
14. Buntin, G.A. Private communication.
15. Jennings, B.H., and Herschbach, G.B. J. Org. Chem. (1965)
        30, 3902.
16. Richey, H.G.Jr., Grant J.E., Garbacik, T.J., and Dull, D.L.
        J. Org. Chem. (1965) 30, 3909.
17. Khalifa, S., Mon, T.R., Engel, J.L., and Casida, J.E.
        J. Agric. Food Chem. (1974) 22, 653.

18. Nelson,J.O., and Matsumura, F. J. Agric. Food Chem. (1975) 23, 984.

19. Department of Health, Education and Welfare, 'Report of the Secretary's Commission on Pesticides and their Relationship to Environmental Health', Parts I and II, p. 47, U.S. Govt. Print Off., Washington DC, 1969.

20. Winteringham, F.P.W., Loveday, P.M., and Harrison, A. Nature (Lond.) (1951) 167, 106.

21. Moorefield, H.H., and Kearns, C.W. J. Econ. Entomol. (1955) 48, 403.

22. Dachauer, A.C., Cocheo, B., Solomon, M.G., and Hennessy, D.J. J. Agric. Food Chem. (1963) 11, 47.

23. Barker, R.J., J. Econ. Entomol. (1960) 53, 35.

24. Hennessey, D.J., Frantantoni, J., Hartigan, J., Moorefield, H.H., and Weiden, M.H.J. Nature (Lond.) (1961) 190, 341.

25. Lipke, H., and Kearns, C.W. 'Advances in Pest Control Research' Vol. 3, p. 253. Metcalf, R.L. Ed., Interscience New York, 1960.

26. Brooks, G.T. J. Chem. Soc. (1958) 3693.

27. Brooks, G.T. Nature (Lond.) (1960) 186, 96.

28. Sellers, L.G. and Guthrie, F.E. J. Econ. Entomol. (1972) 65, 378.

29. O'Brien, R.D. Canad. J. Biochem. (1955) 34, 1131.

30. Tsukamoto, M. Botyu-Kagaku (1959) 24, 151.

31. Agosin, M., Michaeli, R., Miskus, S., Nagasawa, S., and Hoskins, W.M. J. Econ. Entomol. (1961) 54, 340.

32. Sun, Y.P., and Johnson, E.R. J. Agric. Food Chem. (1960) 8, 261.

33. Brooks, G.T., and Harrison, A. J. Insect Physiol. (1964) 10, 633.

34. Tsukamoto, M., and Casida, J.E. Nature (Lond.) (1967) 213, 49.

35. Dahm, P.A., and Nakatsugawa, T., in 'Enzymatic Oxidations of Toxicants' p. 89, Hodgson, E. Ed., North Carolina State University, Raleigh, 1968.

36. Hook, G.E.R., Jordon, T.W., and Smith, J.N., in 'Enzymatic Oxidation of Toxicants' p. 27, Hodgson, E. Ed., North Carolina State University, Raleigh, 1968.

37. Ray, J.W., in 'Pest Infestation Research 1965, The Report of the Pest Infestation Laboratory', p. 59, Agricultural Research Council, London, 1965.

38. Heath, D.F., and Vandekar, M. Br. J. Ind. Med. (1964) 21, 269.

39. Korte, F., and Arent, H. Life Sci. (Oxford) (1965) 4, 2017.

40. Cueto, C., and Hayes, W.J.,Jr. J. Agric. Food Chem. (1962) 10, 366.

41. Brooks, G.T. in 'Pesticide Terminal Residues (IUPAC)' p. 111, Tahori, A.S. Ed., Butterworths, London, 1971.

42. Bedford, C.T., and Hutson, D.H. Chem. Ind. (London) (1976) 440.

43. Robinson, J., and Roberts, M. in 'Society of Chemical Industry Monograph No. 29' p. 106, SCI, London, 1968.
44. Rosen, J.D. in 'Environmental Quality and Safety' Vol. 1, p. 85, Coulston, F., and Korte, F. Eds., Thieme, Stuttgart, 1972.
45. Lu, Po-Yung, Metcalf, R.L., Hirwe, A.S., and Williams, J.W. J. Agric. Food Chem. (1975) 23, 967.
46. Pfaender, F.K., and Alexander, M. J. Agric. Food Chem. (1972) 20, 842.
47. Wright, J.W., and Stiles, A.R. in 'Pesticides', 'Environmental Quality and Safety', Suppl. Vol. III, p. 625, Coulston, F., and Korte, F., Eds., Thieme, Stuttgart, 1975.
48. Brown, L.R. Science (1975) 190, 1053.
49. Holan, G. Nature (London) (1969) 221, 1025.
50. Rogers, E.F., Brown, H.D., Rasmussen, I.M., and Heal, R.E. J. Amer. Chem. Soc. (1953) 75, 2991.
51. Holan, G. Nature (London) (1971) 232, 644.
52. Holan, G. Bull. W.H.O. (1971) 44, 355.
53. Hirwe, A.S., Metcalf, R.L., and Kapoor, I.P. J. Agric. Food Chem. (1972) 20, 818.
54. Nakajima, M., Fujita, T., Kurihara, N., Sanemitsu, Y., Uchida, M., and Kiso, M. in 'Pesticides', 'Environmental Quality and Safety', Suppl. Vol. III, p. 370, Coulston, F., and Korte, F., Eds., Thieme, Stuttgart, 1975.
55. Brooks, G.T., Harrison, A. Biochem. Pharmacol. (1964) 13, 827.
56. Brooks, G.T. Wld. Review Pest Control (1966) 5, 62.
57. Brooks, G.T., Harrison, A., and Lewis, S.E. Biochem. Pharmacol. (1970) 19, 255.
58. Brooks, G.T. in 'Environmental Quality and Safety', Vol. 1. p. 159, Coulston, F., and Korte, F., Eds., Academic, New York, 1972.
59. Busvine, J.R. Nature (Lond.) (1954) 174, 783.
60. Busvine, J.R. Bull. Entomol. Res. (1964) 55, 271.
61. Soloway, S.B. Adv. in Pest Control Res. (1965) 6, 85.
62. Brooks, G.T. in 'Drug Design', Vol. 4, p. 379, Ariens, E.J., Ed., Academic, New York, 1973.
63. Brooks, G.T. Proc. 8th Br. Insect Fungic. Conf. (1975) 381.
64. Morton, T.C., Holan, G., and Virgona, C.T.F. Pestic. Biochem. Physiol. (1976) 6, 209.
65. Lay, J.P., Weisgerber, I., and Klein, W. Pestic. Biochem. Physiol. (1975) 5, 226.
66. Abbott, D.C., Collins, G.B., and Goulding, R. Brit. Med. J. (1972) 553.
67. Deichmann, W.B. Arch. Toxicol. (1972) 29, 1.
68. Cieleszky, V., and Soós, K. in 'Pesticides', Environmental Quality and Safety', Suppl. Vol. III, p. 199, Coulston, F., and Korte, F., Eds., Thieme, Stuttgart, 1975.
69. Aizicovici, H., Cocisiu, M., Nistor, C., and Unterman, W.H. Ibid, p.852.   p.189.
70. Adamovic, V.M., Burke, J.A., Sokić, B., and Petrović, O.,Ibid/

The Progression of Resistance Mechanisms Developed against Insecticides

A. W. A. BROWN

Department of Entomology, Michigan State University, East Lansing, Mich. 48824

As the final item in the symposium on pesticide chemistry in this century, the need was felt for a review of outstanding events in the insecticide resistance field during this period, along with a projection of expectations during its final 25 years. This paper, however, will describe progressions rather than events, since resistance has been a steadily developing problem; this progression will be described in detail, although the Forward Look will be pretty sketchy.

Starting in 1908 in the orchards of the Pacific northwest, the cases of resistance before World War II and the era of the synthetic organics involved the HCN used against scale insects on citrus, the arsenicals used against orchard caterpillars and cattle ticks, and tartar emetic applied against the tiny insect pests called thrips; as now, many instances originated in California (Table I). The resistance mechanisms were investigated in two of

Table I. Development of Insecticide-Resistances, 1908-44.

San Jose Scale	Lime-sulfur	Wash. State	'08
Black Scale	HCN	California	'12
California Red Scale	HCN	California	'13
Citricola Scale	HCN	California	'25
Codling Moth	Pb Arsenate	Colorado	'28
Peach Twig Borer	Pb Arsenate	California	'44
Cattle Tick	Na Arsenite	Argentina	'35
Blue Tick	Na Arsenite	S. Africa	'38
Citrus Thrips	Tartar Emetic	California	'39
Gladiolus Thrips	Tartar Emetic	California	'43
Two-spotted Mite	Selenium	Eastern US	'43
Walnut Husk Fly	Cryolite	California	'43

the cases: — the arsenic-resistant codling-moth larvae were found to be more resistant to starvation and desiccation, and thus had a longer period of effective locomotion to find an unsprayed spot on the skin of the apple (1); the cyanide-resistant California red

scale had a tissue-respiratory electron-transport system less dependent on cytochrome oxidase (2), and the character was found to
be inherited as if it was due to a single sex-linked gene.

The Swiss product DDT was introduced for housefly control in
neutral countries in 1944, and already by 1946 resistance had developed in northern Sweden (of all unlikely places). When housefly resistance appeared near Rome, Italy in 1947, Professor
Missiroli considered that it was a different subspecies which he
named *Musca domestica tiberina* at the very same time that Wilson
and Lindquist in the USDA Orlando laboratory were producing a resistant strain from a susceptible one by laboratory selection.
By 1952 DDT-resistance had been developed in populations of important pests of apple, cabbage, potatoes, tomatoes and grapes,
besides the body louse, the bedbug, two species of fleas, and
several species of mosquitoes (Table II).

Table II.   Development of DDT-Resistance, 1946-52.

Cabbage Worm	Wis.	House Fly	Sweden
Cabbage Looper	N.Y.	Body Louse	Korea
Codling Moth	Ohio	Bed Bug	Hawaii
Apple Plant-bug	Wash.	Human Flea	Peru
Potato Beetle	N.Y.	Dog Flea	Ga.
Potato Fleabeetle	Ind.	House Mosquito	Italy
Diamondback Moth	Java	Salt-marsh Mosquitoes	Fla.
Tomato Hornworm	Fla.	Irrigation-water Mosquitoes	Cal.
Grape Leafhopper	Cal.	Encephalitis Mosquito	Cal.

The mechanism of resistance to DDT in the housefly was at
first thought to be due to reduced penetration through the cuticle,
the Swedish resistant flies having a thicker tarsal integument
than normal laboratory strains (3).   Interstrain differences were
found in the titers of cytochrome oxidase and cholinesterase, but
they bore no correlation with the resistance.   One characteristic
did, and that was the detoxicative dehydrochlorination to the non-
insecticidal metabolite DDE (Fig. 1); and the enzyme responsible,
DDT-dehydrochlorinase, which depended on glutathione for activation, was isolated from resistant strains (4).   A second mechanism
due to nerve insensitivity to DDT was discovered in several housefly strains (5).   An additional mechanism of DDT-resistance found
in Danish and Californian strains selected with OP compounds was
due to oxidation, which could be put into evidence by the addition
of NADH to microsomal preparations *in vitro*, or by adding the mfo-
inhibitor sesamex as a synergist *in vivo* (6).

The cyclodiene group of organochlorines was introduced in
1948, starting with chlordane, then aldrin, dieldrin, endrin and
toxaphene, and then heptachlor; BHC was already available at the
close of the war.   The experience with housefly control in the
Mediterranean countries was that DDT-resistance came in 2 years,
and the substitution of BHC was followed by BHC-resistance a year

later; the same thing happened to the cyclodienes chlordane or
dieldrin, and cross-resistance between BHC and the cyclodiene was
virtually complete. Within 10 years of the introduction of cyclodienes into agriculture in 1949, 8 important cotton pests had gone
decisively resistant to them, the boll weevil being among the last
to go (Table III). This type of resistance developed particularly
fast in flies and mosquitoes, while the Australian beef and wool

Table III. Development of Cyclodiene-BHC-Resistance, 1949-58.

Boll Weevil	La.	House Fly	Sardinia
Cotton Leafworm	Tex.	Sheep Blowfly	NSW
Cotton Spodoptera	Egypt	Body Louse	Japan
Salt-marsh Caterpillar	Cal.	Bed Bug	Italy
Spiny Bollworm	Israel	German Roach	Tex.
Cotton Aphid	SE USA	Blue Tick	S. Africa
Cotton Fleahopper	Tex.	Cattle Tick	Queensl'd
Cotton Perforator	Cal.	Salt-marsh Mosquitoes	Fla.
Sugarcane Froghopper	Trinidad	I-W & Enc. Mosquitoes	Cal.
Cabbage Looper	Ariz.	Malaria Mosquito	Nigeria

industry notably suffered from the failure of lindane and dieldrin
to control the sheep blowfly and the cattle tick. The use of
aldrin against wireworms, rootworms and root maggots in the soil
was soon rewarded by cyclodiene-resistance in 3 wireworm species,
4 species of *Diabrotica* rootworms in cornfields, and 6 species of
Hylemya root maggots on onions, Brassicas and other vegetable
crops (Table IV). Cyclodiene-resistance is very decisive when it
comes, so that its spread through the insect population can be
readily seen, as for example that of the western corn rootworm
Diabrotica virgifera from Nebraska to the rest of the midwestern
states between 1961 and 1964.

Table IV. Cyclodiene-Resistance developed in Soil Insects, 1955-65

Coleoptera		Diptera	
Conoderus fallii	S.C.	*Hylemya antiqua*	Wis.
C. vespertinus	S.C.	*H. brassicae*	Ill.
Limonius californicus	Wash.	*H. liturata*	Ont.
Diabrotica virgifera	Neb.	*H. platura*	B.C.
D. balteata	La.	*H. floralis*	Sask.
D. longicornis	S.D.	*H. arambourgi*	Kenya
D. 11-punctata	N.C.	*Psila rosae*	Ore.
Graphognathus leucoloma	Ala.	*Euxesta notata*	Ont.
Hypera postica	Utah	*Merodon equestris*	U.K.

The mechanism of cyclodiene-resistance has been very difficult
to determine. The hydroxylation of aldrin and dieldrin to aldrin
glycol and dieldrin transdiol is a slow process and is not
peculiar to resistant strains, while the increased lipoid content

frequently noted confers only a slightly increased tolerance. The
most likely mechanism is the sequestration of the cyclodiene epoxide by binding with cellular proteins, thus protecting the presyn-
aptic membranes which are their probable site of action (7).
Lindane-resistant strains are characterized by an increased detoxication, due to dehydrochlorination to PCCH and to dichlorothio-
phenols, the latter process putting SH groups into the molecule
(8). However, increased breakdown is probably only of secondary
importance, the principal resistance mechanism being the same as
for the cyclodiene insecticides.

   At this time, resistance to the organophosphorus insecticides
is of prime importance. First appearing in 1949 in the two-
spotted mite *Tetranychus urticae* in greenhouses, within the next
decade it spread to 14 species of tetranychid mites infesting
pome and citrus orchards, to 7 species of aphids, to flies, midges
and mosquitoes, and finally to cockroaches (Table V). Waiting in
the wings were still more serious OP-resistances in *Heliothis*
caterpillars on cotton, and in *Tribolium* and *Sitophilus* beetles
on stored grain (9).

Table V.   Development of Organophosphorus-Resistance, 1949-59.

Two-spotted Mite	Conn.	House Fly	Denmark
European Spider-mite	Ind.	Coprophagous Fly	Congo
Pacific & McDaniel Mites	Wash.	Lake Midge	Fla.
Citrus Mite	Cal.	German Roach	Ky.
Green Peach Aphid	Wash.	House Mosquito	Cameroon
Green Apple Aphid	Switz'l'd	I-W Mosquitoes	Cal.
Walnut & Alfalfa Aphids	Cal.	Enc. Mosquitoes	Cal.

   The mechanisms of OP-resistance in the housefly were found to
derive not from a decreased oxidation of the thiophosphate to the
powerful phosphate anticholinesterase, — indeed there was usually
a heightened oxidation of parathion to paraoxon, for example —,
but to chemical degradation of the molecular structure (Fig. 2).
The mechanism first to be discovered was a phosphatase-type
hydrolysis resulting from the gene-controlled conversion of an
aliesterase for which the OP compounds were inhibitors, to an
A-esterase for which these OP's were substrates (10). More important, however, was an enhanced oxidative type of cleavage of the
leaving group from the phosphorus, producing the same metabolites
DPTA or DPA as the esterase did, but being put into evidence by
the addition of NADH to microsomal preparations (11). A third
mechanism was enhanced desalkylation by an alkyl transferase
utilizing GSH, and found in the soluble fraction of homogenates
(12). OP-resistant strains also usually become characterized by
reduced cuticular penetration, a characteristic which resistant
houseflies usually had already gained against DDT, which extends
to carbamates and pyrethroids as well. For resistance to mala-
thion, there is an additional mechanism based on hydrolysis of the

succinyl ester side-chain (13) by the enzyme loosely termed
carboxyesterase, or more correctly carboxylic-ester hydrolase.
     With the introduction of the carbamate insecticides in 1956,
resistance to carbaryl appeared between 1963 and 1966 in an orchard leafroller in New Zealand, in the cotton leafworm (*Spodoptera*)
of Egypt, and in *Heliothis virescens* (the so-called tobacco budworm) on American cotton (Table VI). Resistance developed to OP
compounds had already given some cross-tolerance to carbamates

Table VI.   Resistance to Carbamates and Pyrethroids, 1958-66.

Carbaryl		Pyrethrins	
Tobacco Budworm	Tex.	House Fly	Sweden
Cotton Spodoptera	Egypt	Tobacco Moth	Fla.
Light-brown Apple Moth	N.Z.	Mushroom Fly	England

and seemed to predispose the pest for a more rapid development of
carbamate-resistance. Resistance to synergized pyrethrins developed in a Swedish housefly population just 1 year after it had
been taken off a control regime of OP compounds following a
grounding of organochlorine-resistance.
     The mechanism of carbamate-resistance, formerly considered to
be enhanced hydrolysis (e.g. carbaryl to 1-naphthol), was found to
derive almost exclusively from hydroxylation at various points on
the molecule, not only the aromatic leaving group but also the
N-methyl on the carbamate (Fig. 3), as well as some desmethylation
for good measure (14). Pyrethrin-resistance, at first considered
to be due to hydrolysis of the alcohol-acid linkage, was also
found to be due to an oxidation, occurring at the transmethyl
group of the isobutenyl side-chain of the chrysanthemic acid (15).
     By 1975, the development of some type of resistance had been
proved and reported in populations of 268 species of pest arthropods (Table VII). OP-resistance had now spread to involve 85

Table VII. Numbers of Species with Various Types of Resistance, 1975

	DDT	Dld	OP	Carb	Other	Total
Diptera	54	77	23	5	3	103
Lepidoptera	17	20	12	6	3	34
Hemiptera	10	16	20	3	4	42
Acarina	4	8	19	6	8	30
Coleoptera	10	27	7	3	2	38
Other Orders	18	14	4	0	2	21
Total	113	162	85	23	22	268

species, and carbamate-resistance to 23 species. The orchard and
greenhouse mites, particularly *Tetranychus urticae*, had chalked up
such exotic resistance as those to azobenzene, to the dinitro compound binapacryl, to the sulfur-containing organochlorines, to the
formamidines, and even to oxythioquinox (Morestan). When the

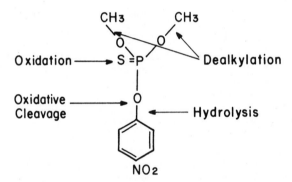

Figure 1. *Detoxicative mechanisms imparting DDT-resistance*

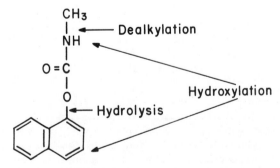

Figure 2. *Detoxicative mechanisms imparting organo-phosphorus-resistance (e.g. to methyl parathion)*

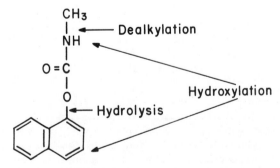

Figure 3. *Detoxicative mechanisms imparting carba-mate-resistance (e.g. to carbaryl)*

report of the FAO working party on resistance is published some
time this year, we will learn that over 300 species of arthropods
have developed some type of resistance in some part of the world.
      The effect of these resistances has been to drive chemical
control from one insecticide to the next.   In most parts of the
Nile delta the cotton leafworms can still be controlled by some OP
compound, such as chlorpyrifos, supplemented where necessary with
the insect growth regulator Dimilin.   But in southern Texas, Mexico,
Nicaragua and Peru the multiple resistances of the tobacco budworm,
and to a less extreme degree of *H. zea* and *Spodoptera sunia*, have
made even 20 insecticide applications a season quite worthless,
and indeed there is less damage to the cotton if no chemicals are
applied at all.   The only materials that can be relied upon to
kill these multiresistant *H. virescens* are the dichlorovinyl
pyrethroid NRDC-143 and the Heliothis nuclear polyhedrosis virus.
It will be noted that the pressure of events, replacing organochlorines with OP's and carbamates, and then replacing them with
more biological-type agents, conforms to the aspirations of those
charged with protecting the environment against pollution.
      Other plant-feeding insects, such as the cabbage looper, have
piled one resistance upon another, so that we must look to pheromones and chemosterilants for their control.   The western corn
rootworm has now joined the onion maggot in going OP-resistant.
Resistance problems on pests of rice in Japan are becoming as
severe as those on cotton in the Americas.
      Among insects affecting man and animals, the three major
mosquito vectors of disease are making the usual rake's progress
from one resistance to another.   The malaria mosquito *Anopheles
albimanus* has gone the whole way, the resistance mainly owing to
the pressure of agricultural insecticides on its breeding places,
and thus malaria is increasing again in Central America.   The
multiple resistance in some strains of *Tribolium* is a serious blow
to the preservation of world food supplies.
      Successive resistances have driven control of the *Boophilus*
cattle ticks all the way to OP compounds, and from them to chlor-
phenamidine (chlordimeform); although it has been recently found
that carbaryl is effective in cattle dips if synergized with
piperonyl butoxide.   The two-spotted mite has gone through a fan-
tastic sequence of acaricides, the only ones to which resistance
has not yet been reported being Pentac and the organo-tin compound
Plictran.
      The pest mosquito *Aedes nigromaculis* of the vast San Joaquin
valley of California went resistant to organochlorines by 1951, to
parathion by 1960, to fenthion by 1965, and to chlorpyrifos
(Dursban) by 1970.   At present reliance is placed on larvicidal
oils, the juvenile-hormone mimic methoprene (Altosid) and the
insect growth regulator diflubenzuron (Dimilin), — and on better
management of surplus irrigation water.   Residual sprays for housefly control, at first so spectacular with the organochlorines, had
to move into the OP compounds, which were then knocked out in

succession by resistance. The experience in Denmark between 1951
and 1967 was that each OP compound lasted for about 2 years, end-
ing with dimethoate, and the only way that its use could be extended was by putting it in housefly baits instead of residual sprays.
    It should be clear to us that the development of resistance
is always to be expected to any insecticide we may choose to apply,
but it is not inevitable. DDT stayed effective against the
European corn borer for at least 15 years (Table VIII) and there
are several other examples, including diazinon and the western
corn rootworm in Nebraska. Some of the species of beneficial
insects which formerly suffered from insecticide damage, such as
braconid parasites, lady beetles, mayfly nymphs and honeybees,
have now developed certain tolerances, while several of the
Phytoseiid mites which feed on the plant-feeding spider mites are
becoming as resistant as their prey to OP's and carbamates.

Table VIII.   Failures of certain insects to develop resistance
              to certain insecticides.

			Field	Lab.
Eur. Corn Borer	DDT	N. Amer.	1950-65	
Fla. Red Scale	parathion	Cal.	1951-63	34 gen's
So. House Mosquito	Flit-MLO	Tex.		60 gen's
Sugarcane Borer	azinphosmethyl	La.	1964-72	6 gen's
Boll Weevil	malathion	W. Tex.	1963-72	
W. Spruce Budworm	mexacarbate	Idaho		14 gen's
W. Corn Rootworm	diazinon	Neb.	1963-73	

    The thing about resistance is that it is inherited, that
highly resistant strains stay resistant even when reared for
generations without exposure to the insecticide, and that they
were produced in the first place by submitting normal strains to
the pruning power of selection. Thus the determinants of resistance may be sought in the genes on the chromosomes. The amazing
thing was that resistance, which was thought *a priori* to be due to
alleles of a number of minor genes (i.e. polyfactorial), time and
time again turned out to be due to a single decisive gene (i.e.
monofactorial). This was first shown in 1953 for DDT-resistance
in the housefly and *Drosophila*, and in 1956 for OP-resistance in
the *Tetranychus* mites. Subsequent studies on the genetics of
resistance in a variety of species showed that the gene alleles
responsible for OP-resistance and carbamate-resistance were
always dominant, those for cyclodiene-resistance were always
intermediate in expression, while DDT-resistance genes turned out
to be dominant in some species and recessive in others (16).
    By the utilization of marker strains bearing visible mutants,
which are available for the housefly and their position on the 6
chromosomes in that species (17) it became possible to locate the
genes responsible for the various DDT-resistance mechanisms
already described (Fig. 4). The resistance due to dehydrochlor-

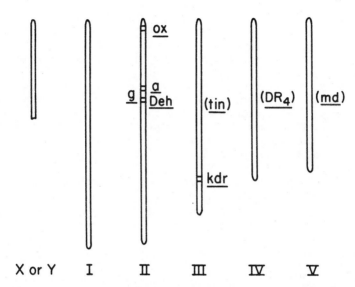

Figure 4.   Location of the genes for various resistances on the chromosomes of the housefly

ination was found to be located on chromosome 2 between the markers *aristapedia* and *carmine*. The heterozygotes for this gene allele, called *Deh*, had half as much DDT-dehydrochlorinase as the resistant homozygotes (18). The gene for enhanced microsomal oxidation *md* was found to be linked with markers on chromosome 5, but it cannot yet be located in a precise position on that chromosome; another gene for oxidation is located at the end of chromosome 2. The gene for reduced nerve sensitivity (essentially knockdown-resistance) was precisely located on chromosome 3, along with the gene (*tin*) for reduced cuticular penetration. (Cyclodiene-resistance in the housefly is located on chromosome 4.) Each DDT-resistance gene compounds with the others to produce resistance intensities which are the multiple rather than the sum of each contributor.

The DDT-resistances in other species have turned out to be due either to oxidation, as in *Drosophila* and the German cockroach, or to dehydrochlorination with reduced penetration added, as in the pink bollworm and the tropical house mosquito (Table 9). In *Heliothis virescens* one strain was characterized by dehydrochlorination, another by reduced penetration (19).

Table IX. Mechanisms of DDT-Resistance in the Housefly and other Insects.

Resistance Mechanism	Gene	Housefly	Tobacco Budworm	Pink Bollworm	Pomace fly	*Culex fatigans*	*Culex tarsalis*
Dehydrochlorin'n	*Deh* (II)	+	+			+	+
Oxidation	*md* (V)				+		+
Oxidation	*ox* (II)						
Insensitive Nerve	*kdr* (III)						
Reduced Penetr'n	*tin* (III)	+		+		+	

For OP-resistance in the housefly, the gene that determines the conversion of aliesterase into an A-esterase, called *a*, is located on chromosome 2 very close to the *Deh* gene. Of the two genes for oxidation found in OP-resistant strains, the gene *ox* (diagnosable by the epoxidation of aldrin to dieldrin) is evidently more important than *md* (first found as determining a sesamex-inhibited DDT-resistance). Desalkylation was found attributable to a gene (called *g*) very close to *a* and *Deh*, and many OP-resistant strains have also acquired the reduced penetration gene allele *tin*. Thus genetics can help us sort out the resistance mechanisms in a given resistant strain or population.

The ability to cleave off the leaving group by a process presumably hydrolytic has been detected in a number of OP-resistant species (Table X). In the tobacco budworm clear evidence for OP-resistance being associated with oxidative cleavage was obtained from the action of microsomes on the phosphorothionate chlorpyrifos

Table X.   Mechanisms of OP-Resistance in the Housefly and other Arthropods.

Resistance Mechanism	Housefly Gene	Housefly	Tobacco Budworm	*Culex fatigans*	2-Spotted Mite	Predaceous Mite	Cattle Tick
Oxidation	*md* (V)	+					(+)
Oxidation	*ox* (II)						
Hydrolysis	*a* (II)	+		+	+	+	(+)
Desalkylation	*g* (II)	+				+	
Reduced Penetr'n	*tin* (III)			+			
Insensitive ChE					+		+

as a substrate (20), while evidence for increased hydrolysis was obtained on the phosphate GC-6506 as a substrate (21). Evidence (22) for desalkylation has been found in the predaceous mite *Amblyseius fallacis* as well as in *Heliothis*. A mutant cholinesterase insensitive to OP inhibition was originally found not to be a resistance mechanism in the housefly, but to characterize some resistant strains of *Tetranychus urticae* (23) and most OP-resistant strains of the Australian cattle tick (24). It has recently been found to be a mechanism in the sheep blowfly (25), the malaria mosquito *Anopheles albimanus*, and a New York strain of the housefly (27).

So we now understand how field populations and laboratory strains exposed generation after generation to an insecticide or insecticides accumulate mutant alleles making for resistance. If susceptible genotypes still remain in the strains, they usually revert since the new resistance genome, being abnormal, generally does not do as well and is thus constantly diluted within the population or by immigration from outside. But strains and populations that have reverted to susceptibility recover their resistance almost immediately when the original insecticide is reapplied; in 1956 the Danish housefly populations which had reverted since organochlorines were discontinued in 1951 recovered their resistance to DDT and chlordane after just one partially-successful reapplication.

The multiresistant strains now extant also show a certain cross-tolerance, but not resistance, to the third-generation insecticides such as the juvenile-hormone mimics and other so-called insect growth regulators, as was found in strains of the housefly, flour beetle and tobacco budworm. Resistance to the JH mimic methoprene and Monsanto-585 has been induced by laboratory selection of *Culex tarsalis* (28) and *Culex pipiens* (29), and to Monsanto-585 in *Culex quinquefasciatus* (30). Whatever insect or IGR is chosen, the result of exposure to selective doses in successive generations is usually the development of resistance, repeating our previous experience with chemosterilants, and the

same applies to diflubenzuron (Dimilin), the new chitin-
synthetase inhibitor derived from urea.

Now for the Forward Look, the projection of expectations for
the remainder of this century. We can expect the continued spread
and accumulation of resistances in direct proportion to our use of
chemicals, which in the United States will be organophosphorus,
carbamate and formamidine compounds, probably with endosulfan,
methoxychlor and lindane among the organochlorines, some pyrethroids, and perhaps with diflubenzurone and some JH mimics among
the insect growth regulators. Since new clearances are barely
keeping up with suspensions, we must make what we have last as
long as possible. Spray calendars which choose the least persistent of the OP compounds, such as trichlorfon, will not exert
selection pressure for so long a period after application as the
more persistent ones, and are easier on the predators and parasites. This is the intention of the integrated control systems
now being developed and followed. We may have learned from the
errors of the past to be sufficiently nervous about our target
populations, every time we put them under insecticide pressure,
to go to the trouble of monitoring their susceptibility status.
Standard test methods for resistance have been developed by FAO
(31) and by the Entomological Society of America (32) for many
important arthropod pest groups, and more are being developed
(Table XI). Their systematic use at regular intervals should be
an integral part of pest management. For insects of public-health
importance, test methods have been made available for all species
groups by WHO (33), and these are systematically used, largely
because they are simple to perform and test kits are available to
carry them out. It is just possible that in the last quarter-
century of this millenium, agriculture departments of states and
nations may be sufficiently well-informed about the overall nature
of the resistance problem, that trouble may be detected when and
where it is imminent and the appropriate change made in the control method before it becomes a reality.

Table XI. Test methods for susceptibility levels to insecticides.

FAO Methods	ESA Methods
	Developed
Hylemya spp. & *Psila rosae*	
Chilo suppressalis	*Anthonomus grandis*
Myzus persicae	*Heliothis zea & virescens*
Nephotettix cincticeps	*Hypera postica*
Tribolium castaneum	*Diabrotica* spp.
Spodoptera littoralis	
Cocoa Mirids	
Tetranychid mites	Developing
Laspeyresia pomonella	
Leptinotarsa 10-lineata	*Conotrachelus nenuphar*
Adult Locusts	*Lygus* bugs
Lucilia larvae & adults	Anthocorid bugs
Beetles in stored cereals	Scarabaeid grubs
	Phytoseiid mites

Literature Cited

1. Hough, W.S. J. Agric. Res. (1934) $\underline{48}$, 533-553.
2. Yust, H.R. and F.F. Shelden. Ann. Entomol. Soc. Amer. (1952) $\underline{45}$, 220-228.
3. Wiesmann, R. Mitt. Schweiz. Entomol. Ges. (1947) $\underline{20}$, 484-504.
4. Lipke, H. and C.W. Kearns. J. Biol. Chem. (1959) $\underline{234}$, 2123-2125.
5. Tsukamoto, M., T. Narahashi and T. Yamasaki. Botyu-Kagaku (1965) $\underline{30}$, 128-132.
6. Oppenoorth, F.J. and N.W.H. Houx. Ent. Exp. Applic. (1968) $\underline{11}$, 81-93.
7. Matsumura, F. and M. Hayashi. Science (1966) $\underline{153}$, 757-759.
8. Bradbury, F.R. and H. Standen. Nature (1959) $\underline{183}$, 983-984.
9. Brown, A.W.A. In R. White-Stevens (ed.) "Pesticides in the Environment", Marcel Dekker, New York (1971) Vol I, Part II, pp. 455-552.
10. van Asperen, K. Ent. Exp. Applic. (1964) $\underline{7}$, 205-214.
11. El-Bashiev, S. and F.J. Oppenoorth. Nature (1969) $\underline{223}$, 210-211.
12. Hollingsworth, R.M., R.L. Metcalf and T.R. Fukuto. J. Agr. Food Chem. (1967) $\underline{15}$, 250-255.
13. Matsumura, F. and C.J. Hogendijk. Ent. Exp. Applic. (1964) $\underline{7}$, 179-193.
14. Shrivastava, S.P., M. Tsukamoto and J.E. Casida. J. Econ. Entomol. (1969) $\underline{62}$, 483-498.
15. Yamamoto, I., E.C. Kimmel and J.E. Casida. J. Agr. Food Chem. (1969) $\underline{17}$, 1227-1236.
16. Brown, A.W.A. Wld. Rev. Pest Control (1967) $\underline{6}$, 104-114.
17. Plapp, F.W. Annu. Rev. Entomol. (1976) $\underline{21}$, 179-197.
18. Lovell, J.B. and C.W. Kearns. J. Econ. Entomol. (1959) $\underline{52}$, 931-935.
19. Vinson, S.B. and J.R. Brazzel. J. Econ. Entomol. (1966) $\underline{59}$, 600-604.
20. Whitten, C.J. and D.L. Bull. Pesticide Biochem. Physiol. (1974) $\underline{4}$, 266-274.
21. Bull, D.L. and C.J. Whitten. J. Agr. Food Chem. (1972) $\underline{20}$, 561-564.
22. Motoyama, N., G.C. Rock and W.C. Dauterman. Pesticide Biochem. Physiol. (1972) $\underline{1}$, 205-215.
23. Smissaert, H.R. Science (1964) $\underline{143}$, 129-131.
24. Nolan, J., H.J. Schnitzerling and C.A. Schuntner. Pesticide Biochem. Physiol. (1972) $\underline{2}$, 85-94.
25. Schuntner, C.A. and W.J. Roulston. Austral. J. Biol. Sci. (1968) $\underline{21}$, 173-176.
26. Ayad, H. and G.P. Georghiou. J. Econ. Entomol. (1975) $\underline{68}$, 295-297.
27. Tripathi, R.K. Pesticide Biochem. Physiol. (1976) $\underline{6}$, 30-34.
28. Georghiou, G.P., C.S. Lin, C.S. Apperson and M.E. Pasternak. Proc. Calif. Mosq. Control Assoc. (1974) $\underline{42}$, 117-118.

29. Brown, T.M. and A.W.A. Brown. J. Econ. Entomol. (1974)
     67, 799-801.
30. Hsieh, M.Y., C.D. Steelman and P.E. Schilling. Mosquito
     News (1974) 34, 416-420.
31. Food and Agriculture Organization. Plant Protection Bull.
     (1969-71) 17, 83-89 & 129-131. 18, 16-18, 53-55 & 107-113.
     19, 15-18, 32-35 & 62-65. 22, 103-126.
32. Entomological Society of America. Bull. Entomol. Soc. Amer.
     (1967 & 1970) 14, 31-37 & 16, 147-153.
33. World Health Organization. Wld. Hlth. Org. Techn. Rep. Ser.
     No 443 (1970), 279 pp.

Herbicides

Introduction

PHILIP C. KEARNEY

Agricultural Environmental Quality Institute, Agricultural Research Center, USDA, Beltsville, Md. 20705

One of the most significant advances in modern chemical technology in the Twentieth Century has been the advent of selective weed control by synthetic herbicides. Growth of the American herbicide industry can be traced through three overlapping but successive stages over the last three decades. The occasion of the Centennial Meeting of the American Chemical Society affords a unique opportunity for examining the impact of chemistry on American agricultural productivity during this three stage developmental process.

The first stage occurred shortly after World War II with the discovery of the selective action of phenoxy herbicides, primarily 2,4-D, against certain broadleaf plant species. It was a period of rapid exploration of other biologically active structures possessing varying degrees of selectivity and persistence. Introduction of the phenylurea, phenylcarbamate, acylanilide, chlorinated aliphatic acid, thiocarbamate and s-triazine herbicides occurred during this first stage. The number of herbicides in general use in the United States and Canada by 1949 was about 25 used on 23 million acres of agricultural land.

The second stage of chemical weed control technology witnessed a period of tremendous growth in the usage of an ever growing arsenal of selected herbicides. The wide acceptability of herbicides in crop production programs was based on the direct economic benefits derived by the users. Market sales and production tonnage of organic herbicides were rapidly gaining on an already developed insecticide industry. By 1959 the number of herbicides in general use was about 100, applied to 53 million acres of agricultural land and the values of sales at slightly less than 500 million dollars.

The third and current stage of herbicide development saw a continuing increase in sales and production. By 1976 more than 165 herbicides are available to the American farmer, with an estimated 500 million pounds being used on about 200 million acres of land. Herbicide sales have increased steadily at about 13% per year since 1970, with a total dollar volume of over 850 million dollars. While production and sales soared, this stage of herbicide development was faced with an ever increasing body of regulatory constraints, coupled with rising development costs prompted primarily by the environmental concerns over the ubiquitous detection of organic compounds in soil, water, and air. The herbicide section of the symposium on "Pesticide Chemistry in the Twentieth Century" highlights chemical advances measured against the background of herbicide development over the last three decades.

Development of the American Herbicide Industry

E. F. ADLER, W. L. WRIGHT, and G. C. KLINGMAN

Lilly Research Laboratories, Eli Lilly and Co., Greenfield, Ind. 46140

From the beginning of recorded history, weeds have limited man's food supply and have imposed a heavy labor burden. Nearly all of early man's time was no doubt spent in obtaining food. Natural food sources permitted man's survival, even though periods of starvation must have been common. From 10,000 B.C. to 6,000 B.C., man began to cultivate crops by primitive methods (Fig. 1) (1). About 6,000 B.C., he fashioned hand-weeding tools. Around 1,000 B.C., animal-powered implements were introduced. Prior to this time, human energy was the sole source available for weed control.

In the 2,900 years between 1,000 B.C. and 1900 A.D., man learned to use animals to till the soil and to control weeds. Improved tools led to better cultural methods and even greater decreases in the human effort required for weed control. By 1920, in this country, perhaps 40% of the energy input to weed control was human, 60% animal.

In the 1920's, tractors were introduced as new agricultural tools and were used, among other things, to increase the amount of land that one man could cultivate. By 1947, tractors with cultivators replaced perhaps 70% of the hand and animal labor formerly required for weed control.

After World War II, modern chemical weed control was introduced. Chemical herbicides not only reduced the human energy required, but also reduced the amount of mechanical cultivation. We estimate human energy input for overall weed control in the United States today at no more than 5%, with only a trace of animal energy input; mechanical, at 40% and declining; with herbicides responsible for the remainder. Thus, the

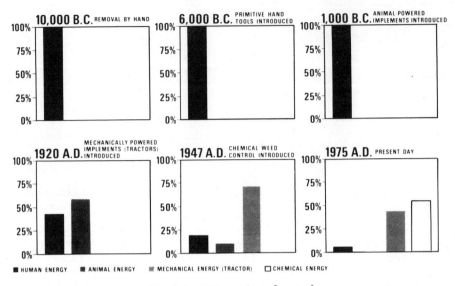

Figure 1.   History of weed control

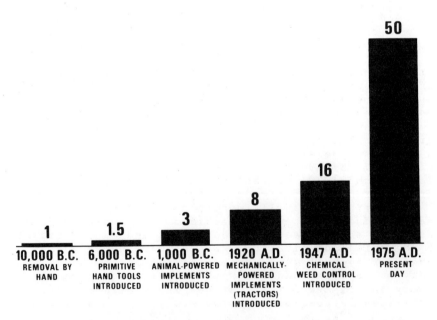

Figure 2.   Crop energy output per man (number of people fed by one farmer)

history of weed control has seen a shift from the use
of all human effort, to animal power, to petroleum-
powered equipment, and now to chemical herbicides.

Using the same time frames, the crop energy
output per man as measured by the number of people
fed by one farmer is presented in Figure 2.

Early man did well to feed himself. When he
began to cultivate crops, by 6,000 B.C., one man was
able to provide a little more food than he himself
could eat. Hence, some time was available for fash-
ioning tools and for other activities. By 1,000 B.C.,
one man could, in many parts of the world, feed as
many as three people. Again, let's move ahead 2,900
years to the United States; we find that by 1920 one
farmer was capable of feeding eight people; by 1947,
16; and today, at least 50 people. The most recent
of these advances would have been impossible without
chemical weed control.

The benefits from herbicide usage are many
(Table I).

Table I.   Herbicides reduce

Hand tillage costs	Harvest costs
Mechanical tillage costs	Grain drying costs
Fertilizer costs	Transportation and storage costs
Irrigation costs	Number of laborers required
Crop yield losses	Acres needed for crop production

They include a <u>reduction of hand tillage costs</u>.
Before herbicides, hand hoeing was regularly practiced
in all vegetable crops and in most agronomic crops.
In vegetable crops, hand hoeing might cost as much as
$300 or more per acre for the season. With herbicides,
total weeding costs can be reduced to a small fraction
of this sum. Before herbicides, 20 hours of hoe labor
time per acre in cotton was usual and weedy fields
could require 100 hours.

You may have heard that herbicides would not be
used in underdeveloped countries where labor is available and inexpensive. But our experience has been to
the contrary. Nowhere in the world do people like to

pull weeds by hand and move soil for weed control.
The abolishment of the drudgery of stoop labor, and
the consequent higher crop yields afforded by herbicides, ultimately betters the lot of the hoe-hand.
It also releases children to attend school and wives
to better tend their families or find more profitable
employment.

Herbicides reduce mechanical tillage costs (2).
Each year in the United States, 250 billion tons of
soil are moved, much of it several times, in tillage
and cultivation operations. This amount of soil
would make a ridge 100 feet high and one mile wide
from New York to San Francisco. The movement of this
soil each year is the world's largest material-
handling operation. At least one-half of this soil-
moving function is practiced solely for the control
of weeds.

Herbicides reduce fertilizer costs. Weeds are
in direct competition with crop plants for nutrients
from the soil. Without weed control, farmers would
be fertilizing the crop and the weeds.

Herbicides reduce irrigation costs. Weeds are
also in direct competition with crop plants for water.
Thus, irrigation water used by weeds is not available
for the production of a crop.

Crop yield losses due to weeds vary according to
the competitiveness of the crop, the weeds present,
and the population density of the weeds. Weed control
is extremely important to any good program of crop
production. Crop loss due to weed competition can be
substantial (3). As an example, it has been estimated
that nearly 100 million bushels of soybeans, or the
equivalent of the production from 4,000,000 acres, was
lost due to weed competition in the year 1970.

Herbicides reduce harvest costs. Weeds often
make it impossible to harvest a crop and may result in
total crop failure. Weeds wrap around, clog, and
otherwise interfere with harvesting equipment, resulting in longer running times, greater fuel consumption,
and increased harvest costs.

Herbicides reduce grain drying costs. Fields
that are filled with green weeds as the crop is matur-
ing and drying result in the grain drying more slowly.
Weed seeds and stems that find their way into the
grain bin are usually high in moisture content. These
green weed parts increase the potential for grain
spoilage and the cost of drying.

Herbicides reduce transportation and storage costs. A good example of the transportation and storage costs of weed seeds was given by a Canadian weed scientist (1). He reported that despite herbicide usage and grain-cleaning processes, 33 railroad carloads of weed seeds are transported across Canada from elevators to ports each day.

Finally, herbicides reduce the number of acres needed for crop production. If, through better weed control, we can obtain higher yields, we can reduce the number of acres required to produce a given amount of food.

The history of the use of chemicals for vegetation control goes back to antiquity. We know that the Romans salted the fields of their defeated Carthaginian foe. Probably salt was used much earlier as a soil sterilant. The first recorded recommendation of sodium chloride for weed control was in Germany in 1854 (4) (Table II). The next year sulfuric acid was recommended and was used for several decades around the world for selective weed control in cereals and onions. Sodium arsenite was introduced in 1902 by the Army Corps of Engineers for the control of water hyacinth in Louisiana. The effectiveness of carbon disulfide as a soil fumigant for weed control was discovered in 1906. It was used in Hawaii, California, and some of the western states. The peak usage was reached in Idaho in 1936 when 350,000 gallons were applied. Petroleum oils were used as early as 1914, and they have been widely used in irrigation and drainage ditches in the western states and as selective herbicides in carrots.

Table II. Chemicals first used as herbicides

Year Introduced	Chemical
1854	Sodium chloride
1855	Sulfuric acid
1902	Sodium arsenite
1906	Carbon disulfide
1914	Petroleum oils
1923	Sodium chlorate
1933	Dinitrophenol compounds
1940	Ammonium sulfamate

Sodium chlorate was first used in France in 1923. It has been used chiefly as a soil sterilant for control of deep-rooted perennial weeds. Dinitrophenol was first utilized in France in 1933 for the control of annual broadleaf weeds in cereals. It has been extensively employed in cereals, legumes, and flax in the northern United States.

Ammonium sulfamate has been used for the control of woody plants since 1940.

These older compounds each represented attempts at weed control, sometimes selective weed control, through chemicals. The last 30 years has been a time of rapid development of new herbicides, mainly organic chemicals, in the United States. Over 40 basic and specialty chemical manufacturers (such as pharmaceutical, oil, rubber, and paint companies) have participated in this chemical revolution of weed control. More than 130 different organic chemicals are currently employed as herbicides in the U.S. All of the main families of organic compounds are represented: aromatic, aliphatic, and heterocyclic. Herbicidal activity is found in a variety of classes of compounds: haloaliphatic, phenoxy, and benzoic acids; carbamates; dinitroanilines; acetanilides; amino triazines; quaternary pyridinium salts; uracils; and ureas. A few selected key examples are reviewed below.

2,4-D, introduced by Amchem in 1945, was the first of a series of phenoxyacetic acid herbicides (Fig. 3). These compounds are highly effective herbicides that selectively kill broadleaf weeds with little or no damage to grasses. They are still widely used to control broadleaf weeds in corn, wheat, barley, sorghum, sugarcane, grass pastures, and in turf.

Dalapon, a chlorinated aliphatic acid, was introduced by Dow Chemical in 1953 (Fig. 3). It is a grass killer, controlling tough perennial grasses such as johnsongrass, bermudagrass, and quackgrass. It possesses almost no crop selectivity.

Diuron was introduced by du Pont in 1954 (Fig. 3). It is one of a series of substituted urea herbicides. Diuron is applied preemergence to crops such as cotton, alfalfa, grapes, fruit and nut crops. Foliar activity is enhanced when a surfactant is added to the spray.

EPTC was introduced by Stauffer in 1959 (Fig. 3). It is a thiocarbamate and an important member of a large family of herbicides. Thiocarbamates are usually soil incorporated. EPTC is used in crops such

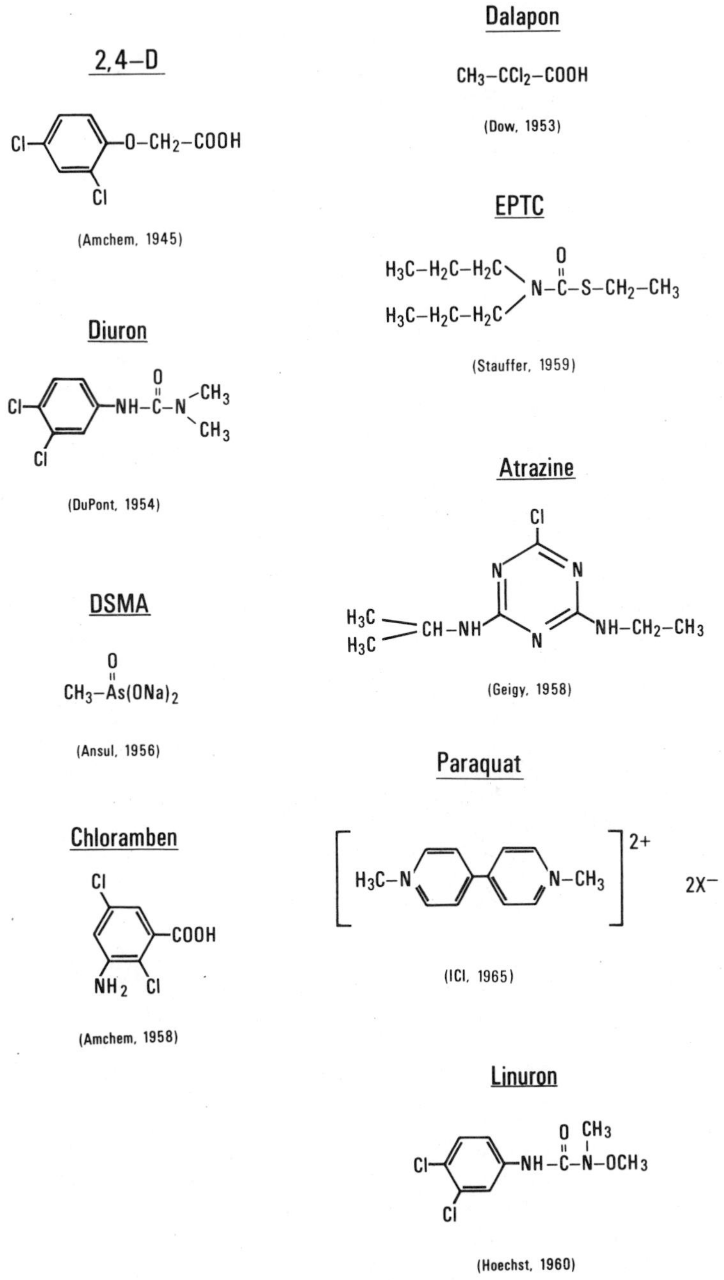

2,4-D

Cl—⟨benzene⟩—O—CH₂—COOH (with Cl)

(Amchem, 1945)

Diuron

Cl—⟨benzene, Cl⟩—NH—C(=O)—N(CH₃)(CH₃)

(DuPont, 1954)

DSMA

CH₃—As(=O)(ONa)₂

(Ansul, 1956)

Chloramben

Cl, NH₂, Cl substituted benzene—COOH

(Amchem, 1958)

Dalapon

CH₃—CCl₂—COOH

(Dow, 1953)

EPTC

H₃C—H₂C—H₂C / H₃C—H₂C—H₂C — N—C(=O)—S—CH₂—CH₃

(Stauffer, 1959)

Atrazine

triazine ring with Cl, (H₃C)₂CH—NH, NH—CH₂—CH₃

(Geigy, 1958)

Paraquat

[H₃C—N⟨pyridine⟩—⟨pyridine⟩N—CH₃]²⁺   2X⁻

(ICI, 1965)

Linuron

Cl, Cl substituted benzene—NH—C(=O)—N(CH₃)—OCH₃

(Hoechst, 1960)

Figure 3.   Selected U.S. herbicides introduced into agriculture—company and year of introduction for each in parentheses

as alfalfa, certain beans, potatoes, and sweet
potatoes. In addition to controlling numerous grass
and broadleaf weeds, it controls nutsedge, one of the
world's worst weeds.

DSMA was introduced by Ansul in 1956 (Fig. 3).
DSMA is an organic arsenical having contact, postemergence activity. It was first utilized for crab-
grass control in turf. It is an effective herbicide
in cotton and in citrus trees, but must be used as a
directed spray to avoid contact with the crop foliage.

Atrazine was introduced by Geigy in 1958 (Fig. 3).
It is a member of a large group of symmetrical triazine herbicides. Atrazine is a preemergence herbicide
to which corn is tolerant. It is the number one
herbicide in acreage treated and in dollars of sales
in the United States. The compound is also used in
orchards, pineapple, sorghum, and sugarcane.

Chloramben, a benzoic acid derivative introduced
by Amchem in 1958, is a selective preemergence herbicide (Fig. 3). It is used principally in soybeans,
corn, and peanuts.

Paraquat, a bipyridyl quaternary ammonium salt,
was introduced by ICI in 1965 (Fig. 3). It is a non-
selective, contact herbicide on plant foliage, but is
immediately inactivated when applied to soil. It is
used in minimum tillage programs and as a postemergence directed spray in sugarcane and in fruit tree
crops.

Linuron, a substituted urea introduced by Hoechst
in 1960, is employed primarily as a preemergence
herbicide; but it also has contact effect on foliage
(Fig. 3). Linuron is used principally in soybeans,
corn, sorghum, wheat, and potatoes. It is often
mixed with other herbicides to broaden the weed
spectrum.

Bromacil is a uracil herbicide introduced by
du Pont in 1963 (Fig. 4). It controls a broad
spectrum of weeds in citrus and pineapple crops. The
chemical is also used for general vegetation control
on noncrop areas such as railroads and industrial
areas.

Picloram is a picolinic acid derivative introduced by Dow Chemical in 1963 (Fig. 4). Picloram is
highly active on most perennial broadleaf and woody
species, and most grasses are resistant.

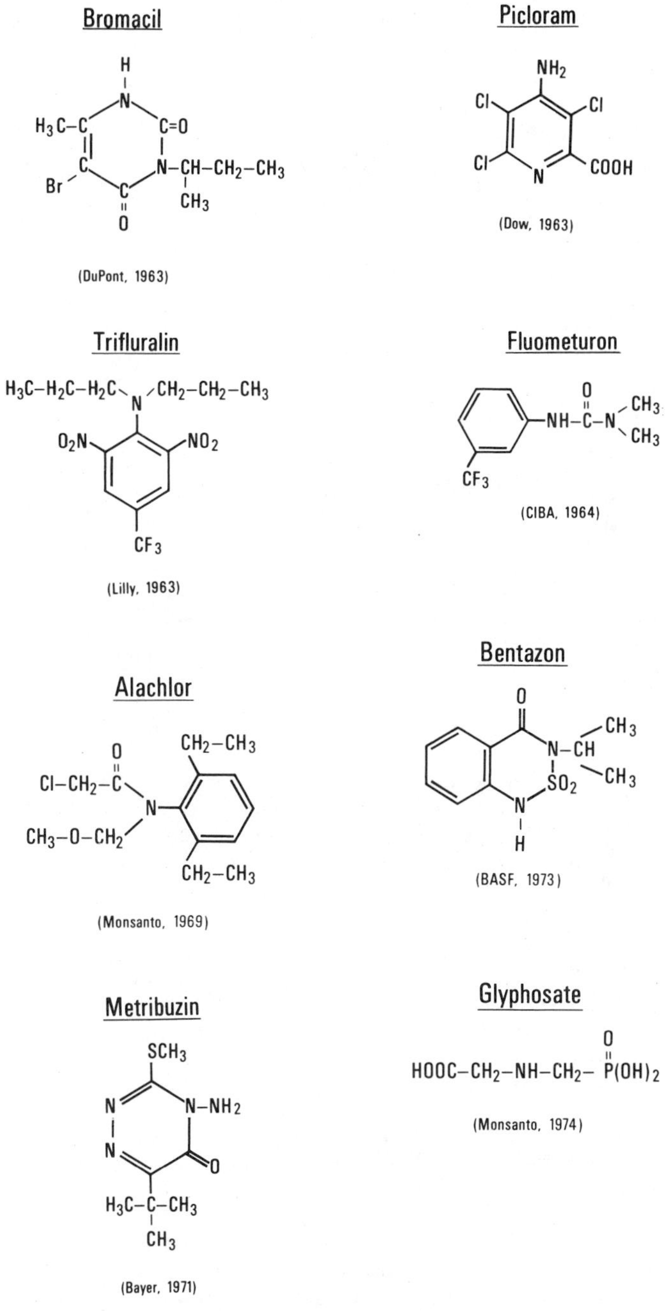

Bromacil

(DuPont, 1963)

Picloram

(Dow, 1963)

Trifluralin

(Lilly, 1963)

Fluometuron

(CIBA, 1964)

Alachlor

(Monsanto, 1969)

Bentazon

(BASF, 1973)

Metribuzin

(Bayer, 1971)

Glyphosate

$$HOOC-CH_2-NH-CH_2- \overset{\overset{O}{\|}}{P}(OH)_2$$

(Monsanto, 1974)

*Figure 4. Selected U.S. herbicides introduced into agriculture—
company and year of introduction for each in parentheses*

Trifluralin is a dinitroaniline and was introduced by Eli Lilly in 1963 (Fig. 4). It was the first of a number of similar dinitroanilines. It is widely used in cotton and soybeans and is labeled for use on more than 50 crops. It is usually incorporated into the soil prior to planting the crop.

Fluometuron is another substituted urea introduced by CIBA in 1964 (Fig. 4). It is a preemergence herbicide and finds its niche primarily in cotton and sugarcane. It is usually applied in combination with other herbicides to broaden the spectrum of weed species controlled.

Alachlor is an acetanilide introduced by Monsanto in 1969 (Fig. 4). Alachlor is a preemergence herbicide, extensively used primarily in corn, soybeans, and peanuts.

Bentazon is a benzothiadiazine introduced by BASF in 1973 (Fig. 4). It is a contact herbicide for selective postemergence control of many broadleaf weeds in soybeans, rice, corn, and peanuts.

Metribuzin is an asymmetrical triazine introduced by Bayer in 1971 (Fig. 4). Metribuzin is used alone or in combination with other herbicides in soybeans, sugarcane, and potatoes.

Glyphosate is a substituted glycine introduced by Monsanto in 1974 (Fig. 4). It is nonselective and when applied to plant foliage, controls both annual and perennial broadleaved weeds and grasses.

The United States has been a leader in the development and use of herbicides. In 1951, herbicides amounted to only 10% of the total of 463 million pounds of pesticides produced in this country (Fig. 5). In 1974, the latest year for which records are available, 604 million pounds, or 43% of the 1,417 million pounds of pesticides produced in the United States, were herbicides (5).

Moving to pesticide sales, in millions of dollars at the manufacturer's level, there is even greater growth (Fig. 6). Herbicides have consistently been more valuable per pound than most other pesticides (5). In 1951, herbicides constituted 13% of the dollars spent for pesticides and in 1974 herbicide sales had grown to 58%. In 23 years herbicide sales dollars had grown nearly fiftyfold, to over one billion dollars per year.

The leadership of the U.S. herbicide industry is evidenced by the fact that, in 1974, over 58% of the worldwide expenditures for herbicides were in the U.S. (6).

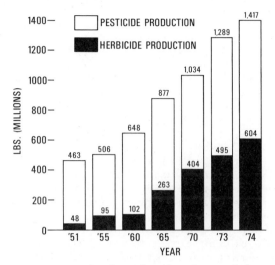

Figure 5. *Herbicide production and pesticide production*

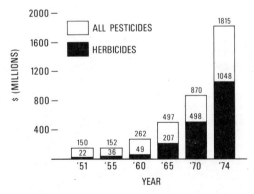

Figure 6. *Pesticide sales—manufacturer's level*

Figure 7 shows the total acres of U.S. cropland
and those treated with herbicides. Those acres
planted to crops (not to pastures, forests, etc.) in
1959 were 359 million acres, and in 1974, 368 million
acres. The acres treated with herbicides have increased from 53 million in 1959 to an estimated 185
million in 1974, or from less than 15% of the acres
planted in 1959 to over 50% in 1974 (7, 8, 9, 10).
There has been rapid growth in usage of preemergence herbicides (Fig. 8) (8, 9, 10). Preemergence herbicides are applied to the soil prior
to germination of weeds and crops. Postemergence
applications are applied to established weeds, such
as the use of 2,4-D on weeds growing in corn or wheat.
In 1959, most herbicide applications were postemergence. Preemergence treatments have grown rapidly
since that time. In 1968, only 45% of the herbicide
treatments were preemergence; but by 1971, 68%; and
in 1974, 70% of the acres treated with herbicides
employed preemergence treatments. However, some of
the newer postemergence materials being developed for
the control of tolerant and resistant weeds may slow
this trend, on a percentage basis, toward preemergence
treatments.
The chemical industry has supported herbicide
research in terms of both scientists and resources.
Estimates of the numbers of herbicide research
workers in industry in the United States adapted from
information provided in the last two surveys of the
National Agricultural Chemicals Association are presented in Figure 9 (11, 12). In 1971, there were
827 industry scientists in herbicide research and
development--319 Ph.D.'s, 183 M.S.'s, and 325 B.S.'s.
Supporting these scientists were 495 other people
serving primarily as technicians. The numbers have
continued to increase until in 1975, there were 451
Ph.D.'s, 247 Masters, 404 Bachelors, with 877 in the
"other" category, for a total of nearly 2,000 people
working in industry herbicide research in the United
States. We would further estimate that of this
number at least half are chemists--organic, physical,
analytical, and biochemists. The remaining half are
biologists and scientists with various agricultural
backgrounds.
Figure 10 shows estimates of the expenditures by
U.S. industry on research and development of herbicides (11, 12). In 1971, 46.3 million dollars was
spent. In four years expenditures had increased 80%
to 83.3 million dollars.

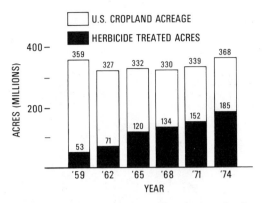

Figure 7. *Herbicide usage on U.S. croplands*

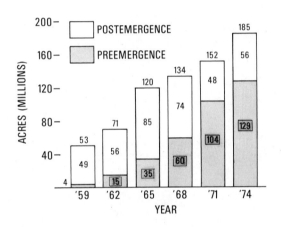

Figure 8. *Herbicide-treated acres*

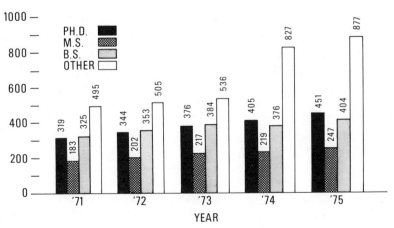

Figure 9. *Herbicide research workers in industry (estimated)*

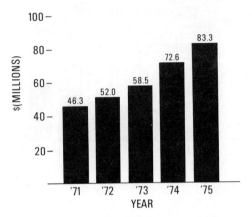

Figure 10.   Estimated herbicide R & D expenditures

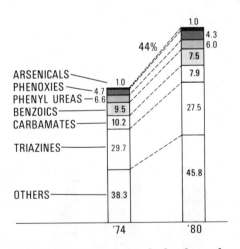

Figure 11.   Projected U.S. herbicide market by product groups

What do we see in the near future for herbicides? Looking ahead five growing seasons to 1980, we see predictions of continued growth in herbicide sales and in research and development.

The publication *Farm Chemicals* recently projected growth of the herbicide market by product group (6) (Fig. 11). In 1974, the first column, we find arsenicals with 1% of the market; phenoxies with 4.7%; phenylureas such as diuron, linuron, and fluometuron with 6.6%; benzoics such as chloramben, dicamba, trichlorobenzoic acid with 9.5%; carbamates such as EPTC, diallate, and chloropropham with 10.2%; and the triazines such as atrazine, prometryne, and cyanazine with 29.7%. The "others" category with 38.3% includes alachlor, paraquat, trifluralin, and some of the more recent product entries such as bentazon, glyphosate, and metribuzin.

The second column depicts the 1980 herbicide market as compared with 1974, with a 44% growth increase overall. All product groups show some real growth, even though percent of the total market declines in all except the "others" category. The "others" category will show an actual increase of 72% and increase its percentage share of the market from 38.3 in 1974 to 45.8% in 1980.

If research and development expenses and industry staffing continue to grow at the rate of the last five years, the expenditures for industry herbicide research and development can be projected to double from 1975 to 1980, reaching 173 million dollars in 1980 (Table III). If industry personnel needs continue to increase during the next five years at the same rate as in the past five, there will be 1,500 scientific and 1,800 support personnel required by industry in 1980, or an increase of 67%.

Table III.   Herbicide R & D projections

1975		1980
	EXPENDITURES	
$83,300	(000's)	$173,500
	PERSONNEL	
1,102	SCIENTIFIC	1,500
877	SUPPORT	1,800
1,979	TOTAL	3,300

With all the work that has gone on the last 30 years, and with over 130 herbicides in use today, are all the weed problems solved? Not at all. Old problems abound and new problems arise each year. There are many opportunities for new developments in herbicidal weed control. Some are:

1. Further development of herbicides with true physiological tolerance to specific crop plants such as is exhibited by atrazine on corn.

2. Better combinations of herbicides are needed to provide the broad spectrum of weed control needed in different localities.

3. The control of persistence needs further consideration. At times only two or three hours or two or three days of herbicide activity are desired. For many crops a persistence of two or three months is needed; whereas in certain conditions, as for soil sterilants and various tree crops, two or three years of persistence may be desired. Through inherent compound characteristics, through the amount applied, and through improved formulations, we can and must tailor persistence of herbicides to fit the period of weed control desired.

4. New and better aquatic herbicides, including aquatic weed growth regulators, are needed since aquatic weeds are not well controlled at present. We must learn how to control weeds in running water and in waterways, as well as lakes and ponds.

5. The transformation of valueless brushlands to productive pasture lands by the use of herbicides holds tremendous potential for increased beef production.

6. The use of antidote chemicals or "anti-herbicides" on crops to counteract the effect of herbicides and thereby increase crop tolerance is a highly promising procedure. This technique is already being used in one series of compounds and may enjoy greater acceptance as more "anti-herbicides" become available.

7. Differences in crop variety tolerance have been known for a long time. Thus, there exists the

possibility of developing, through selective
breeding, crops that are more resistant to
herbicides.

8.   The use of growth regulators to severely inhibit
       weeds may prove of value. In many cases it is
       not really necessary to kill the weed. It is
       usually adequate to inhibit it so that it is
       unable to compete successfully or to reproduce.

       The future of herbicides remains promising. New
and better compounds with greater safety to crops, to
man, and the environment will become available. If
the increased food needs of the world are met, they
will be met and man's labor burden eased, in part, by
the use of suitable herbicidal compounds.

Literature Cited

1.   Hay, J. R.   Weed Science (1974)   22:439-442.
2.   Shaw, W. C.   Weeds (1964)   12:153-162.
3.   Knake, E. L. and Slife, F. W.   Weeds (1962)
       10:26-29.
4.   Timmons, F. L.   Weed Science (1970)   18:294-307.
5.   U.S. Tariff Commission.   Synthetic Organic
       Chemicals, United States Production and Sales of
       Pesticides and Related Products, Annual Reports
       for 1951-1974.
6.   "World Pesticide Markets--FC Special Report"
       Farm Chemicals (1975)   138(9):45-48.
7.   "Agricultural Statistics"   U.S.D.A., Editions
       1959-1974.
8.   "Extent and Cost of Weed Control with Herbicides
       and an Evaluation of Important Weeds, 1965"
       Agr. Res. Service, U.S.D.A., Economic Res.
       Service, Report ARS 34-102, 1968.
9.   "Extent and Cost of Weed Control with Herbicides
       and an Evaluation of Important Weeds, 1968"
       Agr. Res. Service, U.S.D.A., Economic Res.
       Service, Report ARS-H-1, 1972.
10.   "Farmers' Use of Pesticides in 1971"   U.S.D.A.,
       Economic Res. Service, Agricultural Economic
       Report 252, 1974.
11.   "Industry Profile Study, 1973"   National
       Agricultural Chemicals Association, Washington,
       D.C.
12.   "Industry Profile Study, 1975"   National
       Agricultural Chemicals Association, Washington,
       D.C.

4

Mode of Action of Herbicides

DONALD E. MORELAND

U. S. Department of Agriculture, Agricultural Research Service Crop Science Department, North Carolina State University, Raleigh, N. C. 27607

The primary biochemical sites of action of some herbicides have been identified and an appreciation is being gained on how these same herbicides express phytotoxicity by interfering with the plant's biochemistry. The progress being made in this area of research accompanies the increased comprehension that is being achieved on the basic biochemistry of plant growth and on the endogenous control systems that regulate growth and development.

Corbett (1) recently summarized the current status of biochemical knowledge on the mode of action of herbicides in the general form shown in Figure 1. Interference with the processes identified in the left-hand column has been documented for the action of one or more herbicides (1, 2, 3, 4). Interferences are indicated as affecting various interrelated processes (structural organization, energy supply, and growth and reproduction). If the interference is extreme, the treated plant dies.

Thiolcarbamates have been shown to interfere with lipid synthesis and, thereby, to alter the integrity of membranes. Some of the pyridazinones interfere not only with lipid synthesis, but also with the Hill reaction and carotenoid synthesis. The bipyridiliums intercept photoinduced electron flow in the chloroplasts and undergo one-electron reduction to form free radicals. When the radicals are oxidized, hydrogen peroxide is formed, which is thought to react with unsaturated membrane lipids. Membrane permeability is increased and, subsequently, cellular structure is destroyed. Mitochondrial electron transport and oxidative phosphorylation are affected by a large group of herbicides, including the N-phenylcarbamates, acylanilides, phenols, and halogenated benzonitriles. Most of the herbicides that interfere with the mitochondrial reactions also inhibit photosynthetic electron transport as do the phenylureas, s-triazines, and uracils. The N-phenylcarbamates and dinitroanilines, in addition to affecting the mitochondrial and chloroplast reactions, arrest cell division. Glyphosate has been reported to interfere with protein synthesis in *Lemna* (<u>5</u>).

Identification of the biochemical mechanisms involved in the action of the phenoxies continues to challenge investigators. These herbicides are depicted, in Figure 1, as affecting the unknown site at which the native hormone, indoleacetic acid, expresses its growth-controlling action (<u>1</u>).

Of the various biochemical pathways identified as being affected by herbicides, the chloroplast-mediated reactions have received the greatest attention. Approximately 70 percent of the current commercial herbicides, while they may also affect other systems, interfere with chloroplast reactions. Hence, the objectives of this paper are to review some of the work conducted with isolated chloroplasts, evaluate the status of these studies, and relate the observed interferences to the expression of phytotoxicity.

Chloroplast-mediated Reactions.

Interference by certain phenylurea and *N*-phenylcarbamate herbicides with the photochemical reactions of isolated chloroplasts was first reported in 1956 (<u>2</u>). Over the next few years, inhibition by the *s*-triazines, uracils, benzimidazoles, and benzonitriles was reported (<u>2</u>, <u>3</u>, <u>6</u>).

Chloroplasts of higher plants are saucer-shaped, and from 4 to 10 μm in diameter and 1 to 3 μm thick. The chlorophyll is concentrated in bodies within the chloroplasts called grana, which are about 0.4 μm in diameter. Under the electron microscope, the grana appear as highly organized, precisely stacked lamellae, to which the chlorophyll is bound, imbedded in a stroma matrix. The light and associated electron transport reactions take place in the lamellae, whereas enzymes involved in carbon dioxide fixation are located in the stroma.

Photoinduced electron transport and the coupled phosphorylation reactions as they are postulated to occur in chloroplasts are presented schematically in Figure 2. Not all investigators agree on the details of this scheme, and some even question the sequence of the intermediates. The numbers and locations of the phosphorylation sites also remain to be identified precisely. However, the scheme is a reasonable approximation based on available information. Reactions that occur in the light are represented by the open arrows, and the solid arrows represent electron transfers that occur in the dark.

Through a series of oxidation-reduction reactions driven by two light reactions operating in series and involving several hundred chlorophyll molecules, electrons flow from water to NADP. Participating in the overall reaction is a water-splitting complex that includes a mangano-protein and chloride ions. An unidentified chlorophyll α molecule serves as the reaction center of photosystem II, with Q as the primary electron acceptor. Involved sequentially on the electron transport chain are plasto-

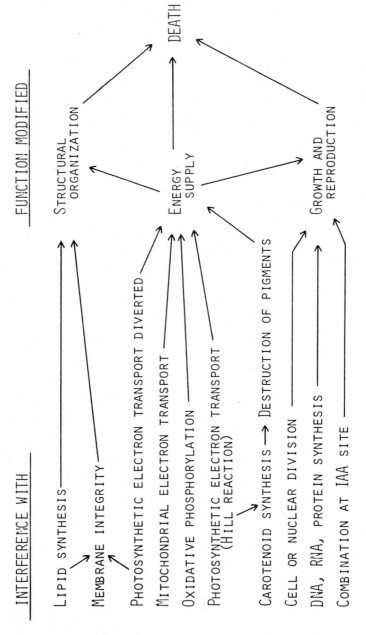

Figure 1. Summary diagram of the mode of action of pesticides [adapted from Corbett (1)]

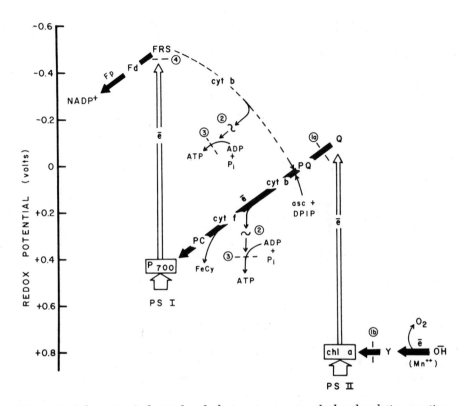

Figure 2. Schematic of photoinduced electron transport and phosphorylation reactions considered to occur in chloroplast lamellae [from Moreland and Hilton (2)]. Open arrows indicate light reactions; solid arrows indicate dark reactions; and the narrow dashed line represents the cyclic pathway. Abbreviations used: PS I, photosystem I; PS II, photosystem II; Y, postulated electron donor for photosystem II; Q, unknown primary electron acceptor for photosystem II; PQ, plastoquinones; cyt b, b-type cytochromes; cyt f, cytochrome f; PC, plastocyanin; P$_{700}$, reaction center chlorophyll of photosystem I; FRS, ferredoxin-reducing substance; Fd, ferredoxin; Fp, ferredoxin-NADP oxidoreductase; FeCy, ferricyanide; asc, ascorbate; and DPIP, 2,6-dichlorophenolindophenol. The numbers 1a, 1b, 2, 3, and 4 indicate postulated sites of action by herbicides. See text for details.

quinone, a b-type cytochrome, cytochrome f (a c-type cytochrome),
and plastocyanin (a copper-protein). Electron passage along the
chain generates at least one molecule of ATP.

P_{700} (a special chlorophyll a molecule) serves as the reaction center of photosystem I, and a bound form of ferredoxin
(ferredoxin-reducing substance) may be the electron acceptor.
Electrons flow subsequently to NADP through ferredoxin (a non-
heme iron protein) and a flavoprotein.

Cyclic electron flow is represented as a shunt in Figure 2.
A site of ATP generation involving a b-type cytochrome is shown
on this bypass. The shunted electrons may return to the central
chain at a point close to plastoquinone as shown; however, some
investigators believe that they reenter nearer to cytochrome f.

Artificial electron acceptors, such as ferricyanide, can be
substituted for NADP; these give rise to oxygen evolution but involve only a short segment of the oxidation chain. This partial
reaction is known as the Hill reaction and compounds that disrupt
it are known as Hill inhibitors. Herbicides that inhibit the
Hill reaction, by blocking electron transport, prevent the production of ATP and NADPH required for carbon dioxide fixation.

Classification of Inhibitory Herbicides.

Herbicides that inhibit the photochemical reactions of
isolated chloroplasts have been called routinely inhibitors of
the Hill reaction. This has been done primarily for convenience
and because, for many years, their action was evaluated under
nonphosphorylating conditions, frequently with ferricyanide as
the electron acceptor. In the past few years, more sophisticated
studies have been conducted with herbicides and more is known
about their differential actions. Consequently, Moreland and
Hilton (2) separated herbicidal inhibitors of the photochemically
induced reactions into the following classes: (a) electron transport inhibitors, (b) uncouplers, (c) energy transfer inhibitors,
(d) inhibitory uncouplers (multiple types of inhibition), and
(e) electron acceptors.

A full comprehension of the specific sites involved in the
inhibitory action of herbicides and the mechanisms through which
inhibition is produced will be achieved only when the uncertain-
ties associated with the sequence and interrelation of components
in the electron transport pathway, the numbers and locations of
phosphorylation sites, and the mechanism of phosphorylation have
been resolved.

Electron Transport Inhibitors.
Electron transport is in-
hibited when one or more of the intermediate electron transport
carriers are removed or inactivated. The site of action of most
herbicidal electron transport inhibitors is considered to be
associated closely with photosystem II. Consequently, reactions
coupled to photosystem II are inhibited, such as basal electron

transport, methylamine-uncoupled electron transport, and noncyclic electron transport with water as electron donor and ferricyanide or NADP as electron acceptor. The coupled phosphorylation is inhibited by the action on the reductive reaction.
Partial reactions not dependent on photosystem II, such as cyclic
phosphorylation or the photoreduction of NADP with an electron
donor that circumvents photosystem II (ascorbate + DPIP), are
either not inhibited or inhibited only weakly. These herbicides
also do not inhibit mitochondrial oxidative phosphorylation.

The action of diuron has been studied more intensively and
extensively than that of any other herbicide. However, its site
of inhibition has not been identified to the satisfaction of all
investigators. In 1962, Duysens and Amesz (7) provided evidence
that diuron acted on the reducing side of photosystem II between
Q and plastoquinone (Figure 2, site 1a). However, other investigators have suggested that diuron may act on the oxidizing side
of photosystem II (Figure 2, site 1b), or directly on the chlorophyll a reaction center of photosystem II (2). Recently, Renger
(8) proposed that diuron may act on both sides of photosystem II:
(a) on the reducing side where it acts as an inhibitor, and (b)
on the oxidizing side where it accelerates the deactivation of
the water-splitting enzyme system Y. The action of many other
diversely structured compounds is compared frequently to that of
diuron; however, their site(s) of action has not been resolved
beyond the general area around photosystem II. The mechanism
through which inhibition is imposed, even by diuron, is unknown.

Herbicides that seem to have a single site of action on the
photochemical pathway, which is associated closely with photosystem II, are the chlorinated phenylureas, bis-carbamates such
as phenmedipham, chlorinated s-triazines, substituted uracils,
pyridazinones, diphenylethers, 1,2,4-triazinones, azido-s-
triazines, cyclopropane-carboxamides, p-alkylanilides, p-alkyl-
thioanilides, aminotriazinones, and urea-carbamates (2).

Uncouplers. Uncouplers dissociate electron transport from
photophosphorylation. Both noncyclic and cyclic phosphorylation
are inhibited, but electron transport reactions are either unaffected or stimulated. Because uncouplers relieve the inhibition of electron transport imposed by energy transfer inhibitors,
they are considered to act at a site closer to the electron
transport chain than the site of phosphate uptake. In Figure 2,
they are shown (site 2) as dissipating some form of conserved
energy represented as $\sim$ on the noncyclic and cyclic ATP-gener-
ating pathways. Perfluidone is the only herbicide identified
to date that functions as a pure uncoupler at pH 8.0 (2). Compounds that uncouple photophosphorylation also uncouple mitochondrial oxidative phosphorylation.

Energy Transfer Inhibitors. Energy transfer inhibitors act
directly on phosphorylation. Like electron transport inhibitors,

they inhibit both electron transport and phosphorylation in
coupled systems. However, addition of an appropriate uncoupler
releases the inhibition of electron flow (but not of ATP formation). The 1,2,3-thiadiazolyl-phenylureas have been reported to
act as energy transfer inhibitors in photophosphorylation (9).
Nonherbicides that behave in this way are the antibiotic Dio-9
and phlorizin. Energy transfer inhibitors are depicted in Figure
2 as affecting site 3 on the noncyclic and cyclic ATP-generat-
ing pathways.

Inhibitory Uncouplers. Inhibitory uncouplers inhibit the
reactions affected by both electron transport inhibitors and uncouplers. Hence, they inhibit basal, methylamine-uncoupled, and
coupled electron transport with ferricyanide as electron acceptor
and water as the electron donor, much like electron transport inhibitors. Coupled noncyclic photophosphorylation is inhibited
and the phosphorylation reaction is slightly more sensitive than
the reduction of ferricyanide. Cyclic photophosphorylation is
also inhibited. NADP reduction, when photosystem II is circumvented with ascorbate + DPIP, is not inhibited; however, the
associated phosphorylation is inhibited. Inhibitory uncouplers
act at both sites 1 and 2 (Figure 2).
Herbicides that act as inhibitory uncouplers are dinitro-
phenols, N-phenylcarbamates, acylanilides, halogenated benzonitriles, substituted imidazoles, substituted benzimidazoles,
bromofenoxim, substituted 2,6-dinitroanilines, pyridinols, and
substituted 1,2,4-thiadiazoles (2).

Electron Acceptors. Compounds classified as electron
acceptors can compete with some component of the electron transport pathway and subsequently be reduced. Ferricyanide, PMS, and
FMN, which are used to study partial reactions of the photochemical pathway, operate in this manner. However, they are not phytotoxic.
Bipyridyliums with redox potentials in the range of -300 to
-500 mV, such as diquat and paraquat, can accept electrons in
competition with the acceptor of photosystem I (Figure 2, site 4)
and have herbicidal activity. Interception of electron flow from
photosystem I essentially shunts the electron transport chain.
The bipyridyliums support both noncyclic and cyclic photophosphorylation, are photoreduced by illuminated chloroplasts under
anaerobic conditions, and inhibit the photoreduction of NADP.
This inhibition is not circumvented by the addition of reduced
DPIP (10).

Structure-activity Studies.

The Hill reaction has served as a target for structure-
activity studies with phenylureas, N-phenylcarbamates, polycyclic
ureas, acylanilides, s-triazines, uracils, dihalogenated benzoni-

triles, azido-*s*-triazines, 1,2,4-triazinones, imidazoles, and
benzimidazoles (6, 11). The objectives of these studies have
been to (a) identify the substituents required for maximum inhibition, (b) relate the chemical and physical properties of the
herbicides to the inhibitory action, (c) determine the environment in which the inhibitors operate, and (d) identify interactions between substituents of the inhibitors and the postulated
receptors in the chloroplasts.

Phenylamide Inhibitors. Some of the earliest structure-
activity studies, which involved the substituted amides, showed
that the strongest inhibitors had a ring system bonded to the
nitrogen of the amide moiety and a free and sterically unhindered
amide hydrogen. Derivatives with unsaturated ring systems,
represented by chloroxuron and diuron, were more inhibitory than
were those with saturated ring systems, such as norea and cy-
cluron. Inhibition was intensified when the ring was chlorinated
in a *meta*- and the *para*-ring positions, as in diuron and propanil.
Derivatives monochlorinated in a *meta*- or the *para*-ring position,
as in chlorpropham and monuron, were less inhibitory than the
3,4-dichlorinated derivatives, but were more inhibitory than the
unsubstituted parent compounds. However, derivatives chlorinated
in an *ortho* position were less active than the unsubstituted
parent compound. Disubstituted isomers in which an *ortho* chlorine was paired with a *meta* or a *para* chlorine were also quite
inactive (6).
  Inhibitory action was associated with a wide variety of
structural groups substituted on the carbonyl carbon of the
amide moiety. In general, derivatives with nonpolar side chains
were more active than those with polar side chains. The most
active inhibitors, represented by diuron, possessed a dialkyl-
amino substituent. However, derivatives with aliphatic side
chains, such as propanil, and alicyclic side chains, such as
cypromid, were also strong inhibitors (6).
  The requirement for a free and sterically unhindered amide
hydrogen led to the postulation that the amide moiety interacted
with the receptor in the chloroplasts. Because of the reversibility of the inhibition, the interaction was considered to involve weak bonds, conceivably hydrogen bonds.

Substituent Parameters. A significant advance was made, in
the structure-activity studies with the Hill reaction, when
Hansch and Deutsch (12) evaluated some of the published Hill inhibition data with a multiple regression analysis, an extra-
thermodynamic approach, or the so-called sigma, pi (σ, π) regression analysis. The principle of the approach rests on the
assumption that changes in biological activity can be correlated with measurable molecular or substituent parameters. This
analysis involved equations of the following type:

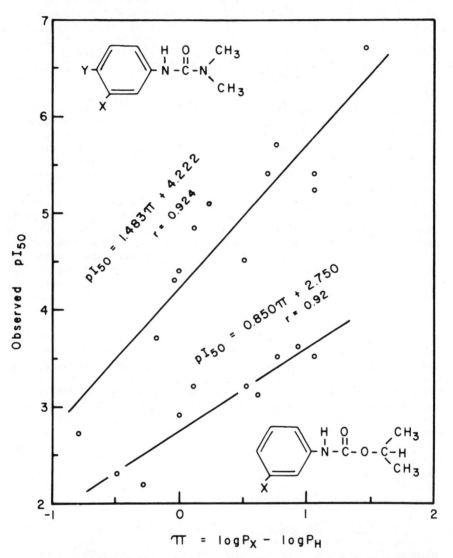

Figure 3. Correlation of pI_{50} and partition data for some substituted phenyldimethyl-ureas and isopropyl N-phenylcarbamates [adapted from Hansch and Deutsch (12)]

$$pI_{50} = a\pi + b\sigma + cE_s + d$$

where π is a partition coefficient obtained in an octanol/water system, σ is the Hammett substituent parameter, E_s is the Taft steric factor, and a, b, c, and d are constants. The partition coefficient was obtained from the following equation:

$$\pi_X = \log P_X - \log P_H$$

where P_H is the partition coefficient of the unsubstituted parent molecule and P_X is the partition coefficient of the derivative. Hence, π becomes the logarithm of the partition coefficient of the substituent X.

Examples of correlations published by Hansch and Deutsch (12) are shown in Figure 3. The relation between π and observed pI_{50} values for a series of *meta*-substituted isopropyl *N*-phenyl-carbamates is presented in the lower curve. The upper curve shows a similar relation for a series of *meta*- and *para*-substituted phenylureas. In both examples, regression analyses suggested that approximately 92% of the observed responses could be attributed to the lipophilicity, or the hydrophobic bonding power, of the ring substituents. The addition of Hammett substituent and Taft steric constants to the equations did not improve significantly the regression coefficients. Hence, electronic contributions were considered to be of minor importance in the expression of inhibition.

Based partly on the above results, Hansch (13) subsequently postulated that for the acylanilides, uracils, benzimidazoles, imidazoles, and triazines, the site of action in the chloroplasts involved the amide linkage of strategically located proteins (Figure 4). A good inhibitor had a large lipophilic moiety that bound to the hydrophobic area and a polar function that anchored the inhibitor to the receptor. The system had a planar arrangement. Inhibitors were also characterized by having an N-H group attached to an electron-deficient sp^2 carbon atom. Binding of the inhibitor was visualized as occurring between the lone-pair electrons of the herbicide nitrogen and the electron-deficient carbonyl of the protein amide group. Binding was postulated to involve something between a complete charge-transfer complex and a simple dipole interaction, possibly reinforced by hydrogen bonds (13).

Heterocyclic Inhibitors.   Around 1968, results obtained with a new generation of Hill inhibitors, which lacked a free amide hydrogen, began to appear in the literature. A very complete structure-activity study was conducted by Draber *et al.* (14, 15) with numerous 1,2,4-triazinones. Correlations were made with the multiple regression approach introduced by Hansch. From this study, Draber *et al.* concluded (Figure 5) that R_1 was involved in the binding to the receptor, possibly by creating a

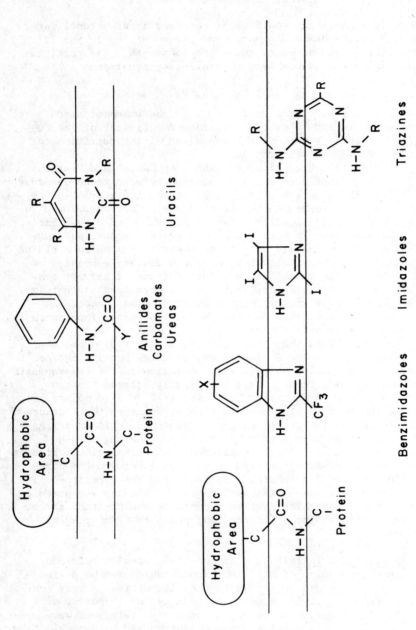

Figure 4. Interaction of structural elements of herbicidal inhibitors of photosystem II with a postulated receptor protein [adapted from Hansch (13)]

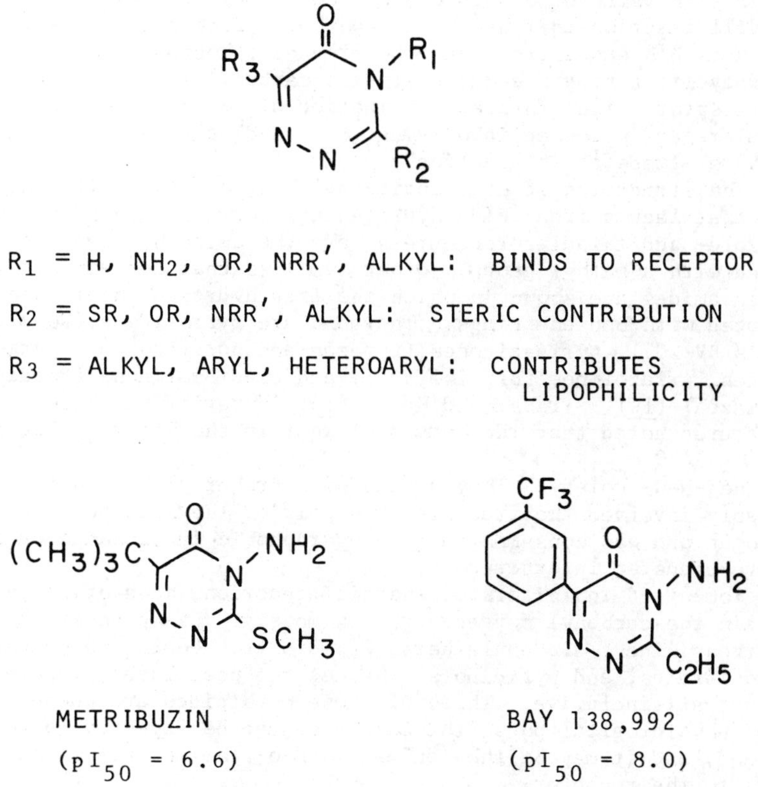
R3
R1
R2
R1 = H, NH2, OR, NRR′, ALKYL: BINDS TO RECEPTOR
R2 = SR, OR, NRR′, ALKYL: STERIC CONTRIBUTION
R3 = ALKYL, ARYL, HETEROARYL: CONTRIBUTES LIPOPHILICITY
(CH3)3C
NH2
SCH3
CF3
C2H5
METRIBUZIN
(pI50 = 6.6)
BAY 138,992
(pI50 = 8.0)

Figure 5. 1,2,4-Triazinones tested and contributions made by molecular substituents in the inhibition of photosystem II [adapted from Draber et al. *(15)]*

favorable electron distribution on the heterocyclic ring. R_2
contributed or possessed a steric property that was especially
critical for a good fit at the receptor. R_3 contributed lipophilicity to the whole molecule and thus influenced penetrability
and unspecific binding. These properties were maximized in
metribuzin and in compound BAY 138,992. The latter compound,
with a pI_{50} value of 8.0 is one of the strongest inhibitors of
the Hill reaction that has been reported. Draber *et al.* agreed
with Hansch's suggestion that the free electron pair of the
heterocyclic nitrogen adjacent to the carbonyl function bound to
the receptor. They favored elimination of the hydrogen bonding
postulate and stressed involvement of a hydrophobic interchange
or charge-transfer interaction.

The structures of some additional heterocyclic Hill inhibitors that lack a free amide hydrogen are shown in Figure 6. Benz-
thiazole- and thiadiazolone-ureas have the amide hydrogen replaced with a methyl group. Other families that contain heterocyclic amides are shown in which the free hydrogens have been
replaced with benzene rings. Included are pyrrolidone (Rohm &
Haas's BV-207), pyridazinones (pyrazon and norflurazon), pyra-
zolones, triazolones (BAY 143,873), and oxadiazolinone (Rhodia's
oxadiazon) (16). Trebst and Harth (16) in reviewing these
structures noted that the common element in the heterocyclic ring
was the $-\overset{\overset{\displaystyle O}{\|}}{\underset{\diagdown}{N}-C-}$ moiety. They agreed with Draber *et al.* that binding
probably involved the free electron pair of the heterocyclic
nitrogen and was consummated by a hydrophobic interchange or a
charge-transfer interaction.

Some good inhibitors of the Hill reaction, however, do not
contain the carbonyl oxygen-nitrogen moiety. Examples are the
dinitroanilines, diphenylethers, 2,4-dinitrophenols, halogenated
benzonitriles, and pyridinols. Hence, the postulates proposed
are not all inclusive. Three of these herbicides are phenols.
Under physiological pH's, the molecules can be expected to be
ionized, and it may be the ionized form of the molecule that
binds to the receptor.

Steric Relations. Some interesting specificity has been
documented that reflects a requirement for a definite steric
approach of an inhibitor to the receptor in the chloroplasts.
One example is provided by the optical isomers of 1-(α-methyl-
benzyl)-3-(3,4-dichlorophenyl)urea (17). This chemical is an
inhibitory uncoupler. The S-isomer inhibits electron transport,
but the R-isomer is noninhibitory. The inactive isomer does not
compete with the active isomer at the photosystem II site. The
phosphorylation site shows no optical specificity. The two
isomers do not differ significantly in their lipophilicity.
Hence, the difference in inhibitory activity is not related to
partitioning behavior.

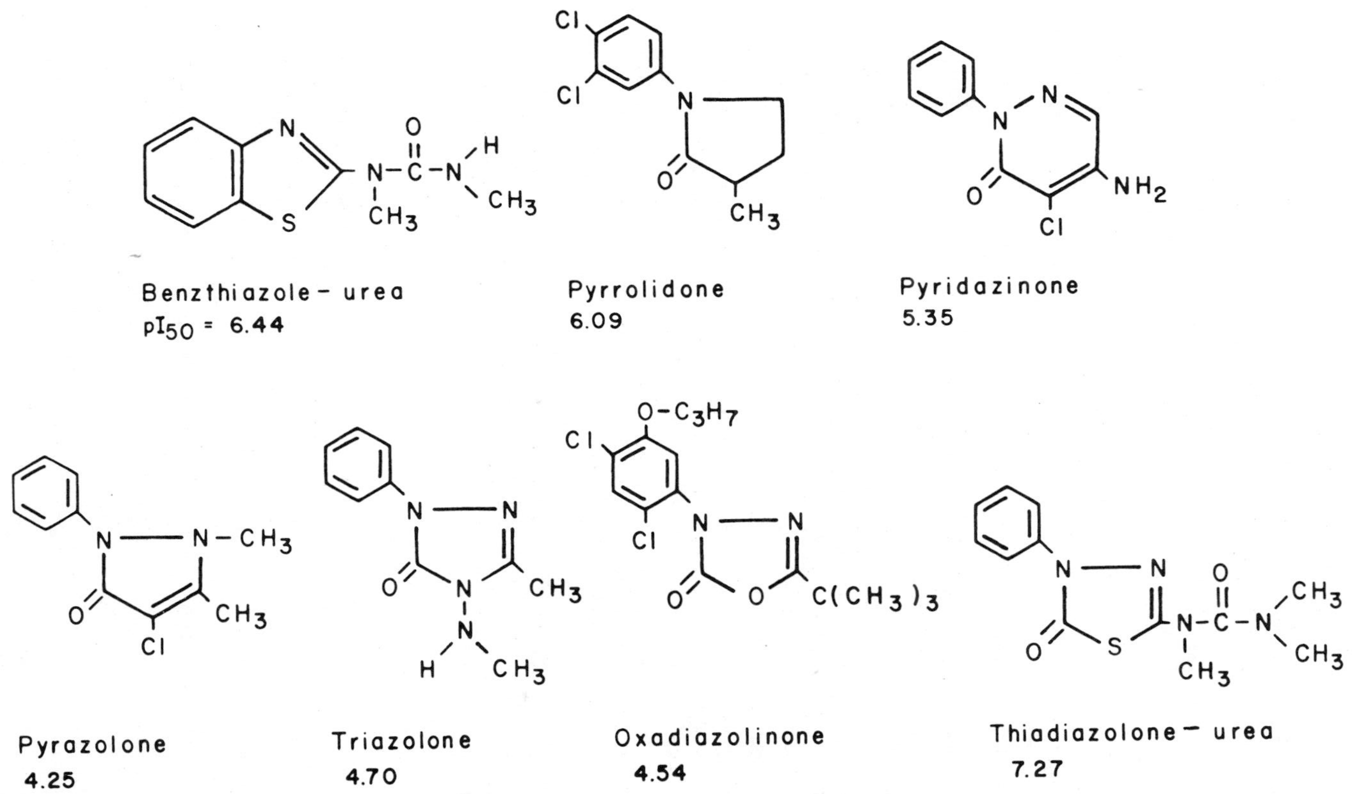

Figure 6. Structural elements of some heterocyclic inhibitors of photosystem II [adapted from Trebst and Harth (16)]. Numbers below the chemical names are pI$_{50}$ values.

An example of geometric isomerism is provided by the dimethylpyrrolidinecarboxanilides (18). Only when the methyl groups substituted on the pyrrolidine ring are in the *cis*-conformation is electron transport inhibited and phytotoxicity produced. The *trans*-isomer neither inhibits the Hill reaction, nor is it phytotoxic.

Status of Structure-activity Studies. Many diversely structured chemicals are known to inhibit the photoinduced chloroplast reactions. Each year, additional types of chemistry are added to the lengthy list of inhibitory structures. However, to date, no postulate has been presented that satisfactorily explains where and how inhibition is produced.

Part of our inability to fit the many structure-activity observations into a given model relates to our uncertainty as to whether all of the inhibitors function at precisely the same site through a common mechanism or whether the different inhibitors affect different, but possibly closely situated, sites. In view of the extreme structural dissimilarities among the various inhibitors, one could conclude that it is unlikely that all react at the same site. However, we have little evidence that they do not do so.

The regression analyses have shown that inhibitory potency expressed against the Hill reaction can be correlated with physico-chemical parameters within a particular group of herbicides. However, no investigator has successfully correlated mathematically activities between different chemical families (11). Also, no evidence exists for the "special" protein amide postulated by Hansch (13). Even though the models are only crude approximations, they provide a basis for the development of hypotheses that can be critically investigated. In addition, an insight is being gained into how herbicides and receptors might interact.

Studies with Intact Plants.

Insofar as they have been studied, all herbicides that inhibit the Hill reaction of isolated chloroplasts also inhibit photosynthesis of intact plants and photosynthetic microorganisms (2, 3). Phytotoxicity is produced only in the light, and severity of symptoms is proportional to light intensity. Studies with light quality have indicated that the chlorophylls are the principal absorbing pigments involved in the production of phytotoxicity.

The development of toxic symptoms on plants treated with pure electron transport inhibitors, such as simazine, diuron, and the uracils, can be prevented if the plants are supplied exogenously with a respirable carbohydrate (2). This observation suggests that the glycolytic or the mitochondrial system can provide sufficient energy to prevent the appearance of phytotoxic symptoms, if respirable substrates are provided. In contrast, carbohydrate protection could not be demonstrated with inhibitory uncouplers or with uncouplers, such as chlorpropham, ioxynil, and dinoseb, that interfere also with oxidative phosphorylation.

A number of herbicides that interfere with the photochemistry of chloroplasts have been reported also to alter the ultrastructure of chloroplasts. These include bromacil, haloxydine, pyrazon, 2,4-D, monuron, diuron, Sandoz 6706, and the bipyridyliums (2, 19). The first effect observed is a swelling of the intergranal thylakoids, sometimes within 2 hours after the herbicide is applied to the roots. Subsequently, the thylakoids swell, beginning with the outer thylakoids, until the whole lamellar system becomes disorganized. Later, the tonoplast and chloroplast envelopes rupture, and finally the thylakoid membranes rupture. Mixing of plastid and cytoplasmic contents has been observed within 4 hours after treatment. External symptoms of injury are usually not apparent until 3 or 4 days after treatment with electron transport inhibitors. Hence, the internal morphology in leaves is destroyed (within a few hours) long before external symptoms appear.

In every study, light was required for the effects of the inhibitors to become apparent. Chloroplasts of herbicide-treated plants kept in the dark resembled, in all respects, chloroplasts of the dark-control plants. The modifications produced in chloroplasts are not unique to herbicides. Mineral and vitamin deficiencies, antibiotics, unnatural pyrimidines, and genetic alterations all cause similar aberrant ultrastructural changes in chloroplasts; however, the extent of the disruptions produced by herbicides is more extreme. The changes induced by herbicides are similar in many respects to those that occur in normal senescence, reflecting the characteristic pattern associated with degeneration and death of a cell.

Sucrose has been shown to reverse the effect of at least monuron alterations to the fine structure of chloroplasts. All of the injury, including that detectable at the ultrastructural level, apparently can be prevented if the energy supply can be kept fully charged through the glycolytic and mitochondrial systems, by the feeding of respirable substrates. However, carbohydrates will not protect against the herbicides that interfere with oxidative phosphorylation (uncouplers and inhibitory uncouplers).

Postulated Modes of Action.

The relation between inhibition of the photoinduced responses in isolated chloroplasts and the expression of phytotoxicity remains to be identified positively. Any hypothesis proposed to account for the mode of action must take into consideration that: (a) phytotoxic symptoms develop only in the light, and severity is proportional to light intensity; (b)

carbon dioxide fixation is inhibited only in the light; (c)
toxic effects can be alleviated by the exogenous application of
respirable carbohydrates; (d) severe morphological and cytologi-
cal changes are induced only in the light; and (e) external
symptoms become apparent in higher plants several days after
treatment, except for the bipyridyliums (2). Several hypotheses
have been proposed to account for the phytotoxicity of the Hill
inhibitors, but none has been substantiated by rigorous experimentation.

Starvation. The early reports that Hill inhibitors limited
photosynthesis and that starch disappeared from treated plants,
prompted some investigators to refer to these compounds as
photosynthesis inhibitors. Photosynthesis is inhibited because
ATP and NADPH are not available for carbon dioxide fixation.
However, there is little evidence that the plants starve to
death. If this were the only process affected, phytotoxic symptoms should resemble those that appear on plants kept in total
darkness. Deficiency of photosynthate does limit new growth,
but does not account for the morphological alterations that occur
within a few hours after treatment. The mechanisms that lead to
phytotoxicity appear to be considerably more complex than would
result from limiting carbohydrate synthesis by suppression of
carbon dioxide fixation (2).

Free Radical Mechanisms. The appearance of phytotoxic
symptoms only in the light after treatment of plants with herbicides such as diuron and atrazine prompted some investigators to
propose "light-activation" hypotheses, the formation of toxic
substances, or the formation of reactive free radicals. However,
except for the strong documentation on the formation of free
radicals by bipyridiliums, there is no direct evidence that toxic
components are formed from an interaction between a herbicidal
Hill inhibitor and light (2).

Pigment Synthesis. Amitrole, fluometuron, dichlormate,
metflurazone, Sandoz 9774, haloxydine, and pyriclor inhibit or
interfere with carotenoid biosynthesis (2). Carotenoid pigments
in photosynthetic systems may protect against photosensitized
oxidations, which occur when light-excited chlorophylls combine
with molecular oxygen. Amitrole is the only herbicide, of this
group, that does not affect the Hill reaction. Most of the Hill
inhibitors do not affect carotenoid synthesis. Interference with
either the Hill reaction or pigment synthesis could cause plant
death.

Energy (ATP) Availability. All of the herbicides that
interfere with the photoinduced reactions limit the availability
of ATP. Action is expressed at different sites on the electron
transport and energy generation pathways, but the net result is

the same. Interference with ATP production has focused attention
on how this action might relate to the production of phytotoxicity.

ATP has a ubiquitous and dominant role in cellular metabolism. This role can be appreciated more fully if cognizance is
extended to the energy requirements of cells, to the regulation
of cellular activity and metabolism imposed by ATP, and to what
interference with ATP production means to the growth of a chlorophyllous plant. Plants store oxidative and photochemical energy
in the terminal phosphate bonds of ATP. The terminal bond energy
is used subsequently to perform the chemical, mechanical, and
osmotic work of the cell.

Only ADP is phosphorylated to form ATP in glycolysis, oxidative phosphorylation, and photophosphorylation. ATP provides
the energy, directly or indirectly, to drive most biosynthetic
reactions. The functions of membranes such as active transport
and osmotic relations, which regulate the volume of cells, are
energy dependent. The structural organization, contraction, and
orientation of chromosomes and microtubules of the spindle appar-
atus during mitosis depend on ATP energy. The intracellular
concentrations and stoichiometric relations of ATP, ADP, and AMP
also modulate cellular metabolism.

The observations that phytotoxic symptoms develop only in
the light suggest that the demand for ATP is increased when
chlorophyllous organisms are illuminated. Actually, a large
number of energy-requiring biosynthetic reactions are now known
to be light-activated. These include RNA and protein synthesis;
various enzymes involved in the synthesis of chlorophyll, other
pigments, and lipids; and many of the enzymes of the carbon
dioxide fixation pathways. Turnover of other cellular components
is also activated by light. All of the light-activated synthetic
activity places a much higher demand upon the plant for energy in
the light than in the dark.

In evaluating the role of ATP in the cellular metabolism of
higher plants, all processes that contribute to the ATP pool
(glycolysis, oxidative phosphorylation, and photophosphorylation)
must be considered. Even though the photosystem II inhibitors
block noncyclic photophosphorylation, ATP can still be produced
in vivo under some conditions by cyclic photophosphorylation, by
glycolysis, and through oxidative phosphorylation. Apparently,
sufficient energy can be provided through the last two processes,
if respirable carbohydrates are supplied exogenously, to satisfy
the light-induced demands and prevent phytotoxic symptoms. The
uncouplers and inhibitory uncouplers interfere with the mitochondrial production of ATP, and carbohydrates do not protect
against their action (2).

Many, if not all, of the biochemical, physiological, and
morphological alterations observed following application of the
Hill inhibitors to plants can be accounted for on the basis of
interference with ATP production. Without the needed ATP, growth
stops, cellular functions are arrested, the integrity of the

cell's structural morphology is lost, and the plant dies.

Conclusions.

Future research may show that none of the hypotheses discussed accounts for the action of herbicides that interfere with
the photochemistry of isolated chloroplasts. No single hypothesis may explain adequately the action of all inhibitory herbicides under all conditions. With a given herbicide, at one concentration, when applied to a certain species or variety of
plant, and under particular environmental conditions, one hypothesis may account for the observed phytotoxicity. However,
under other conditions or situations, another hypothesis may be
more applicable (2).
Based on current knowledge, it seems likely that whatever
form the final hypothesis may take, it will center around what
happens when the formation of ATP or NADPH, or both, is inhibited
after interference with the photochemical reactions of the chloroplasts. Hopefully, the postulates will serve as models that
can be subjected to rigorous and sophisticated experimentation,
and will be modified as our knowledge of biochemical control
systems in higher plants increases.

Literature Cited.

1. Corbett, J. R. "The Biochemical Mode of Action of Pesti-
    cides", 330 p. Academic Press, London, 1974.

2. Moreland, D. E., Hilton, J. L. In "Physiology and Bio-
    chemistry of Herbicides", pp. 493–523, L. J. Audus (ed.),
    Academic Press, London, 1976. (In press).

3. Moreland, D. E. Annu. Rev. Plant Physiol. (1967)
    18:365–386.

4. Ashton, F. M., Crafts, A. S. "Mode of Action of Herbicides",
    504 p. John Wiley & Sons, New York, 1973.

5. Jaworski, E. G. J. Agri. Food Chem. (1972) 20:1195–1198.

6. Moreland, D. E. In "Progress in Photosynthesis Research",
    Vol. III, pp. 1693–1711, H. Metzner (ed.), Tübingen, 1969.

7. Duysens, L. N. M., Amesz, J. Biochim. Biophys. Acta (1962)
    64:243–260.

8. Renger, R. Biochim. Biophys. Acta (1973) 314:113–116.

9. Hauska, G., Trebst, A., Kötter, C., Schulz, H.
    Z. Naturforsch. (1975) 30c:505–510.

10. Zweig, G., Shavit, N., Avron, M. Biochim. Biophys. Acta
    (1965) 109:332-346.

11. Büchel, H. Pestic. Sci. (1972) 3:89-110.

12. Hansch, C., Deutsch, E. W. Biochim. Biophys. Acta (1966)
    112:381-391.

13. Hansch, C. In "Progress in Photosynthesis Research",
    Vol. III, pp. 1685-1692, H. Metzner (ed.), Tübingen, 1969.

14. Draber, W., Büchel, K. H., Dickoré, D., Trebst, A.,
    Pistorius, E. In "Progress in Photosynthesis Research",
    Vol. III, pp. 1789-1795, H. Metzner (ed.), Tübingen, 1969.

15. Draber, W., Büchel, K. H., Timmler, H., Trebst, A. In
    "Mechanism of Pesticide Action", ACS Symposium Series,
    Number 2, pp. 100-116, G. K. Kohn (ed.), Washington, D. C.
    1974.

16. Trebst, A., Harth, E. Z. Naturforsch. (1974) 29c:232-235.

17. Moreland, D. E., Boots, M. R. Plant Physiol. (1971)
    47:53-58.

18. Holm, R. E., Stallard, D. E. Weed Sci. (1974) 22:10-14.

19. Anderson, J. L., Thompson, W. W. Residue Rev. (1973)
    43:167-189.

5

The *s*-Triazine Herbicides

ENRICO KNUESLI

CIBA-GEIGY Ltd., Agrochemicals Division, Basle, Switzerland

The invitation to give a lecture at this place under these festive circumstances is a high privilege indeed. The confrontation with this privilege caused concern to the speaker in so far as a review can hardly furnish much evidence not known to such experts in the matter as you all, Ladies and Gentlemen, are. What remains without reservation, however, is the challenge to communicate to you something of the fascination experienced for about twenty years now on the way to and on the way with triazine herbicides.

With this in mind, allow me to recall the scene at the middle of our century. How young an art was chemical weed control then! For a long time man had evidently not felt himself so helpless against weeds as against other pests. It is not by chance that neither thorns nor thistles but mosquitoes, gadflies and grasshoppers figure in the range of the ten biblical plagues. Pyrethrum, nicotine, copper, sulfur were chemical control measures long before chemistry entered the field of weed control. In the late thirties, chemistry - and organic chemistry in particular - made a decisive follow-up in the field of insecticides and fungicides, while   the field of herbicides   was in its infancy.

In the mid fifties the range of practically-used organic herbicides was dominated by phenoxyacetic acids; in this country (USA) the production of 2,4-D had reached an output of 34,000,000 pounds with a sales value of 28×10^6 $ out of a total herbicide market of 38×10^6 $ and out of a total pesticide market of 260×10^6 $. The range offered to interested herbicide users included, in 1951, besides 2,4-D the O-alkyldinitrophenols, pentachlorophenol, trichloroacetic acid, sodium isopropylxanthate, additional chlorophenoxyacetic acids, isopropyl-$\underline{N}$-phenylcarbamate, endothal, maleic acid hydrazide and $\underline{p}$-chlorophenyldimethylurea. The concept of a pre-emergence treatment of weeds had just been inaugurated by the last-mentioned compound.

Herbicides, 1951

Cl—⟨benzene ring, X top, Y bottom⟩—OCH$_2$COOH   2,4-D
                                                     2,4,5-T
                                                     MCPA

Cl—⟨benzene ring, Cl bottom⟩—OCH$_2$CH$_2$OSO$_3$Na   2,4-Dichlorophenoxyethylsulfate,
                                                         Na salt

⟨benzene ring⟩—NHCOOiC$_3$H$_7$ Isopropyl N-phenylcarbamate

⟨bicyclic ring, O⟩—COOH   3,6-Endoxohydrophthalic acid
             —COOH   ENDOTHAL

⟨pyridazinone ring, O top, NH, N, OH bottom⟩   6-Hydroxy-3-(2H)-pyridazinone
                                                  MH

Cl—⟨benzene ring⟩—NHCON⟨CH$_3$, CH$_3$⟩   3-(4'-Chlorophenyl)-1,1-dimethylurea
                                             CMU

     This was the status when we commenced, in 1952, a project for
the discovery and the development of herbicides and defoliants.
The decision to initiate such a project was taken by the management of our company, then J.R. GEIGY Ltd., a year earlier. The
company had at that time experience in the field of pharmaceuticals, dyestuffs, insecticides, moth-proofing agents, and fungicides. It is a pleasure, and an expression of gratitude, for me
to recall that Dr. Hans Gysin was the inspiring and enthusing
leader of the project and that Dr. Albert Gast cared, with high
expertise, for a major part of the greenhouse and field evaluation.
     How did we attack the problem? In the conventional way: by
establishing work hypotheses, by synthesizing, by screening, by
discarding many compounds.

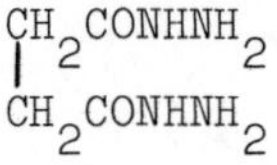

$CH_2CONHNH_2$
$CH_2CONHNH_2$

G 25264

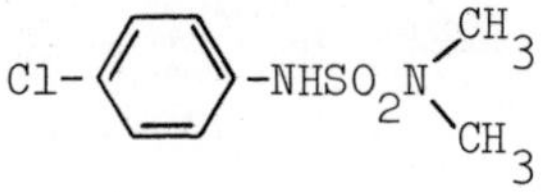

$Cl-\langle\bigcirc\rangle-NHSO_2N\begin{smallmatrix}CH_3\\CH_3\end{smallmatrix}$

G 25490

$Cl-\langle\bigcirc\rangle-NHCOCON(C_2H_5)_2$

G 25374

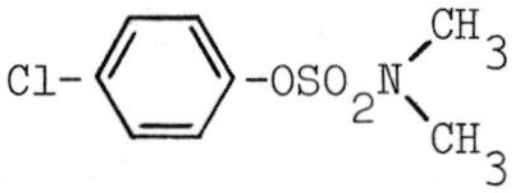

$Cl-\langle\bigcirc\rangle-OSO_2N\begin{smallmatrix}CH_3\\CH_3\end{smallmatrix}$

G 25491

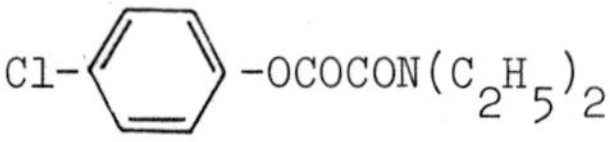

$Cl-\langle\bigcirc\rangle-OCOCON(C_2H_5)_2$

G 25377

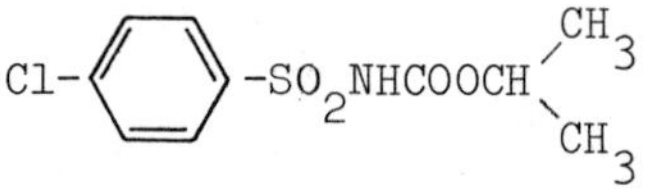

$Cl-\langle\bigcirc\rangle-SO_2NHCOOCH\begin{smallmatrix}CH_3\\CH_3\end{smallmatrix}$

G 25494

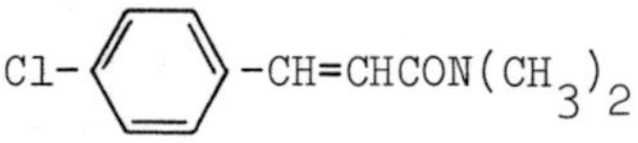

$Cl-\langle\bigcirc\rangle-CH=CHCON(CH_3)_2$

G 25486

$Cl-\langle\bigcirc\rangle-NHCH_2COOC_2H_5$

G 25795

In a first round, we tried to obtain, through structural variation of known active molecules, new and superior biological effects. We were particularly interested to check the consequences of the isosteric replacement of structural elements in chlorophenyl derivatives as shown above.

In the greenhouse, during biological evaluation G 25486 showed defoliant properties which led to structural variation work. However, no compound useful under practical conditions could be found. G 25795 demonstrated remarkable root-promoting activity so that many further analogues and homologues were synthesized.

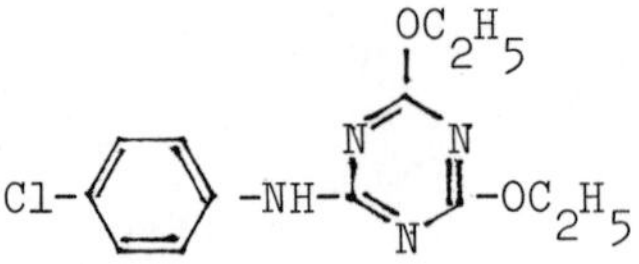

$Cl-\langle\bigcirc\rangle-NH-\langle\text{triazine}\rangle-OC_2H_5$ with OC_2H_5 substituent   G 25798

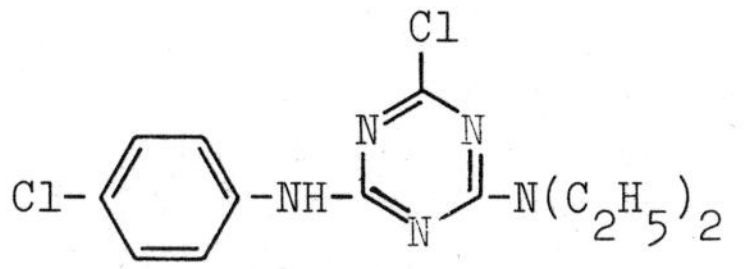

$$Cl-\langle\phi\rangle-NH-\text{[triazine, Cl]}-N(C_2H_5)_2 \qquad G\ 27902$$

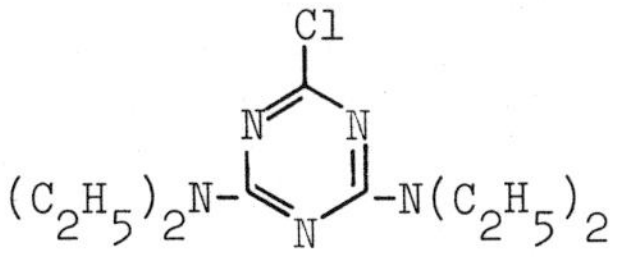

$$(C_2H_5)_2N-\text{[triazine, Cl]}-N(C_2H_5)_2 \qquad G\ 25804$$

$$C_2H_5O-\text{[triazine, Cl]}-OC_2H_5 \qquad G\ 25814$$

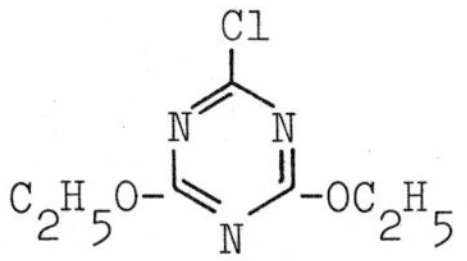

G 25804 revealed   substantial herbicidal activity and in
quite early tests a distinct selective behaviour versus corn and
cotton.

Why, you may ask, did they include, rather unexpectedly,
this s-triazine ring system? The background has already been
reported repeatedly.

We knew that in the field of dyestuffs and pharmaceuticals
the substitution of an urea bridge by a bis-amino-s-triazine
group had **on occasion** not fundamentally changed the respective
properties.

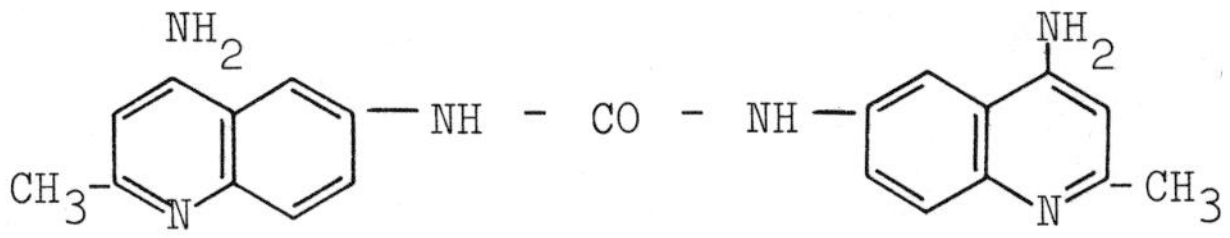

Surfene

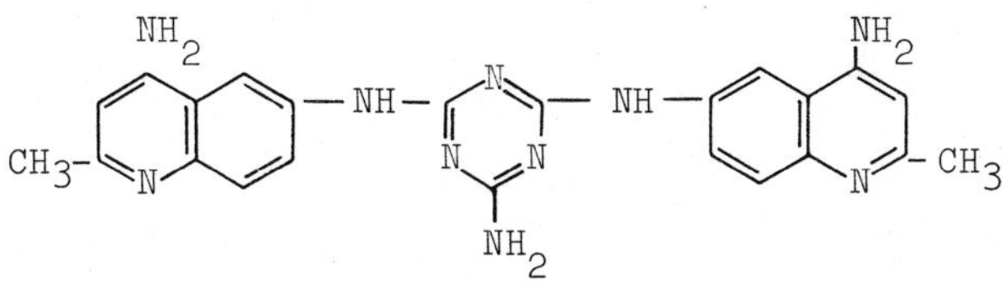

Surfene C
or
Congasine
Jensch,Angew.Ch. 50 891 (1937)

Surfene shows, as an example, such a structural combination having protozoidicidal activity, developed by a German scientist.

So we were induced to try this approach, too, and we started synthesis work in the field of s-triazines. The result of our primary working hypothesis was disappointing; derivatives bearing anilino radicals showed no herbicidal effects. Surprisingly, however, the herbicidal activity reappeared in the structure 2-chloro-4,6-bis-diethylamino-s-triazine, compound G 25804 shown previously. The awareness that we were confronted with a completely new herbicidal matrix with apparently superior usefulness led us to intensive work around the s-triazine ring system.

What a beautiful tool is cyanuric chloride for the chemist working in chemical synthesis! Three chlorine atoms offer reaction with a large proportion of the chemicals listed in the Beilstein Handbook or the Chemical Abstracts Index. Not only that: the chlorine atoms are reasonable enough not to react simultaneously but, under adequate conditions, stepwise, allowing myriads of potential combinations. Furthermore: cyanuric chloride has been and is a relatively cheap key material; it can be produced quite easily from such basic materials as chlorine and hydrocyanic acid.

As we assemble under the auspices of the American Chemical Society, you may ask whether it has not been a boring task to deal with this chemistry where the reaction scheme is usually quite transparent. No doubt, the major attractiveness has been and is the structure/activity evaluation and the respective deductions. But now and then it occurred that a rather nice unexpected chemical offspring resulted from this work, and the chemical accent of our meeting may justify the quoting of some examples:

We identified the structure of a side product obtained in a liquid phase process for the production of cyanuric chloride; this tetramer of chlorocyan had not been described before and we studied its reactivity:

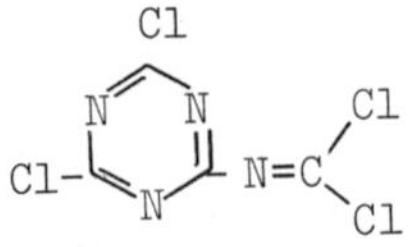

We identified a yellow compound which poisoned for a certain time the carbon-catalyst in the trimerization of chlorocyan as cyameluric chloride:

$$C_6Cl_3N_7$$

Cyameluric chloride

We found that cyanuric chloride reacts easily but in a controllable manner with dimethylformamide, CO_2 being **evolved**. The reaction was fully elucidated later by H.Gold:

$$3 \ HCON(CH_3)_2$$

$$\left[Cl(CH_3)_2NCHO\text{-}\!\!\diagdown\!\!\diagup\text{-}OCHN(CH_3)_2Cl \right]$$

$$3 \ HCON(CH_3)_2$$

$$3 \ CO_2 \ + \ 3 \ \left[(CH_3)_2NCH=N-CH=N(CH_3)_2 \right] Cl$$

H.Gold, Angew.Chem. 72 956 (1960)

But let us return to the problem of selecting, out of the myriads of possible 2,4,6-s-triazine derivates, those which have herbicidal activity and from these, those which will be useful under practical conditions.

Starting from the structure of G 25804 we initiated variation along four main lines in order to explore the consequences with regard to the biological characteristics:

G 25804

a) by varying the N-alkyl radicals
b) by substituting the chlorine atom by other
   suitable groups
c) by permuting most different radicals on the
   three ring positions allowing substitution and
d) by replacing the s-triazine ring by other N-
   heterocycles mainly provided with halogen and
   alkylamino radicals.

After having synthesised and tested many representatives we
can conclude now that, in general, the following criteria must
be fulfilled in order to obtain substantial herbicidal activity:
- two nitrogen functions bound to ring carbon atoms are essential for the typical triazine activity pattern.
- the presence of one to three N-alkyl substituents is needed,
  those compounds bearing one alkyl group on each nitrogen
  function being of special interest.
- alkyls C_1 to C_4 are most suitable, including methoxyalkyls.
- substitution of the chloro atom by alkoxy and alkylthio groups,
  preferably methoxy and methylthio, conserves the high herbicidal activity but leads to a change of the crop selectivity pattern.

Substitution of the chloro atom by bromine, by fluorine, by
nitrilo-, hydrazino-, alkyl-, haloalkyl-, alkoxyalkoxy groups
leads very often to remarkable herbicidal but seldom - from the
practical point of view - to superior activity.

It is thereby obvious to everybody active in this field that the qualification "superior activity" can never relate to one parameter alone; activity against the target organisms is, of course, an absolute prerequisite but this activity can, outside the field of industrial weed control, only be made valuable by a complementary suitable crop selectivity pattern.

The following compounds resulting from our project reached the level of practical use:

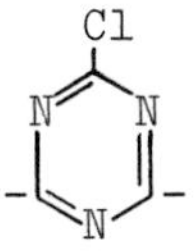

Common name:

G	27692	C_2H_5NH-	$-NHC_2H_5$	SIMAZINE
G	27901	C_2H_5NH-	$-N(C_2H_5)_2$	TRIETAZINE
G	30027	C_2H_5NH-	$-NHiC_3H_7$	ATRAZINE
G	30028	iC_3H_7NH-	$-NHiC_3H_7$	PROPAZINE
G	13528	C_2H_5NH-	$-NHsec.C_4H_9$	SEBUTHYLAZINE
G	13529	C_2H_5NH-	$-NH-t.C_4H_9$	TERBUTHYLAZINE

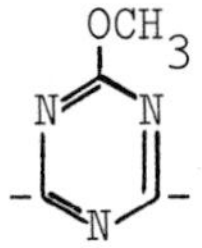

Common name:

G	31435	iC_3H_7NH-	$-NHiC_3H_7$	PROMETONE
G	32293	C_2H_5NH-	$-NHiC_3H_7$	ATRATONE
GS	14254	C_2H_5NH-	$-NHsec.C_4H_9$	SECBUMETONE (proposed)
GS	14259	C_2H_5NH-	$-NH-t.C_4H_9$	TERBUMETONE (proposed)

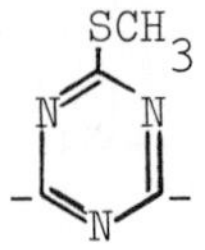

Common name:

G	32911	C_2H_5NH-	$-NHC_2H_5$	SIMETRYN
G	34161	iC_3H_7NH-	$-NHiC_3H_7$	PROMETRYN
G	34162	C_2H_5NH-	$-NHiC_3H_7$	AMETRYN
G	34360	CH_3NH-	$-NHiC_3H_7$	DESMETRYN
G	36393	iC_3H_7NH-	$-NHCH_2CH_2CH_2OCH_3$	METHOPROTRYN
GS	14260	C_2H_5NH-	$-NH-t.C_4H_9$	TERBUTRYN

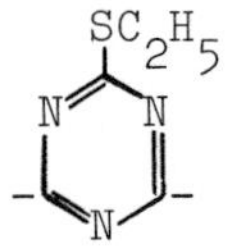

Common name:

GS 16068 iC_3H_7NH- $-NHiC_3H_7$ DIPROPETRYN
                                                          (proposed)

They differ, of course, substantially as to the importance
they assumed. As an example G 27901, Trietazine, was sold once
in a quantity of a couple of thousand pounds for weed control in
chrysanthemums in Japan and can, therefore, not be put in line
with for example G 30027, Atrazine.

No research group, be it academic or industrial, can expect
unlimited exclusivity after having identified a field which in-
vites **further exploitation.**   The compilation and analysis of
the main contributions, experimental or sales products, **developed**
by groups other than ours show the following picture:

a) Our conclusion that interesting activity is mainly connected with the presence of two monosubstituted amino radicals
and a halogen, halogenoid, alkoxy or alkylthio group has been
confirmed.

b) One tendency circled around the grafting of a hydroxy or
alkoxy group directly on the amino function or into the alkyl
radical:

Hydroxy or alkoxyalkyl radicals:

DuPont   Cl $-NHCH_2CH_2CH_2OCH_3$ $-NHCH_2CH_2CH_2OCH_3$
1957/1965

Monsanto CH_3S $-NHCH_2CH_2CH_2OCH_3$ $-NHCH_2CH_2CH_2OCH_3$ LAMBAST
1963

Allied   Cl $-NHiC_3H_7$ $-NHCH_2OH$ ACD 15M
1969

BASF   Cl $-NHC_2H_5$ $-NHCH \overset{\diagup CH_3}{\underset{\diagdown CH_2OCH_3}{}}$ 55547
1967

Further lines comprise:
    c) The insertion of unconventional alkyl, alkenyl or
alkynyl substitutes.

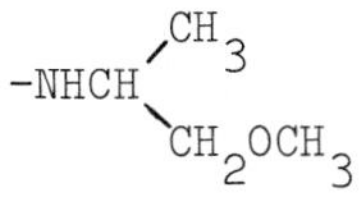

Unconventional hydrocarbon radicals:

Monsanto CH_3S $-NHC_2H_5$ $-N \overset{\diagup C_2H_5}{\underset{\diagdown CH=C \overset{\diagup CH_3}{\diagdown CH_3}}{}}$ MON 0385
1971

BASF   Cl $-NHC_2H_5$ $-NHCH \overset{\diagup CH_3}{\underset{\diagdown C \equiv CH}{}}$ BASF 54187
1967

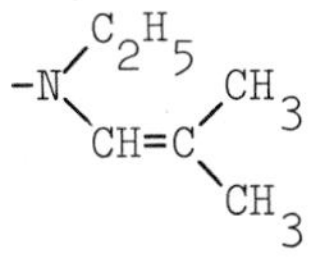

GULF   Cl $-NHiC_3H_7$ $-NHCH \overset{\diagup CH_2}{\underset{\diagdown CH_2}{|}}$ CYPRAZINE
1966

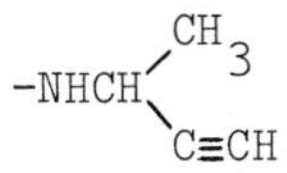

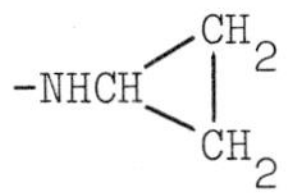

CIBA CH_3S $-NHC_2H_5$ $-NHCH \overset{CH_3}{\underset{}{|}} - CH \overset{CH_3}{\underset{}{|}} - CH_3$ DIMETHAMETRYN
1967   (proposed)

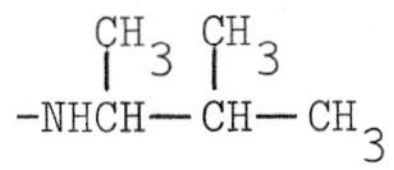

d) The introduction of acyl radicals.

Acylation:

Matolcsy et al.   Cl $-NHiC_3H_7$ $-NHCON(C_2H_5)_2$
1959/1961

                     Cl $-NHC_2H_5$ $-NHCON(CH_3)_2$

Stauffer   Cl $-NHiC_3H_7$ $-N\begin{smallmatrix} C_2H_5 \\ COCOOC_2H_5 \end{smallmatrix}$
1973

DEGUSSA $-N\begin{smallmatrix} alk. \\ SCCl_3 \end{smallmatrix}$
1959/1964

$\left. \begin{matrix} Cl \\ OCH_3 \\ SCH_3 \end{matrix} \right\} \cdot$ -NHalk. $-N\begin{smallmatrix} alk. \\ SO_2N\begin{smallmatrix} CH_3 \\ CH_3 \end{smallmatrix} \end{smallmatrix}$

                            $-N\begin{smallmatrix} alk. \\ CONH_2 \end{smallmatrix}$

                            $-N\begin{smallmatrix} alk. \\ P{=}O\begin{smallmatrix} OR \\ OR \end{smallmatrix} \end{smallmatrix}$

e) The introduction of cyanoalkyl radicals.

Cyanoalkyl radicals: Common name:

Matolcsy et al.   Cl $-NHC_2H_5$ $-NHCH_2CN$
1959/1961

DEGUSSA/SHELL   Cl $-NHC_2H_5$ $-NH-\underset{CH_3}{\overset{CH_3}{C}}-CN$ CYANAZINE
1967

DEGUSSA/SHELL CH_3S $-NHC_2H_5$ $-NH-\underset{CH_3}{\overset{CH_3}{C}}-CN$ CYANATRINE
1966

Because of the susceptibility of the 1-cyano-1-methylethylamino
group to hydrolysis Cyanazine has a relatively short residual
activity.
    A further possibility of variation of the non-amino posi-
tions is illustrated by the next example:

Variation in the non-amino function:

			CH_3
DEGUSSA	N_3	$-NHiC_3H_7$	$-NH-C-CN$
1958/62			CH_3

DEGUSSA   SCN $-NHalk.$ $-NHalk.$
1959

DEGUSSA SCH_2CN $-NHalk.$ $-NHalk.$
1960

**The azido group is also able to substitute for one of the two
alkylamino groups:**

N_3^- as a replacement for an alkylamino group

CIBA CH_3S $-N_3$ $-NHiC_3H_7$ AZIPROTRYN
1963

    Is it really possible to give in a few minutes   condensed
information on the activity and selectivity pattern of the triazine herbicides, on the way they act and degrade and on the
impact they made on world-wide agriculture? I shall try, but not
without drawing your attention to the various recent monographs
where the names of the contributors of information are also
cited.
    s-Triazines were and are herbicides with a remarkable broad
spectrum of activity. At the same time they display selectivity
towards important crops. The unique, physiologically based lack of
activity   of the chlorotriazines towards corn and sorghum and
the resulting crop safety rapidly gained them the favour of the
growers. In fact, I think it would not be immodest to say that
chlorotriazines meant a new dimension in the area of corn growing.
    Besides corn, sorghum and grapes, chlorotriazines have been
applied mainly in citrus, in pip-fruits, in ornamental and berry
bushes and in the field of general weed control. Selective
behaviour can, of course, also be observed on the part of certain
weeds:

Characteristic
residual flora:

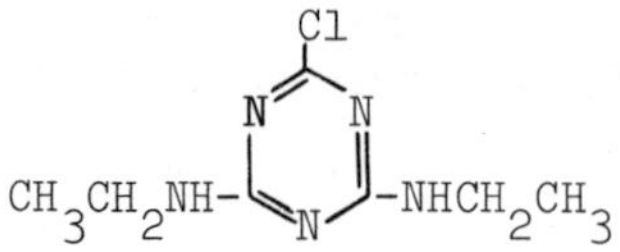

CH$_3$CH$_2$NH-[triazine with Cl]-NHCH$_2$CH$_3$ SIMAZINE   birdsfoot trefoil
                                                      G 27692   (Lotus corniculatus)

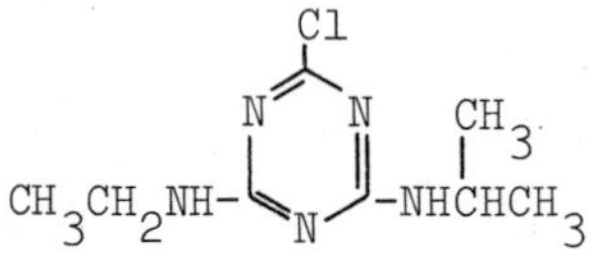

CH$_3$CH$_2$NH-[triazine with Cl]-NHCHCH$_3$ (CH$_3$)   ATRAZINE   crab grass
                                                      G 30027   (Digitaria sanguinalis)

                                                                     green foxtail
                                                                       (Setaria spec.)

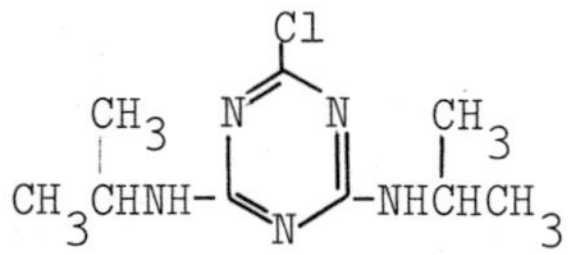

CH$_3$CHNH- (CH$_3$) -[triazine with Cl]-NHCHCH$_3$ (CH$_3$)   PROPAZINE   wild carrot
                                                      G 30028   (Daucus carota)

Increased stands of wild carrots show up, for example,
after Propazine treatment, of birdsfoot trefoil after Simazine
treatment and of green foxtail and crab grass after Atrazine
treatment. Are these biological particularities not amazing in
view of the very small structural differences?

The last mentioned behaviour led to practical consequences.
At the time of their introduction chlorotriazines were particularly welcome because they were able to control the grass flora
which had developed for years after 2,4-D treatments, especially
quack-grass. In the meantime, the broad application of Atrazine
has led at many places to the build-up of a new and different
residual grass flora which can be controlled, however, by combination with suitable grass-killers.

Methoxytriazines are applied where a hard to kill weed
flora has to be controlled in woody crops and sugarcane; alfalfa
is, surprisingly enough, also quite tolerant, due to the presence
of a pronounced degrading system.

In the series of the alkylthiotriazines the field of
application covers a broad range of crops like sugarcane, small
grains (under European conditions), cotton, sunflowers, some
vegetables, rice.

As the mode of action has been treated in detail in Dr.
Moreland's paper, I shall only summarize that the exact site of
action of the inhibitor molecule seems to be at the water-
splitting site of the photosystem. Inhibition of energy transfer in chloroplasts is, apparently, essential for the plant
killing action. Chlorophyll is thought to be the principal

pigment involved in triazine phytotoxicity; in the dark no toxicity occurs.

Looking over the whole mosaic of findings related to
degradation, be it in plants, in animals or in the soil, it becomes evident that chemical and biochemical reactions occur at
similar sites of the triazine molecule.
    Three main pathways and their combinations dominate the de-
gradation scene:

a) Replacement of the C-2 substituent by a hydroxy group
   (in plants, animals, soils)

   $-Cl \longrightarrow -OH$

   $-OCH_3 \longrightarrow -OH$

   $-SCH_3 \longrightarrow -SOCH_3 \longrightarrow -SO_2CH_3 \longrightarrow -OH$

b) Replacement of the C-2 substituent by peptides and aminoacids
   (in plants and animals)

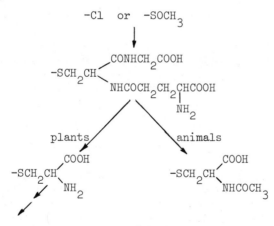

The search for the enzyme responsible for the conjugation of
chlorotriazines resulted in the identification of a glutathione
S-transferase.

c) Reactions of the $\underline{N}$-functions
   (in plants, animals, soils)

$$-NHC_2H_5 \longrightarrow -NH_2$$

$$-NHCH{\Large\langle}^{CH_3}_{CH_3} \longrightarrow -NHCH{\Large\langle}^{COOH}_{CH_3}$$

$$-NH\overset{\overset{\displaystyle CH_3}{|}}{\underset{\underset{\displaystyle CH_3}{|}}{C}}CN \longrightarrow -NH-\overset{\overset{\displaystyle CH_3}{|}}{\underset{\underset{\displaystyle CH_3}{|}}{C}}-CONH_2 \longrightarrow -NH-\overset{\overset{\displaystyle CH_3}{|}}{\underset{\underset{\displaystyle CH_3}{|}}{C}}-COOH$$

$$-NHCH{\Large\langle}^{CH_2CH_3}_{CH_3} \longrightarrow -NHCH{\Large\langle}^{CHOHCH_3}_{CH_3}$$

$$-NHCH_2CH_2CH_2OCH_3 \longrightarrow -NHCH_2CH_2CH_2OH \longrightarrow -NHCH_2CH_2COOH$$

$$-N_3 \longrightarrow -NH_2$$

$$-NH_2 \longrightarrow -OH$$

Triazine tolerance is mainly regulated by the pathway and the rate of detoxication in a given plant species. The hydrolytic and conjugation processes which were listed in a) and b) allow resistant plants to transform the phytotoxic triazines rapidly into non-phytotoxic metabolites. Moderately susceptible plants may do this more slowly or for example through $\underline{N}$-dealkylation, as listed in c), whereby metabolites are formed which may still possess some phytocidal activity.

    In mammals degradation mainly proceeds via conjugation, N-dealkylation and side chain oxidation, less by hydrolysis. Also 2-hydroxy-4-amino-6-alkylamino derivatives are completely excreted when directly applied to animals. No organospecific retention or accumulation of s-triazines or metabolites have been observed in animals.

    In soils hydrolysis of the 2-substituents and $\underline{N}$-dealkylation dominate the transformation of the $\underline{s}$-triazines. Further degradation of the primary metabolites proceeds as follows (shown be-low):   The dealkylation steps are relatively slow, whereas ring cleavage, probably at the cyanuric acid stage, with the liberation of CO_2 is high once ammeline is reached on the pathway:

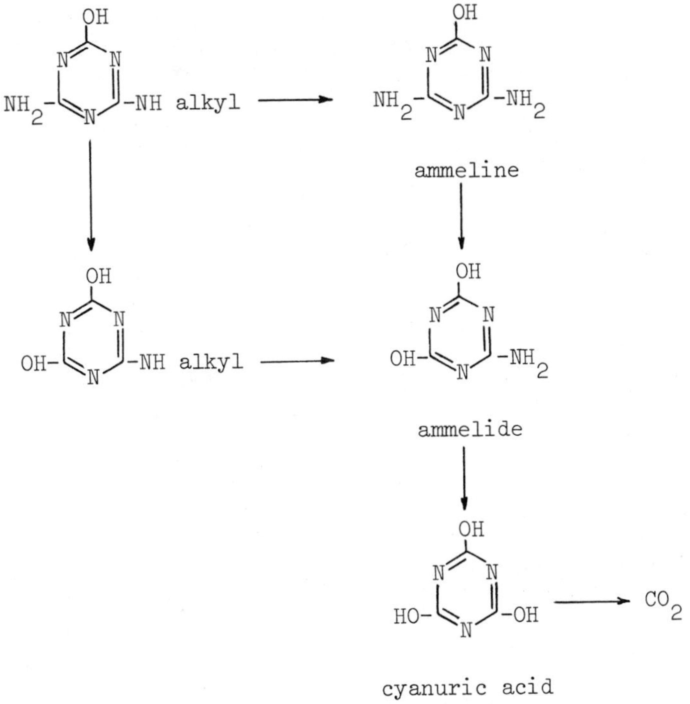

$$
\begin{array}{ccc}
\text{OH} & & \text{OH} \\
\text{NH}_2\text{—}\boxed{\text{triazine}}\text{—NH alkyl} & \longrightarrow & \text{NH}_2\text{—}\boxed{\text{triazine}}\text{—NH}_2 \\
& & \text{ammeline} \\
\downarrow & & \downarrow \\
\text{OH} & & \text{OH} \\
\text{OH—}\boxed{\text{triazine}}\text{—NH alkyl} & \longrightarrow & \text{OH—}\boxed{\text{triazine}}\text{—NH}_2 \\
& & \text{ammelide} \\
& & \downarrow \\
& & \text{OH} \\
& & \text{HO—}\boxed{\text{triazine}}\text{—OH} \longrightarrow CO_2 \\
& & \text{cyanuric acid}
\end{array}
$$

It is interesting to note that the presence of certain amounts of cyanuric acid in USA soils was already mentioned by two USDA scientists in 1917; in that case cyanuric acid was recognized as being a step in the uric acid allantoin degradation cycle.

Triazine herbicides are applied world-wide and in important agricultural sectors. They are, evidently, able to resolve major weed problems in such a way and to such a degree that they are quantity-wise the top herbicides used today. Although there is no technology which will not be confronted at some time with a superior technology there is strong evidence for the future utility of this class of compounds.

To create usefulness -- this is the challenge which animates our branch of applied chemistry. In the case of successful achievement, it would be wrong to applaud a few individuals. Esteem and high appreciation must go to the community of hundreds and hundreds of practitioners and scientists spread over the whole world who devoted their interest and their talents to the matter and contributed to the insight which we have today.

No technology can be successful unless applied correctly and consciously. No technology can be accepted and justified unless supported by basic knowledge. Only through knowledge are we able to circumscribe our possibilities and our limits.

The Environmental Chemistry of Herbicides

DONALD G. CROSBY

Department of Environmental Toxicology, University of California, Davis, Calif. 95616

One of the principal problems in discussing the environmental chemistry of herbicides lies in deciding where to start and where to stop. As an initial oversimplification, one could write

Herbicides → Nontoxic Inorganic Products

and be close to the truth. However, the recent history of public and scientific concern over herbicide efficacy, toxicity, side-effects, and similar issues requires that we consider at least some of the intermediate steps of that process.

This consideration is overdue, not only among herbicide chemists but particularly among other scientists and scientifically-aware attorneys, public officials, managers, and even professors. Therefore, this Chapter is not so much directed toward "experts" as it is toward a more diverse and perhaps more critical audience.

By "environment", I refer to the physical and chemical world which surrounds us. We usually tend to think of it in terms of "compartments"--atmosphere, soil (lithosphere), water (hydrosphere) and living plants and animals (biosphere)-- although a moment's reflection on soil microorganisms, airborne dust, or the clouds in the sky should tell us that this categorization, too, is oversimplified. However, the compartment concept does form a framework of chemistry by which our all-encompassing surroundings can be assigned some chemical characteristics--characteristics which existed before, and exclusive of, man-made chemicals. For example, from the composition of the atmosphere, we may surmise that oxidations will represent an important group of reactions in that compartment, ionic reactions such as nucleophilic displacements should be especially important in the hydrosphere, and so on.

Unlike other pesticide groups such as the insecticides or fungicides, herbicides now encompass a very wide range of structural types (Fig. 1). Aliphatic, aromatic, and heterocyclic systems; a variety of common and less common functional groups

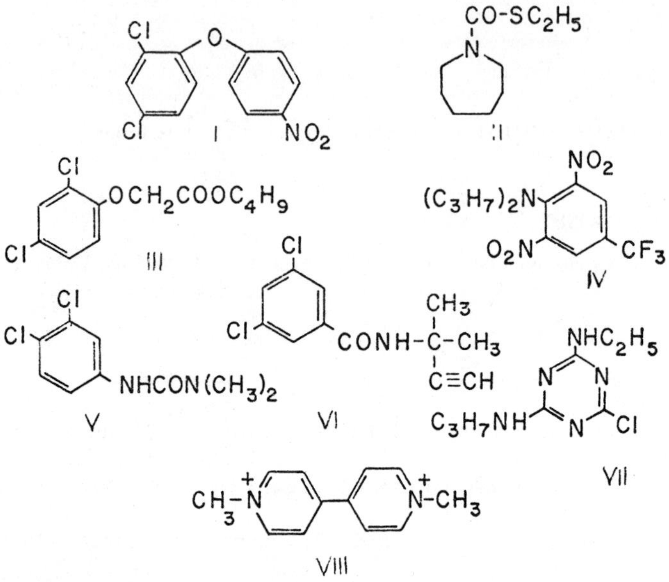

Figure 1.   Chemical structures of some important herbicides

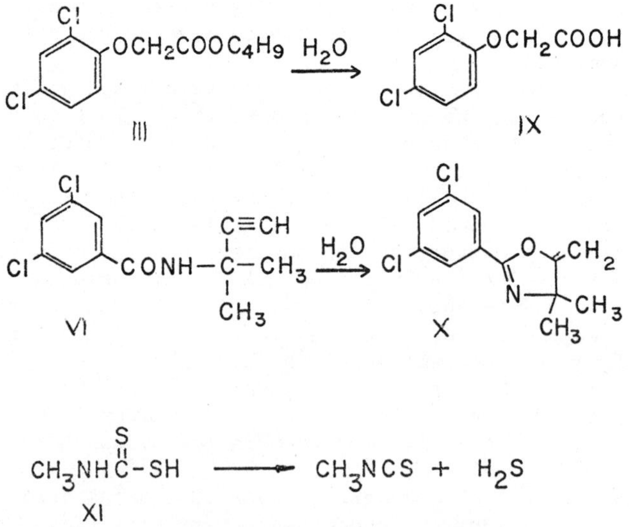

Figure 2.   Typical dark reactions of 2,4-D butyl ester (III), pronamid (VI), and metham (XI)

including esters, acids, amines, nitro compounds, and thio-acids;
a continuum of polarities from water-soluble salts to hydrophobic
hydrocarbons--all seem to share a common property: reactivity.
It is with the chemical consequences of the intentional or inad-
vertent introduction of the two--reactive herbicides and the
chemical compartments of the environment--that this paper will
deal.

Interactions

Despite the chemical diversity of the several hundred
structures representing herbicidal activity, most reactions of
herbicides fall within only a limited number of mechanistic types:
oxidation, reduction, nucleophilic displacements (such as hydrolysis), eliminations, and additions. "Herbicides", after all, are
more-or-less ordinary chemicals, and their principal transformations in the environment are fundamentally no different from
those in laboratory glassware. Figure 2 illustrates three typical
examples which have received their share of classical laboratory
study--the alkaline hydrolysis of a carboxylic ester (in this
case, an ester of 2,4-dichlorophenoxyacetic acid, IX), the cyclo-
addition of an alcohol to an olefin (as in the acetylene, VI), and
the β-elimination of a dithiocarbamate which provides the usual
synthetic route to an isothiocyanate (conversion of an N,N-
dimethylcarbamic acid salt, XI, to methyl isothiocyanate). Allow
the starting materials herbicidal action (which they have), give
them names such as "2,4-D ester" or "pronamide" or "Vapam", and
let soil form the walls of an outdoor reaction kettle; the reactions and products remain the same.

Generally these environmental reactions in soil or water
proceed rather slowly compared to what we might be used to under
the forcing conditions of the laboratory. For example, the
hydrolysis of half the 2,4-D ester in natural water requires 220
days at pH 6 (1), and appreciable cyclization of VI takes 40 days
in soil (2). However, react they do. As seen from Table I,
comparison of the transformation rates of a number of common
herbicides in sterile and nonsterile soil clearly show that such
nonbiological reactions must be at least as important as metabolism in bringing about fundamental environmental changes among
herbicides when provided enough time.

Many of these same reactions are markedly accelerated by the
energy of sunlight (3), and a number are unexpectedly rapid. For
example, after the 2,4-D esters are hydrolyzed by water and light
(1), the resulting acid undergoes oxidation, reduction, and
nucleophilic displacement of ring-chlorines, at ambient tempera-
tures, which would be very difficult to perform under ordinary
(dark) laboratory conditions (4). Besides light, the degradation
of these phenoxy acid herbicides requires atmospheric oxygen, the
hydroxide ion normally present in water (10^{-7} M at neutrality),
water, and some extractable source of hydrogen (Fig. 3) (5). The

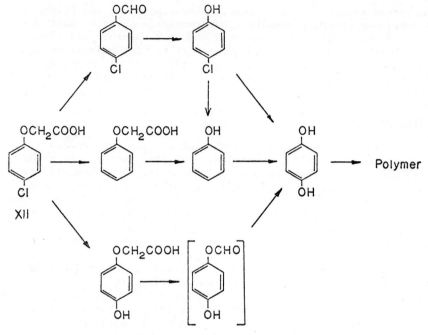

Figure 3.   *The photodecomposition of 4-CPA in water*

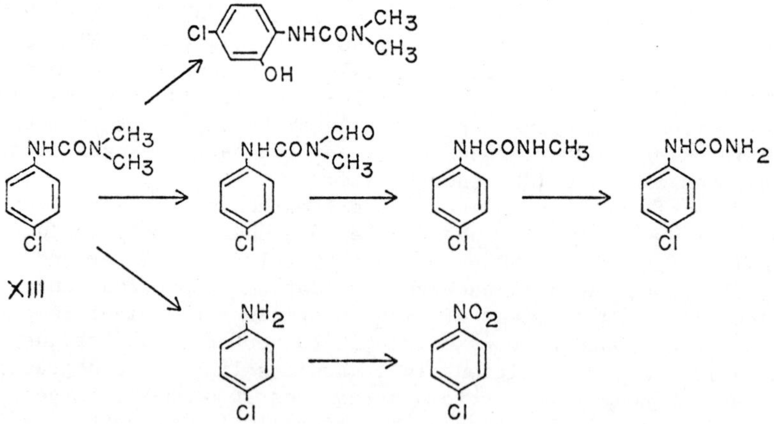

Figure 4.   *Metabolism and photodecomposition products of monuron (XIII)*

Table I.   Degradation of Herbicides in Sterile and Non-sterile
           Soil.

Herbicide	Sterilization Method	Relative Rate (sterile/non-sterile)
Amiben (ester)	Steam	1/1
Amitrole	KN_3; ethylene oxide	1/1
Atrazine	NaN_3	1/1
Bromoxynil	Autoclave	1/10
Pronamid	Steam	1/1
Dalapon	Autoclave	<1/10
Dichlobenil	Autoclave	1/0.5
Diphenamid	Radiation	1/1.5
Diuron	Chloropicrin	1/5

importance of the makeup of such a nonliving microchemical environment to herbicide transformations cannot be overemphasized (6).
   Of course, the biochemical action of living plants and
animals cannot be discounted (Table I) and often rivals or exceeds
abiotic action. Monuron (XIII) is readily degraded by microorganisms, higher plants, and animals (7) by the routes shown in Fig.
4. These metabolites then are at least partially converted
further to oxidized products, conjugates with amino acids or
carbohydrates, or other representatives of the remarkable synthetic abilities of organisms (8), although they often are
reconverted to the parent metabolite upon return to soil or water.
   A sign of the integrity of environmental chemistry is that
the primary metabolites of monuron, shown in the Figure, are
identical with the major products of monuron photodecomposition in
water (9); the basic reactions and reagents probably are the same.
Recall that the final fate of monuron and other herbicides
undoubtedly will be the inorganic state--water, carbon dioxide,
ammonia or nitrogen oxides, and chloride ions--but without a
consistent time frame. It is the intermediate stages which can be
frustrating, dangerous, unpredictable, and occasionally scientifically delightful.

The Directions of Environmental Chemistry

   With those qualities in mind, what may we expect of the
Environmental Chemistry of Herbicides as we enter the "Second
Century of American Chemistry?" Perhaps a great many more contributions to both basic science and practical art than most people
have considered. By way of example, I would like to mention just
four areas: fundamental chemistry, chemical biology, human
safety, and agronomic efficacy.

Revealing the Surprising Chemistry of Nature. Figures 1 and
4 showed amines and their derivatives to be important environmental breakdown products as well as herbicides in their own
right. In the laboratory, such substances can be oxidized by the
most powerful agents (e.g., peroxytrifluoroacetic acid) to the
corresponding aromatic nitro compounds (10). However, the simple
illumination of at least several representatives in water (p-
chloroaniline, bentazone, and Sustar) resulted in detectable
levels of corresponding nitro derivatives (Fig. 4) (11-13). What
natural oxidants are generated which are both reactive enough and
stable enough to carry out such transformations?

Another common laboratory reaction of amines is diazotization
to provide unstable and highly reactive diazonium salts. Plimmer
et al.(14) have isolated an aromatic triazene (XV) from soil
containing 3,4-dichloroaniline (XIV) and presented evidence that
it is formed by "natural" diazotization of the aniline followed by
coupling with a second amine molecule (Fig. 5). If this is true--
that the natural nitrite commonly found in soil and water can
bring about diazotization--a new dimension must be added to both
the natural mechanisms of herbicide degradation and the generation
of new series of potentially dangerous transformation products.

Photodecomposition of a substance previously has been
considered to require the prior absorption of light--the first
rule of photochemistry. Yet, first ethylenethiourea (15) and more
recently molinate (II), compounds which do not absorb ultraviolet
light in the sunlight wavelength range, were observed to undergo
photooxidation in sterilized field water (Fig. 6). Through the
work of Ross (16), we now know that natural waters contain photo-
oxidants (just as the atmosphere does) which cause oxidative
degradation of herbicides even though no light is actually
absorbed by the pesticide.

Providing Insight Into the Chemical Basis of Plant Processes.
A wide variety of carbamates, triazines, amides, ureas, quinones
and other herbicides are known to exert their action by inhibiting
the plant's photosynthetic process (17). However, some of the
same compounds have been used very effectively as probes into the
pathways of photosynthesis and electron transport in plants.

The photosynthetic process consists of two chlorophyll-
mediated, light-energized systems, an electron-transport system
bridging them, and the "dark-reaction" in which light-generated
ATP and NADPH reduce carbon dioxide to carbohydrate. The locus of
action of the principal herbicidal inhibitors has been ascertained
in a number of instances (Fig. 7), but, with few exceptions, the
exact chemical mechanism by which inhibition takes place remains
unknown. As more herbicides are examined and more is learned of
structure-activity relations, an increasingly detailed picture of
the chemistry by which light energy generates chemicals via
"photosynthesis" is assured.

However, in a number of instances, both the fundamental biochemistry and its extension to the search for improved herbicide

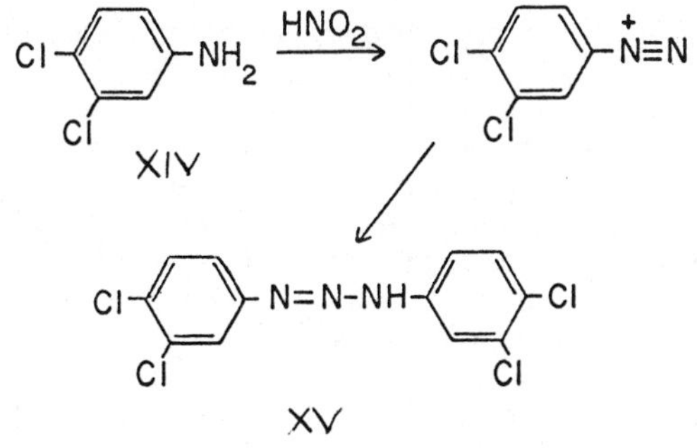

*Figure 5.   Formation of bis(3,4-dichlorophenyl)-
1,3-triazene in soil*

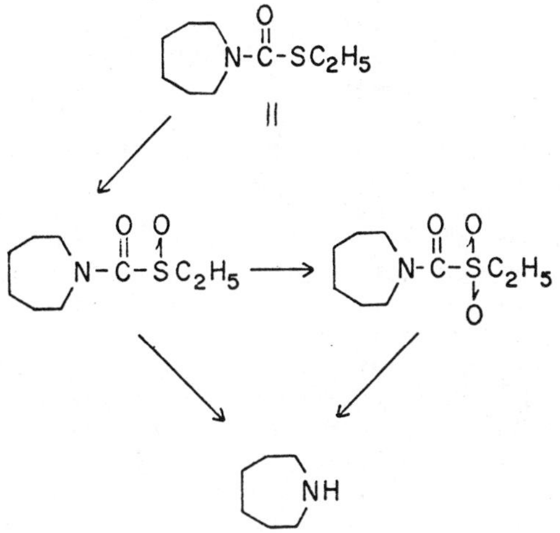

*Figure 6.   Photodecomposition of molinate (II) in
water*

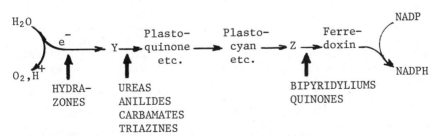

Figure 7.   Effects of herbicides on photosynthetic processes

candidates will depend upon prior in vivo environmental transfor-
mations--the reactive (toxic) form within the plant indeed may not
be identical to the more stable one applied. For example, most of
the spectacular action of paraquat (VIII) on plants actually
appears due to the in situ generation of toxic hydrogen peroxide
(18), diphenatrile almost certainly is converted to its amide or
acid before action (19), and the activation of phenoxy herbicides
by metabolism to chloroacetic acid has been proposed (20).

     Plants obviously have mechanisms by which to resist disease,
but it is largely through the study of herbicides that other plant
defense mechanisms have been revealed. Detoxication as a defense
against foreign chemicals is now generally accepted to have major
importance for herbicide selectivity. Resistant species display
abilities for oxidation, reduction, hydrolysis, and conjugation
almost unrecognized a decade ago (8,21). However, one especially
intriguing mechanism is that which causes maize to be resistant to
intoxication by simazine (XVI). In this instance, the plant
contains a natural but very reactive nucleophile, 2,4-dihydroxy-7-
methoxy-1,4-benzoxazin-2-one (XVII) which displaces chloride from
the reactive chlorotriazine (Fig. 8); the resulting O-substituted
hydroxylamine is much more susceptible to hydrolysis than was the
simazine, and the benzoxazinone is regenerated along with non-
toxic hydroxysimazine XVIII (22,23).

     The degradation processes within plants still provide a
source of amazement for me, expecially when such supposedly
"simple" organisms routinely carry out chemical reactions which a
chemist is hard put to do in his laboratory. These abilities also
may eventually provide some keys into the fundamental biochemical
processes shared by all living things. The relatively strenuous
oxidation of an aromatic amine to the corresponding nitro compound
was mentioned earlier; however, bean plants can convert the urea
herbicide diuron (V) into 3,4-dichloronitrobenzene (24). Unlike
their halogenated relatives, trifluoromethyl groups attached to
aromatic rings are hydrolyzed to acids only under extreme laboratory conditions; carrots convert the trifluoromethyl group of
trifluralin (IV) to the corresponding acid at ambient temperature
(25).

     Investigation of the photochemical degradation of trifluralin
(26) demonstrated the formation of benzimidazoles and their intermediate dihydroxybenzimidazolines through what initially must be a
free-radial mechanism (Fig. 9). Yet investigation of the facile
plant metabolism of such dinitroaniline herbicides reveals the
same or analogous products. Can plants use such radical reactions
in detoxication activities? If so, how are the radicals generated
and controlled? If not, what other mechanisms might account for
these peculiar trifluralin metabolites? The observation has been
made before (8) that metabolites and photoproducts often turn out
to be identical. Again, why?

     Obviously, plants differ widely in their ability to resist
and dispose of otherwise toxic substances. Might it be possible

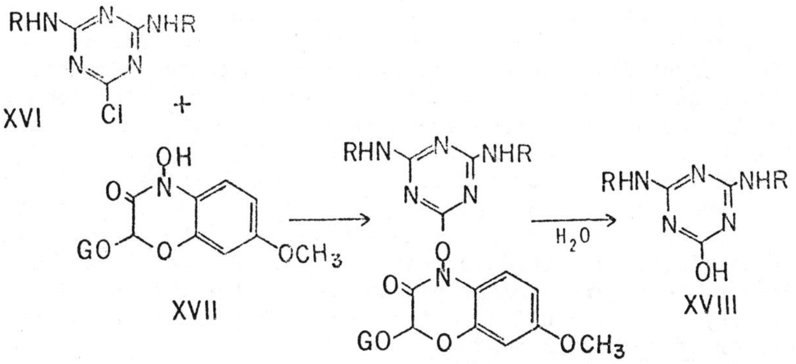

Figure 8.   Mechanism of simazine (XVI) detoxication in corn

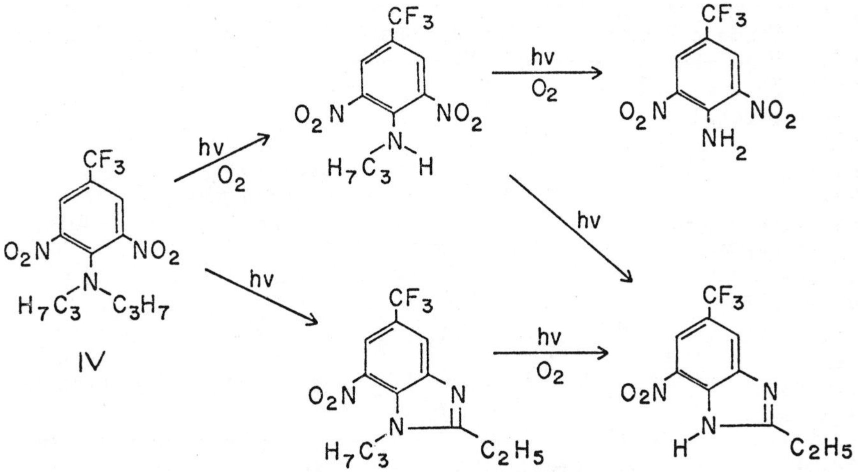

Figure 9.   Photodecomposition of trifluralin (IV)

to use herbicides as taxonomic probes? In recent years, the field
of biochemical systematics has developed rapidly (e.g., 27), based
largely on structural analogies among alkaloids, terpenes, cyano-
genic glycosides, etc. Still, the variety of detoxication mechanisms demonstrated within the plant kingdom suggests that ability
to defend against chemical stress had evolutionary value long
before the advent of modern-day chemicals and that present taxa
must be the current product of those eons of coping with an
hostile environment. For example, red currants (Ribes rubrum)
oxidized over half of an applied dose of 2,4-D and tolerated the
herbicide, while the susceptible black currents (R. nigrum) failed
almost completely at the detoxication (28). How does the genetic
history of these very similar plants account for this species-
specificity and how could such information be used to predict
effects of other herbicides?

Protecting Human Well-being. The growing popularity of
herbicides and plant growth regulators is not accidental. The
proven value of these agents for crop production, health,
commerce, forestry, and many other areas has caused the use of
plant-control chemicals to double in the past 10 years. Of
course, the fact that a substance is usefully toxic against a weed
does not preclude toxic effects on desirable plants, higher
animals, or even on man himself (Table II). Wisely, society is
demanding a certain amount of assurance that the toxicity of
environmental chemicals be harnessed.

Table II. Acute Toxicity of Common Herbicides (29).

Common Name	Structure	Trade Name	LD_{50} (mg/kg)[a]
Dinitrocresol (DNOC)		Sinox	30
Allyl alcohol			64
Sodium pentachlorophenate		Dowicide G	78
Paraquat (chloride)	VIII	Gramoxone	157
2,4-D	IX	Weedone 638	375
Molinate	II	Ordram	501
2,4-D butyl ester	III	Esteron 76	620
Metham	X	Vapam	820
Nitrofen	I	Tok	2630
Atrazine	VII	Aatrex	3080
Diuron	V	Karmex	3400
Trifluralin	IV	Treflan	3700-10,000
Pronamid	VI	Kerb	8350

[a]Acute rat oral toxicity.

What happens to herbicides after they are applied? A proportion will be taken up by plants and either stored or metabolized (biochemically transformed to other substances, as we have seen). The metabolites, as well as the remaining parent and other break-down products, eventually will reach water and soil (6), from which they may volatilize into the atmosphere or move on suspended dust or silt [sometimes for great distance (30)] eventually to decompose or be returned to earth in an ever-diminishing cycle. How the chemicals move and break down increasingly determine a grower's relations with his neighbors, his customers, and his governments.

MCPA application to rice provides an example. This phenoxy herbicide (2-methyl-4-chlorophenoxyacetic acid) has been of vital importance to California's rice production for a number of years, and its volume for that purpose regularly has exceeded 10^5 kg/yr. However, as MCPA is applied after the fields are flooded and the rice seedlings have emerged, there has been increasing concern that it might concentrate in the rice grain, move in air and water, and eventually exert toxic effects on people or on other crops. Careful analysis of MCPA's environmental chemistry (31) shows that as long as the field water is held for a few days, the MCPA does not move and is decomposed to harmless products by sunlight and microorganisms as well as by the rice plant itself.

Yet, herbicides or their by-products can be hazardous. Perhaps the most renowned example is the extensively-used 2,4,5-T (2,4,5-trichlorophenoxyacetic acid), or rather the 2,3,7,8-tetrachlorodibenzo-p-dioxin (TCDD) impurity which sometimes accompanies it. During massive use of the herbicide as a defoliant in the Vietnam war, TCDD was found almost by accident to be one of the most toxic synthetic substances ever tested. Soon, it was shown to be present in domestic 2,4,5-T as well as in the chemical warfare agents. Tests in laboratory animals demonstrated that some of the observed levels indeed were quite high enough to cause toxic effects (32).

Miraculously, few human tragedies have definitely been traced to 2,4,5-T or TCDD, in war or peace. Further investigation indicates that environmental break-down may be largely the reason. TCDD is very unstable to sunlight when it is present as a trace contaminant in commercial pesticides (Fig. 10) (33,34), especially when applied to inert surfaces or leaves. The present lack of evidence for widespread occurrence of TCDD in the environment may be directly related to its environmental chemistry. The knowledge that the detoxication and loss occur through reductive dechlorination by the solvent also opens the way for intentional TCDD destruction or decontamination.

Maximizing Herbicide Utility. Most herbicides dissipate rather rapidly after application. That is, they volatilize, are decomposed by light or microorganisms, and are leached into soil, etc. In any case, they become unavailable to perform their function. Ultimately, this dissipation becomes desirable in that

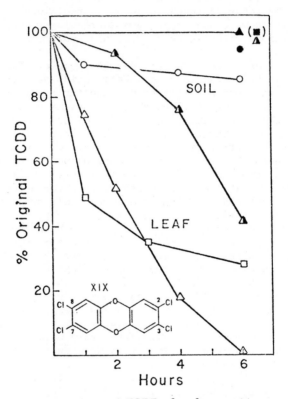

Figure 10. Rates of TCDD photodecomposition on soil (○), leaves (□, △), and glass (△). Closed symbols represent dark controls.

it prevents a buildup of potentially toxic chemicals, but the
pest-control efficiency of many herbicide applications is low
because of it. Only in recent years have we begun to understand
something about the dissipating forces--for example the photo-
chemically-generated oxidants or plant metabolism mentioned
earlier. A lot of herbicide has been wasted.

In order to minimize waste as well as to direct selectivity,
a number of approaches toward dissipation-control are being
examined. For example, both volatilization and photodecomposition
often can be regulated to a desired degree by incorporation of a
non-volatile resin additive into the pesticide formulation (35).
The technique appears promising for insecticides, and there is no
reason to believe it should not work for herbicides also. Another
approach is inhibition of microbial break-down; for example, N-
methylcarbamate inhibitors of hydrolytic enzymes, such as PCMC
(p-chlorophenyl N-methylcarbamate), applied together with a herbicide such as chloropropham [isopropyl N-(3-chlorophenyl)carbamate]
which is inactivated by soil microbes, more than doubled the
effectiveness (36,37).

However, controlled or specific environmental degradation
sometimes is necessary for herbicidal action. For example, the
phenoxy herbicide sesone (sodium 2,4-dichlorophenoxyethyl sulfate)
has no effect on plants until it can be oxidized to 2,4-D by a
specific soil microorganism, Bacillus cereus (38). The growth
regulator ethophon (Ethrel) relies upon slow environmental conversion into ethylene for its activity (39). And metham (Vapam)
depends upon hydrolysis in soil to release toxic methyl isothiocyanate (40).

Surely, many such common reactions could be utilized for the
intentional destruction of unwanted herbicides and their residues
(41). Metham might be caused to react simply with aqueous ammonia
to form harmless methylthiourea; many herbicides including
prometryne and metribuzin (Sencor) might be degraded by dilute
hypochlorite ("chlorinated lime") of the type used to purify
swimming pools, and the photodecomposition of others (such as
2,4,5-T) might be accelerated by cheap nontoxic photosensitizers
such as acetone (Table III) (42). The variations of environmental
chemistry applications to control and direct herbicide persistence
and effectiveness now appear endless.

What Can We Do

For centuries, people have observed the transport and transformations of chemicals in the environment without really thinking
in terms of "environmental chemistry". The odor of flowers (or
of stockyards), the Fall coloration of maple leaves, and the
bleaching of fabrics were all taken for granted. Even into the
Age of Chemistry, no one really worried much about where the smoke
went or why the water tasted funny. That has changed.

Table III.   Sensitized Photolysis of 2,4,5-T (42).

| Sensitizer | Sunlight | 2,4,5-T Concentration | | % Loss |
		0 Hrs (mg/l)	48 Hrs (mg/l)	
None	−	1.00	0.93	7
None	+	1.00	0.86	14
Acetone (0.4%)	−	1.00	0.98	2
Acetone (0.4%)	+	1.00	0.20	80
Riboflavin (5 mg/l)	−	1.00	0.84	16
Riboflavin (5 mg/l)	+	1.00	0.20	80

Still, our knowledge of the forces and reagents which act on chemicals in the environment is largely rudimentary. However, through their structural variety and growing use, herbicides act as socially-acceptable chemical probes into that environment; environmental data on them could be invaluable for predicting the mobility and fate of much more toxic, persistent, and consequently dangerous substances which society releases daily with so little knowledge of what becomes of them. A rice-field or a corn patch can be viewed as a chemical reactor full of reagents into which is injected a structurally unique indicator. The environmental chemistry of herbicides is there to study, and the test tube is as close as your front porch.

When the American Chemical Society was founded in 1876, no more than half a dozen weed-killers were in use (43). In 1936, 60 years later, that number still remained almost unchanged. There now are over 200 herbicides and other plant growth regulators in common use, but the world requirements for food, fiber, and forest products--the principal beneficiaries of herbicides--never were greater. Still, the public is saying clearly that it must know what happens to all these chemicals and what some of the consequences will be.

Perhaps ironically, it was a herbicide--aminotriazole--which started the present regulatory trend and resulted most recently in rather specific government demands for environmental chemistry data to permit the registration of new herbicides and reregistration of old favorites (44). Modern society is being pushed inexorably toward a most serious dilemma: the requirement for pest control vs the need for human and environmental safety. As we have seen in just the few examples of this Chapter, much-- perhaps most--of our uncertainty arises from ignorance of the forces which act upon chemicals in the environment. Time is growing short for chemists to learn and apply the scientific fundamentals of the photochemical, microbial, and transportive phenomena which have been observed for centuries to influence us and our environment.

Just how short that time is, is being felt by regulatory agencies faced with setting criteria and efficiently (and safely) reregistering most existing pesticides. Yet, recently provided a prime opportunity to acquire some of the most urgent data, the EPA failed to act; surely, the burgeoning burden of registration decisions must point toward a basic need for environmental chemistry predictability--soon. Industry, too, needs that fundamental knowledge to find safer, more effective products. As we now see, the environmental chemistry of herbicides often provides the key to selectivity, persistence, residue distribution, and mode of action; registration requirements for new data actually may be looked upon as an opportunity to <u>apply</u> the demanded data toward finding new compounds, new formulations, and new control methods rather than only as an expensive chore. At the least, universities must start to teach the subject to our nation's future chemists.

I am convinced that the environmental chemistry of herbicides provides for their safer and more efficient use, less cost to consumers, more benefits to industry, and exciting advances in basic science. Look around you: in the <u>next</u> century of American Chemistry, this new field of work will affect each of us more than we could ever have imagined.

Literature Cited

(1) Zepp, R.G., Wolfe, N.L., Gordon, J.A., Baughman, G.L., Environ. Sci. Technol. <u>9</u>, 1144 (1975).
(2) Yih, R.Y., Swithenbank, C., McRae, D.H., Weed Sci. <u>18</u>, 604 (1970).
(3) Crosby, D.G., in "Herbicides: Chemistry, Degradation, and Mode of Action" (P.C. Kearney, D.D. Kaufman, eds.), Vol. 2, p. 835, Marcel Dekker, New York, 1976.
(4) Crosby, D.G., Tutass, H.O., J.Agr. Food Chem. <u>14</u>, 596 (1966).
(5) Crosby, D.G., Wong, A.S., J. Agr. Food Chem. <u>21</u>, 1049 (1973).
(6) Crosby, D.G., in "The Physiology and Biochemistry of Herbicides" (L.J. Audus, ed.), 2nd Ed., Academic Press, London, 1976.
(7) Menzie, C.M., "Metabolism of Pesticides", Spec. Sci. Rept: Wildlife 184, Fish and Wildlife Service, USDI, Washington, D.C., 1974.
(8) Crosby, D.G., Ann. Rev. Plant Physiol. <u>24</u>, 567 (1973).
(9) Crosby, D.G., Tang, C.-S., J. Agr. Food Chem. <u>17</u>, 1041 (1969).
(10) Emmons, W.D., J. Am. Chem. Soc. <u>79</u>, 5528 (1957).
(11) Crosby, D.G., Leitis, E., unpublished, 1973.
(12) Nilles, G.P., Zabik, M.J., J. Agr. Food Chem. <u>22</u>, 684 (1974).
(13) Miller, G., Crosby, D.G., unpublished data, 1976.
(14) Plimmer, J.R., Kearney, P.C., Chisaka, H., Yount, J.B., Klingebiel, U.I., J. Agr. Food Chem. <u>18</u>, 859 (1970).
(15) Ross, R.D., Crosby, D.G., J. Agr. Food Chem., <u>21</u>, 335 (1973).

(16) Ross, R.D., Thesis, Univ. of California, Davis, CA., 1974.
(17) Büchel, K.H., Pestic. Sci. 3, 89 (1973).
(18) Calderbank, A., Adv. Pest Control Res. 8, 127 (1968).
(19) Fawcett, C.H., Taylor, H.F., Wain, R.L., Wightman, F., Proc. Roy. Soc. (London), B148, 543 (1958).
(20) Tutass, H.O., Thesis, Univ. of California, Davis, CA., 1967.
(21) Casida, J.E., Lykken, L., Ann. Rev. Plant Physiol. 20, 607 (1969).
(22) Roth, W., Knüsli, E., Experientia 17, 312 (1961).
(23) Hamilton, R.H., Moreland, D.E., Science 136, 373 (1962).
(24) Onley, J.H., Yip, G., Aldridge, M.H., J. Agr. Food Chem. 16, 426 (1968).
(25) Golab, T., Herberg, R.J., Parka, S.J., Tepe, J.B., J. Agr. Food Chem. 15, 638 (1967).
(26) Leitis, E., Crosby, D.G., J. Agr. Food Chem. 22, 842 (1974).
(27) Alston, R.E., Turner, B.L., "Biochemical Systematics", Prentice-Hall, Englewood Cliffs, N.J., 1963.
(28) Luckwill, L.C., Lloyd-Jones, C.P., Ann. Appl. Biol. 48, 613 (1960).
(29) Bailey, J.B., Swift, J.E., "Pesticide Information and Safety Manual", Univ. of Calif., Berkeley, 1968.
(30) Risebrough, R.W., Huggett, R.J., Griffin, J.J., Goldberg, E. D., Science 159, 1233 (1968).
(31) Soderquist, C.J., Bowers, J.B., Crosby, D.G., J. Agr. Food Chem., submitted for publication (1976).
(32) PSAC, "Report on 2,4,5-T," OST, Exec. Office of the President, Washington, D.C. 1971.
(33) Crosby, D.G., Wong, A.S., Plimmer, J.R., Woolson, E.A., Science 173, 748 (1971).
(34) Crosby, D.G., Wong, A.S., Science, submitted for publication (1976).
(35) Aller, H.E., Dewey, J.E., J. Econ. Entomol. 54, 508 (1961).
(36) Dawson, J.H., Weed Sci. 17, 295 (1969).
(37) Kaufman, D.D., Kearney, P.C., Von Endt, D.W., Miller, D.E., J. Agr. Food Chem. 18, 513 (1970).
(38) Vlitos, A.J., Contr. Boyce Thompson Inst. 17, 127 (1953).
(39) Warner, H.L., Leopold, A.C., Plant Physiol. 44, 156 (1959).
(40) Turner, N.J., Corden, M.E., Phytopathol. 53, 1388 (1963).
(41) Foy, C.L., Bingham, S.W., Residue Rev. 29, 105 (1969).
(42) Crosby, D.G., Wong, A.S., J. Agr. Food Chem. 21, 1052 (1973).
(43) E. Bourcart, "Insecticides, Fungicides, and Weedkillers", Scott, Greenwood, and Son, London, 1913.
(44) U.S. Environmental Protection Agency, "Guidelines for Registering Pesticides in the United States," Federal Register 40(123), 26802 (1975).

Fungicides

Introduction

GUSTAVE K. KOHN

Zoecon Corp., 975 California Ave., Palo Alto, Calif. 94304

This section of the symposium on Pesticide Chemistry of the
Twentieth Century has a unique distinction. The earliest extant
written reference to a pesticide relates to plant disease problems of the Mediterranean area. The pesticide is sulfur and
Homer makes reference to it. This discovery dating back some
3500 years ago, may be the first written comment on successful
agricultural chemotherapy.

Fungus disease and plant disease in general play a limiting
role in the developing of agriculture of much of the third world,
particularly for those countries in Asia, Africa and South America where the climate is tropical or semi-tropical. Fungicides
in relation to food production at this particular time of world
history have a very special significance.

It is appropriate that as we review plant disease
chemotherapy, we <u>limit</u> our discussions to agents that are
<u>fungicides and bactericides</u>. We are well aware, of course, of
broader aspects - of the increasing recognition of virus caused
plant disease. We are just beginning to understand the natural
plant mechanisms for immunity - but we have as yet made no sub-
stantive progress toward the stimulation of phytoalexins nor the
synthesis of products that successfully mimic them. These deficiencies of knowledge and of practice will at least be partially
reduced in the decades that follow. Meetings similar to this in
the periods ahead will transcend the area of fungicides and
bactericides and deal with agents that control plant infections
from other causes and by different mechanisms.

Our first author needs no introduction to those who practice
in this field. He is a plant pathologist of eminence, the author
of fundamental and definitive studies in plant pathology whose
books and whose researches on chemotherapeutic agents and their
mode of action stimulated several generations of chemists and
biologists. He worked on Homer's first plant disease combatting
agent as he did on the early inorganic fungicides and the early
organic composition. He was for many years the director of the
Connecticut Agricultural Station and professor at Yale University.

We could have made no better choice for our first author than scholar, productive researcher and pioneer than Dr. James G. Horsfall.

The research of Dr. van der Kerk and his institute at Utrecht, the Netherlands, on fundamental organometallic chemistry as well as on fungicides also requires no introduction.

Organometallic compositions in the form of simple basic salts, the dithiocarbamate metal compounds and the organotins are among our most useful plant protecting agents.

The third author is an industrial chemist associated in various capacities with the research department of Chevron Chemical Co. His area of competence in the fungicide field relates to the sulfenimide group of compositions. The sulfenimide fungicides today are a versatile group of protective fungicides employed in agriculture throughout the world.

Systemics provide us with the nearest approach currently available to a practical form of plant immunity. Though this is certainly not immunity in the mammalian sense, it nevertheless provides the farmer with compositions of protectant and prophylactic value. In a paper presented at the Symposium but not included in this volume, Dr. Hugh D. Sisler of the University of Maryland, who is recognized for his mode of action studies, explored the diverse mechanisms of action in the area of fungicide chemistry exhibited by these systemics, a rapidly proliferating area for current synthesis and investigation.

Dr. Tomomasa Misato of the Institute of Physical and Chemical Research, Saitama, Japan, among his many contributions, pioneered in the investigation of certain antibiotics particularly as relating to structure and activity and mode of action but including also application to Japanese agriculture. Antibiotics are one of the newer areas in plant chemotherapy, and we welcome one of the most eminent investigators in the field who explores this area from its inception to the most recent applications to plant protection.

Through the papers above described, we hope to give our readers some historical perspective, a view of the present state of the art with regard to plant chemotherapy and finally some visisions for the future.

Fungicides—Past, Present, and Future

JAMES G. HORSFALL

The Connecticut Agricultural Experiment Station, Box 1106, New Haven, Conn. 06504

The year 1976 is surely the year for celebration, first the bicentennial of the Nation, then the centennial of the American Chemical Society (ACS). In this context it is pertinent to examine the past, present, and future of the chemicals that are called fungicides, the compounds widely used to protect the food of the world from plant disease. I shall limit my remarks to fungicides for food, not for fiber.

Why Use Fungicides On Food Crops?

A basic principle in plant pathology is that fungicides are used for crops that lack natural resistance to the fungus involved. Two notorious examples are Phytophthora infestans on potato and Venturia inaequalis on apple. No farmer would go to the labor and expense to spray his potatoes or his apples if he could have plants that successfully fight off their fungi. This principle says further that the amount of fungicide needed or the frequency of application is inversely proportional to natural resistance.

If natural resistance in the host breaks down, farmers often turn to fungicides. A classic example is the breakdown in 1970 in the U.S. of resistance of maize to Helminthosporium maydis. Farmers turned to zineb in 1970 even though it is expensive. Had not resistance been restored, zineb might well be widely used on maize by 1976.

Wheat is a curious case. Resistance to the rust disease periodically breaks down in wheat. As soon as the search discovers a new gene for resistance in wheat, a new race of the rust fungus appears. This is the classic case of the gene-for-

113

gene hypothesis. Despite this periodic collapse of
resistance in wheat, no fungicides are used in
really significant amounts. This is due to the low
cost/benefit ratio. Wheat returns such a relatively
low value per hectare that it cannot carry the cost
of an expensive chemical control regime. This is
especially true since society, not the farmer, now
bears the cost of the research to produce new
varieties, not the cost of chemical treatment.

Rice in Japan is a special case for cereals
that normally are not sprayed with fungicides. The
rice price in Japan is maintained high by the
government and, hence, farmers can afford to spray
and all or almost all do spray (Ou, 1).

Fungicides Of The Past

In 1776 when the Nation was born, we had two
useful fungicides for food crops, elemental sulfur
and copper sulfate. During the century before the
founding of ACS, we added only one more, lime-sulfur
in 1803 and this was only a variant of elemental
sulfur. Six years after ACS was founded, Bordeaux
mixture was born of one of those accidents that
Pasteur said happens to the prepared mind.

In 1876, the year that ACS was founded, the
French wine growers inadvertently imported on
American rootstocks, a new disease for them, downy
mildew. They had been protecting their grapes from
pilferage along the roadsides with a horrendous-
looking slurry of copper sulfate and hydrated lime.
Professor Alexis Millardet, having the needed prepared mind, was walking down a road in Bordeaux
Province during the harvest season of 1882. He
noticed that the treated grapes were free of downy
mildew while the others farther back from the road
were infected. And thus was born the material that
became the holy water of plant pathologists who, for
sixty years or more, annointed their crops with it
until it was largely replaced by organics.

In 1888 formaldehyde, the first synthetic
fungicide appeared. Unless you count chlorophenol
mercury in 1913, little really new happened until
1934 when Tisdale and Williams of DuPont revealed
the dialkyldithiocarbamates. They were expensive
to make, however, and it was depression days, and so
DuPont was skittish about trying to sell them to
farmers when copper sulfate could be bought for
6 cents a pound.

The price barrier was breached, however, when

Horsfall (2) introduced chloranil for legume seed
treatment in the late thirties. It sold for about
$1.50 per pound. In 1943 Dimond et al (3) introduced
the ethylenebisdithiocarbamates. These have gone on
to dominate the fungicide market for agricultural
crops. In 1943, 2,3-dichloro-1,4-naphthoquinone
appeared; in 1947, 2-heptadecyl-2-imidazoline; in
1949, 6-(1-methylheptyl)-2,4-dinitrophenyl crotonate;
in 1952, N-trichloromethyl thio-4-cyclohexene-1,2-dicar-
boximide (captan).

Fungicides Of The Present

Perhaps, we can begin the present with captan
in 1952. That gives us a quarter of a century. The
development of new compounds exploded in the 'fifties, as did insecticides, and nematicides.

The Forty Fungicides Of The World. By now the
world uses about forty fungicides on its crops.
The number depends on whether you count the mixtures
and on how you count the variants - say of the
dithiocarbamates.
The best listing of fungicides that we know of
is published annually by the Meister Publishing
Company of Willoughby, Ohio in their Farm Chemicals
Handbook. They list the following compounds or
types of compounds as officially "registered" for
use on plants in the United States: allyl alcohol,
ammonium isobutyrate, antibiotics, benzimidazole
types, carbofuran, cadmiums, captan types, coppers,
carboxin, dehydroacetic acid, Dexon (sodium [4-(di-
methylamino) phenyl] diazo sulfonate), diphenyl,
dodine, Dyrene (anilazine), formaldehyde, glyodin,
halogenated hydrocarbons, hypochlorite, Karathane
(dinocap types), mercuries, mineral oils, nitro-
phenols, organic tins, organic acids, pentachloronitrobenzene types, phenols, pyrimidines, propylene
oxide, pyridines, piperidines, quaternary ammoniums,
quinolinols, quinones, sulfurs, and Terrazole (5-
ethoxy-3-trichloromethyl-1,2,4-thiadiazole).
(4)
The Major Crops Of The World. Mangelsdorf has
said that since the dawn of history man has used
about 3000 species of plants for food. Perhaps 150
of these are in world commerce today, but only
10 percent of these really feed the people of the
world. Mangelsdorf's 15 species include five cereals; rice (Oryza sativa), wheat (Triticum spp.),
maize (Zea mays), sorghum (Sorghum cereale), and

barley (Hordeum vulgare); two sugar plants: sugar
cane (Saccharum officinarum) and sugar beet (Beta
vulgaris): three root crops: potato (Solanum
tuberosum), sweet potato (Ipomea batatas), and
cassava (Manihot esculenta); three legumes: common
bean (Phaseolus vulgaris), soybean (Glycine max),
and peanut (Arachis hypogaea); and two tree crops:
coconut (Cocos nucifera) and banana (Musa spp.).
In discussing fungicides we must add some non-food
crops; rubber (Hevea brasiliensis), coffee (Coffea
spp.), cotton (Gossypium spp.), tea and tobacco
(Nicotiana tabacum).

The Major Diseases Of The Crops Of The World.
The major diseases of rice are blast and bacterial
blight; wheat, rusts and smuts; maize, stem and root
rots; barley, helminthosporial leaf spot and root
rots; sugar cane, viruses; sugar beet, viruses and
cercosporal leaf spot; potato, late blight and
viruses; sweet potato, stem rot; cassava, mosaic;
common bean, viruses, bacterial blights, and root
rots; soybean, root rot; peanut, leaf spots and root
rot; coconut, practically none; banana, wilt and
Sigotoka; rubber, leaf blight; coffee, rust; cotton,
wilt and rots of seedlings and bolls; tobacco, blue
mold; tea, blister blight.
The massive tonnages of fungicides used in the
world are applied to foliage diseases of the crops
with high value per acre - banana, potato, apple,
citrus, vegetables, tobacco, peanut, coffee, tea,
rubber. Few fungicides go on the foliage of the
cereals (except rice in Japan), legumes, and cotton.
The root crops generally remain aloof from
fungicidal treatment. Yes, the world treats seeds
for damping off, and treats soil in seedbeds and
greenhouses for root rot, but seldom in the field.
There is some spraying of cotton seed as it is
planted. The world uses some fungicides for seed
borne diseases like the cereal smuts and it uses
some fungicides to prevent decay of fruits and
vegetables enroute to market. The tonnage is small,
however.
Despite the great array of forty fungicides, one
is depressed to see how many of the world's major
plant diseases are still not properly controlled -
bacterial diseases, viral diseases, root rots, and
wilts.
The challenge beckons.
Chemotherapy is one possible answer to the
challenge. Treat the plant from the inside and not

on the outside only as in the past. The Germans
call this "inneretherapy".

The Drive For Chemotherapy. Chemotherapy of
plant disease has advanced rapidly in recent years
following a slow start in the 'forties. It has gone
so far that we now have a whole book (5) devoted to
it and a revision underway after only three years.
  Perhaps the front-running chemotherapeutant is
benomyl and its benzimidazole relatives which have
achieved dramatic results on vascular diseases.
Other selective therapeutants are carboxin, several
pyrimidines, triforine, several morpholines, 6-
azauracil, azepines, phenylthioureas, chloroneb, and
others.
  Like any new field, chemotherapy of plant disease has its semantic problems. When we helped
initiate it in 1940, we called it chemotherapy in
line with our medical confreres. Literally it
means, of course, chemical cure, but it is given a
connotation of internal therapy as well. There is
a strong tendency, particularly in Britain to label
it "systemic fungicide." The semantic problem here
is that not all chemotherapeutants are systemic
fungicides. Even benomyl, the leading contender, is
not a true fungicide. It is a fungistat.
  Chemotherapy of plant disease has a built-in
weakness, not confronting that of animal therapy.
Plants have no phagocytes to clean up the stragglers
that are missed by the therapeutant. Penicillin is
only bacteriostatic. It does not kill the bacteria
but it keeps them few enough for long enough to
give the phagocytes a chance. Benomyl does not enjoy the benefit of phagocytes. It has a partially
compensating advantage, however. It is not excreted
by the kidneys and it therefore lasts longer in the
plant. A less stable compound would be less effective.

The Rachel Carson Syndrome. In June 1962 in
the middle of one of the world's great cities and
far from the farm, there appeared in one of the
world's sophisticated journals (The New Yorker), an
article that set the agricultural segment of the
world on fire. It was written by a lady missionary
named Rachel Carson. Later in 1962 it was expanded
into a book, Silent Spring (6). She said that the
world was suffocating in a poisonous rain of pesticides and she accused the farmers of poisoning her
food. The scare she set in motion has spread around

the globe. Constraints have sprung up like dragons'
teeth.

The Rapid Rise In Constraints. Her book
changed most of the rules of the game in developing
and using fungicides. For instance, chloranil
(Spergon) was first tested on spores in the laboratory in 1938 (2). By April 1940, farmers of New
York State were using it by the hundred weight and
by 1941 by the ton to treat pea and lima bean seed
to protect against seed decay. That was two years
from laboratory to field. And now it takes six or
seven years to go the same distance. In the meantime uncounted numbers of rats and mice, even dogs,
must be sacrificed on the Carson altar. When law-
yers and control officials by the score get into
the act, developmental costs shoot sky high and the
end is by no means in sight.
        The constraints have increased the hazards of
farming because diseases are now more difficult to
control. Carson's book has spawned a host of "new
ecologists" who enjoy baiting farmers by saying that
they pollute the environment and the food of man.
Farmers are fighting back. A bumper sticker on a
farmer's truck now reads, "If you criticize agriculture, don't talk with your mouth full." The mouths
of the new ecologists are all full.
        Despite all the alleged poisons in the food,
stomach cancer is declining; sons and daughters are
growing taller than their parents; and athletes
continually break world's records. The DDT in the
fat of the athletes must be responsible for the new
records!!
        The Carson syndrome has had important impacts
on the scientific base of fungicides. For example,
a study of the membership lists of the American
Phytopathological Society shows that the number of
plant pathologists who work with fungicides is
falling.

The Search For Selectivity. I had the honor of
serving on a committee appointed at the request of
President John F. Kennedy to examine the significance of Carson's book. Our report to him in the
spring of 1963 was entitled "The Use of Pesticides"
(7). Among other things, we recommended that pesticides, including fungicides, be made more selective.
And they were.
        Blastin (pentachlorobenzyl alcohol) is selec-
tive for rice blast, Dexon (sodium [4-(di-

methylamino) phenyl] diazo   sulfonate) for <u>Pythium</u>,
pentachloronitrobenzene for <u>Rhizoctonia</u>, and carboxin for Basidiomycetes.

Selectivity is brilliantly displayed by a
multiplicity of compounds developed for the control
of powdery mildews. For 148 years from 1803 until
1951 sulfur was the only significant fungicide for
powdery mildew. In 1949 a new fungicide appeared
with the publication of 6-(1-methylheptyl)-2,4
dinitro-phenyl crotonate (8). Two years later
Yarwood reported (9) its anti-powdery mildew properties. It went on to worldwide usage and thus stimulated a vast search for others. Now we have many
effective compounds, including benomyl, binapacryl,
dodemorph, folpet, parinol, piperalin, pyrazophos,
thiophanate, tridemorph, triforine, and others.

The Rise Of Fungus Resistance. The drive for
selectivity that is urged on by the Carson pressure
has exaggerated a small trend that had already shown
up before Carson. Fungi had developed resistance to
some of the selective fungicides. When Horsfall
published (2) his second book six years ahead of
Carson, he had difficulty identifying any resistant
fungi. A few were noted, but within five years
after Carson, Georgopoulos and Zarcovitis demonstrated dramatically that selectivity is a tricky solution to a very difficult problem posed so non-
chalantly (12).

The biology is fairly simple. The more selective we make our fungicides, the fewer the blocks
in the path of the fungus, and the easier it can
find a bypass around the block. However promising
a compound may be as an original killer of the pest
fungus, its use may be eroded by resistance almost
by the time it is able to pass through all the maze
of official approval.

The rapid biological erosion of new compounds
is very discouraging to those who must develop them
to control plant disease.

Fungicides For The Future

We all want answers to the question, where
next? Where does fungicide research go now? I
agree with the Danish humorist, Victor Borge, who
has said, "Forecasting is a difficult business, especially for the future". Still, we must look
ahead.

The Tactics And Strategy Of Discovery. By and

large the world's fungicides have come from the industrial countries of U.S.A., Britain, Switzerland, German, and Japan. It seems reasonable to say that the development of new fungicides by industry is becoming an increasingly more difficult business. There are at least three reasons for this.

(1) The regulators are introducing an ever-increasing number of tests that must be done over an ever-increasing number of years and over an ever-increasing number of test organisms. This diminishes the likelihood of finding a useful compound and multiplies the cost. As a result the smaller less well capitalized companies are deserting the field and those that remain seem to be spending a larger proportion of their time defending the compounds they have already marketed or are hoping to market, and proportionally less time on exploring.

(2) Since enormous numbers of compounds have already been made and screened, the odds of finding a new one seem to be diminishing (von Rumker et al, 11).

(3) The competition for old markets is keen and new markets seem to develop slowly.

Some will say, "Let the public sector of society take over the job." This won't solve the cost problems of regulation or the probability of finding new and useful structures, and besides, society does not do well in the manufacturing business.

Society may well be forced, however, to take over the terrible costs of safety determination.

That we are still greatly challenged is witnessed by the large number of uncontrolled fungal diseases, not to mention viral and bacterial diseases. The root rots, the vascular wilts, and the cereal rusts comprise the major challenges. We probably will find the greatest success by testing candidate compounds on the plants themselves. This will encourage selectivity and thus runs a severe risk of developing resistance.

Cooperate With Plant Breeders. Surely the odds run heavily against success in finding therapeutants that can escape the resistance problem, but plant breeders face hazards as great. Perhaps, we should join hands with the breeders. Perhaps we could outwit the fungus by combining a resistance gene with a chemotherapeutant. This would multiply the odds in our favor.

Cooperate With Physiologists. Another possi-

bility is to join hands with those who study the
physiology of disease. Plants do have biochemical
and physical means for protecting themselves from
disease attack. Here is a potent possibility of a
synergistic approach.

Still another possibility is to search for
compounds that act on the features that characterize
and distinguish fungi from higher plants and humans.

Antidifferentiation Compounds. Fungi differ-
entiate their living structures differently from
their hosts and from humans. For example, fungi
have walls of chitin. They reproduce through spores.
Humans and higher plants do not. Very few screens
have been deliberately developed to exploit these
differences. We have discovered enough compounds
accidentally to be able to say that possibilities
exist, however. Griseofulvin, for example, curls
and twists the germ tubes so that' they are unable
to infect the tissue. Polyoxin interferes with
chitin synthesis. Blastin prevents an appressorium
of the rice pathogen from sending down an infection
peg into the leaf, and so it goes.

In our laboratory we have developed a highly
effective and rapid screen to pick out antisporu-
lants (12). We can use the same techniques for
picking out anticonidiophore compounds (13).

Summary

We discuss the major crops of the world and
their major diseases and indicate how discouragingly
few are those that can now be adequately controlled
by fungicides or otherwise. We list the world's
40 fungicidal types. The environmentalists are
adding more and more constraints of more and more
complexity on the process of developing new compounds. They are insisting on selectivity. This
leads into fungus resistance. This lowers the odds
of eventual success and discourages the innovators.
We urge research on screening procedures so that
they may be more directly aimed at the fungal life
processes (chitin synthesis, for example) that are
different from host or human rocesses.

Literature Cited

1. Ou, S.H. "Rice Diseases." 368 pp. Common-
        wealth Mycol. Inst. Kew, Surrey, England.
        1972.

2. Horsfall, J.G. "Principles of Fungicidal Ac-
    tion." 279 pp. Chronica Bot. Co. Waltham,
    Mass. 1956.
3. Dimond, A.E., Heuberger, J.W., and Horsfall,
    J.G. Phytopathol. 1943. 33:1005-1007.
4. Mangelsdorf, P.C. Proc. Nat. Acad. Sci. U.S.A.
    1966. 56: 370-375.
5. Marsh, R.W. Editor. "Systemic Fungicides."
    321 pp. Halstead Press. New York. 1972.
6. Carson, Rachel. "Silent Spring." 368 pp.
    Houghton Mifflin Co. Boston, Mass. 1962.
7. President's Science Advisory Committee. "The
    Use of Pesticides." The White House. Wash-
    ington, D.C. 1963.
8. Rich, S. and Horsfall, J.G. Phytopathol. 1949.
    39:19.
9. Yarwood, C.E. Proc. IInd Int. Congr. of Crop
    Protection. 1951. p. 1-22.
10. Georgopoulos, S.G. and Zaracovitis, C. Ann.
    Rev. Phytopathol. 1967. 5: 109-130.
11. Von Rumker, R., Guest, H.R., and Upholt, W.M.
    Bioscience. 1970. 20: 1004-1007.
12. Lukens, R.J. Phytopathol. 1960. 50: 867-868.
13. Lukens, R.J. and Horsfall, J.G. 1971. Phyto
    pathol. 1971. 61:13.

Metallo-Organic Fungicides

G. J. M. VAN DER KERK

Der Rijksuniversiteit te Utrecht, Croesestraat 79, Utrecht, The Netherlands

Metals - or rather metal ions - are indispensable for the regulation of life processes and are thus essential for all forms of life. In the first place metal ions play an important role as cationic components of the systems that regulate the osmotic phenomena within cells and tissues. Further, they can act as matrixes in the folding and unfolding of macromolecular cell components and thus influence the molecular shapes of such components, so important for their biological functioning. But more related to the subject occupying us today are the functions of metal ions as constituents of oxygen carriers and in particular of biocatalysts, such as co-enzymes and enzymes. In fact, a great number of metal ions, both of main group and of transition metals, are known to be of essential significance for the proper functioning of widely varying biocatalytic systems. I refer to the occurrence of iron, copper and vanadium in the oxygen-carrying systems in the blood of vertebrates, many invertebrates and tunicates, respectively. Further, to the presence of magnesium in the photosynthetic pigment chlorophyll, of zinc in the enzyme carbonic anhydrase, essential for an adequate respiratory exchange in mammals and birds, and in several other enzymes occurring both in higher and lower animal and plant species. Finally, to the necessity, for a great variety of life processes, of many transition metal ions frequently in very small amounts, which has led to the indication "essential trace metals".

On the other hand, it is well known that many metal ions for which no physiological functions are apparent - e.g. those of silver, mercury, cadmium, thallium, lead and arsenic - are more or less toxic for all types of living organisms and that they exert inhibitory activity, sometimes in extremely low concentrations, toward enzymic reactions both in vivo and in vitro.

When discussing "metallo-organic fungicides", it is clear that one important aspect of this topic is to define the subject. Metals do not occur as such in life processes and this is even true for metal ions in a strict sense. Metal atoms and ions are very reactive electron-deficient centers which surround themselves by all kinds of electron-donating groups, molecules and ions. These surrounding groups are called <u>ligands</u> and modern organo-metal and metal-coordination chemistry studies the bonding interactions between metals (either atoms or ions) and ligands, as well as the structures and properties of organometallic and metal-coordination compounds.

The arrangement of ligands around a metal center has important consequences. The chemical and physical properties of both the metal and the ligands are changed as a result of charge transfer. The number of ligands surrounding a metal center - the coordination number - and the nature of the metal center and of the ligands determine the geometry and the bond characteristics of coordination compounds.

Ligands may be bound to the metallic center very loosely and for this reason be susceptible to exchange for other ligands with higher affinity for the metal center. Also, metal ions may expel other metal ions from their coordination complexes because of better coordinating capacity. On the other hand, the bonding interaction between metal ions and ligands may be so strong that certain complexes are stable even in biological systems containing a variety of potential ligand molecules.

This brief exposition just serves to impress upon you that the interaction of metal centers with ligands gives rise to metal-coordination structures with specific chemical and physical properties, which may result in similarly specific physiological effects.

The traditional copper fungicides are in fact inorganic copper coordination compounds   The still most important group of organic protectant fungicides, the dithiocarbamates, are applied in the form of their metal-coordination compounds. Dimethyldithiocarbamate as the iron complex ferbam and the zinc complex ziram, ethylenebisthiocarbamate as the zinc complex zineb and the manganese complex maneb.

From our own work I cite two examples which just may serve to illustrate the importance of metal-ligand interactions in the functioning of dithiocarbamate fungicides.

The first example originates from older work ($\underline{1}$) on the mode of antifungal action of dimethyldithiocarbamates. It could be proven that fungitoxicity is not connected with the dimethyldithiocarbamate ion as such or with its iron or zinc complexes used in practice, but with the very special properties of its 1:1 copper complex which is formed from the very minute but ubiquitous amounts of copper present in all natural waters, even in "pure" tap water.

In fact, this 1:1 complex Cu^+DDC serves as a "copper carrier", bringing it to the copper-susceptible intracellular system, which is the dithiol compound lipoic acid or the dithiol system lipoic acid dehydrogenase:

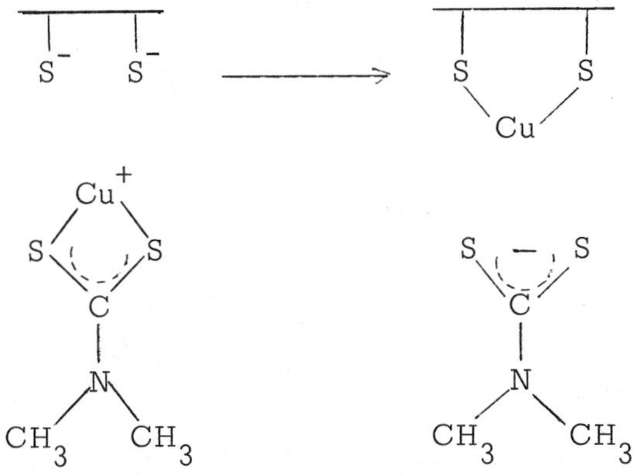

As a consequence, the antifungal action of the dimethyl-dithiocarbamates is antagonized by all ligand molecules which can effectively compete with the cellular dithiolsystem for the 1:1 complex Cu^+DDC. One very effective antagonist is the generally occurring amino acid histidine. But, to our surprise, the most effective antagonist appeared to be a higher homologue of the dimethyldithiocarbamate ion, viz. the dibutyldithiocarbamate ion, which itself or in the form of its metal-coordination compounds is completely inactive as a fungicide. Of course, this observation could be rationalized: it depends on the complex stabilities and the solubility properties of the 1:1 and the 1:2 copper/dialkyldithiocarbamate complexes which are different for the methyl and butyl derivatives.

The second example demonstrates impressively the influence of coordinating metals on the chemical properties of ligands (2). Aromatic dithiocarbamate derivatives of the type:

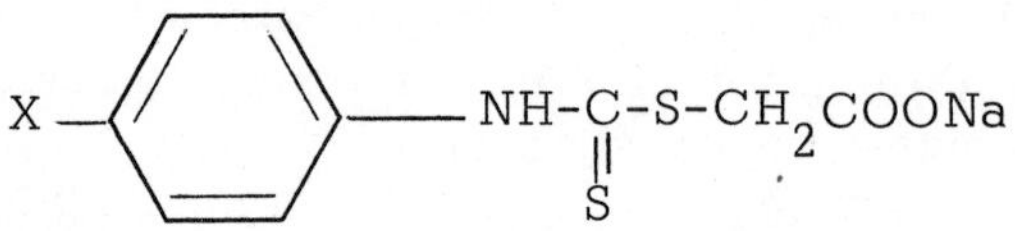

$$X-\text{(benzene ring)}-NH-\underset{\underset{S}{\|}}{C}-S-CH_2COONa$$

are stable at pH 4-7 and are not fungitoxic within this pH range. Upon adding a zinc salt to such a compound at low pH an insoluble stable zinc coordination complex is formed:

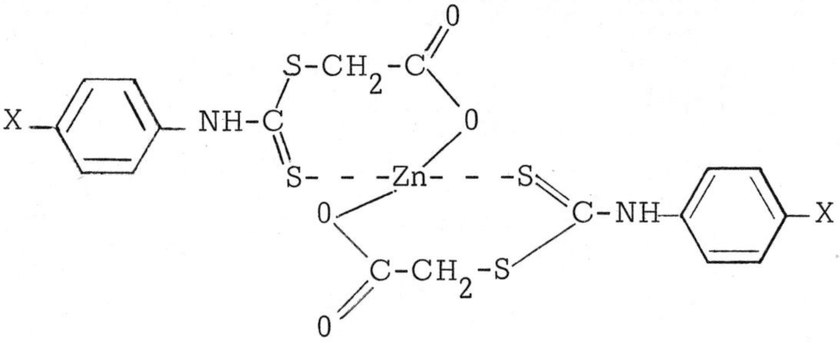

Upon suspending this complex in water or a nutrient medium and bringing the pH value to about 7, the following reaction occurs spontaneously:

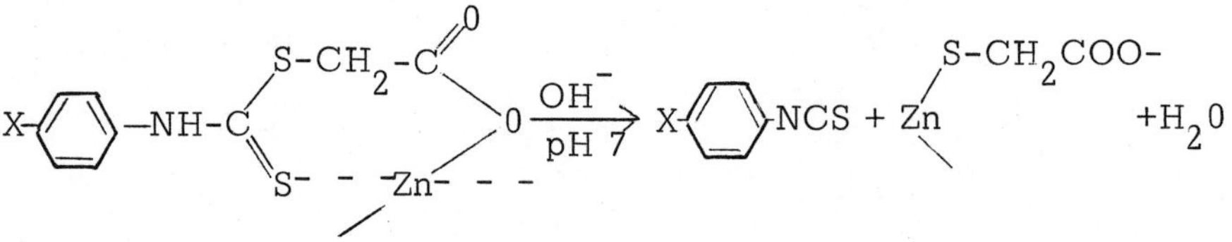

An aromatic isothiocyanate is formed which, depending on the nature of the substituent X, may be moderately to highly fungitoxic. I will not discuss the mechanism of this reaction but just want to emphasize the change in chemical behaviour resulting from complex formation.

Fungi require iron, copper, zinc and a few other metals for proper growth and development, but zinc and in particular copper ions, when supplied in more than optimal amounts, are notorious as well for their fungicidal effects. On the other hand, a number of metal ions for which no physiological functions are known, such as the ions of silver, mercury, cadmium, nickel and lead, may exert powerful fungicidal activity.

Still another category is represented by the <u>organometal-
lic</u> compounds, i.e., metal compounds in which at least one
direct metal-carbon bond occurs. The great majority of these
types of compounds are real artifacts since living systems are
very restricted in their capability to establish such bonds.
The one exception is the capacity of some micro-organisms to
methylate certain metals, e.g. arsenic, antimony and mercury,
probably as a kind of detoxification mechanism. Methylcobal-
amin is the only organometallic compound known to have a
physiological function in life processes.

It has been observed that quite generally the toxic
effects of organometallic compounds are stronger than those
of the underlying metal ions. This is particularly true for
the antimicrobial effects. The metal tin shows this phenomenon in a rather dramatic way. Whereas scarcely any pronounced biological effect is known for tin, either in the stan-
nous or the stannic form, certain trialkyltin compounds belong
to the most active fungicides known at present.

One reason for the enhanced activity of organometallics in
comparison to the corresponding inorganic forms may be the
generally higher lipid solubility of the former. It is certainly true that owing to this property, organometallics can
reach places that are inaccessible to metal ions. It has
been found, however, that frequently profound differences
exist between the mode of action of organic and inorganic
metal compounds. Moreover, of many multivalent metals,
different types of organometallic compounds exist, depending
on the number of available valencies that are occupied by a
carbon atom of an organic group. The most "organic" types
in general are not necessarily the most active ones. Moreover, the biochemical mode of action of the several types
may be different for one and the same metal.

Whatever explanations will be found, it is very clear
that bringing a metal to the organic form is likely to change
its chemical properties and its physiological effects very pro-
foundly. Of course, this has been known for a long time
for mercury and arsenic. But in particular the study of organotin compounds has led to the insight that organylation of
metals not only modifies existing chemical and physiological
properties but rather introduces the conditions for completely
new ones.

Keeping in mind that the periodic system contains about
75 elements that are generally considered to be metals, it

would seem that a tremendous field of exploration still lies
ahead of us. This is certainly true but it should be realized
that there are a number of important limiting factors.

The first limitation is related to the chemical properties
of metal-carbon bonds. All main group, and first and second
subgroup metals form "normal" two-electron metal-carbon
bonds which vary from strongly polar (ionic) to rather covalent.
All of the strongly polar and many of the covalent metal-carbon bonds are chemically very reactive and, in particular,
are sensitive toward water and/or oxygen. This eliminates
all the metals occurring in the first three groups of the
periodic system with the exception of mercury. In fact, only
the fourth main-group metals silicon, germanium, tin and lead,
and the fifth main-group metals arsenic, antimony, and bismuth
are left. All remaining electropositive elements, known as
the transition metals, are able to form organometallic derivatives but these are of a very peculiar nature. In bond formation leading to metal-carbon bond relations coordination numbers that are higher than the usual valencies are involved.
The study of this class of organometallic compounds is rather
new and is still in progress. Both stable and unstable representatives are known. So far no clear picture exists regarding the physiological properties of the chemically stable organo-transition metal compounds. With a view to the great
range of transition metals and to their widely varying capacity
for bond formation, a systematic study of the physiological
properties of the organo-transition metal compounds seems
very attractive. It should be recalled that several transition
metals play a decisive role in normal cell metabolism. Further,
it is known that a group of compounds belonging to this class,
the metal carbonyls, are extremely toxic toward mammals.
On the other hand, there are indications that our expectations
must not be set too high. A great variety of chemically
extraordinary interesting transition metal organometallics has
been prepared during the past decades. I think in particular
of the types known as "sandwich compounds", exemplified
by ferrocene, bisbenzenechromium, bisπ-allyl nickel and
cyclobutadienemetal complexes:

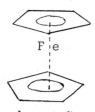

F e

biscyclopentadienyliron
"ferrocene"

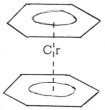

C r

bisbenzenechromium

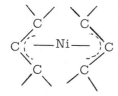

bis (η -allyl)nickel

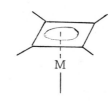

M

cyclobutadienemetal
complexes

Using direct or indirect methods, an astonishing number and variety of functionally-substituted structural variants of these types of compounds have been prepared and investigated. So far, the search for variants with interesting physiological properties in the widest sense has been pretty much in vain.

A further limitation has been the difficulty of introducing functional groups into organometallic compounds of the main group metals. Until quite recently, organometallic chemistry was simple insofar, that organic groups bound to such metals were mostly unsubstituted hydrocarbon radicals, both aliphatic and aromatic. This restriction depended on the special methods required for establishing metal-carbon sigma bonds which were not very suitable for the introduction of radicals containing functional groups such as hydroxyl, amino, carboxyl, etc. It is well known that in organic chemistry proper the presence of different and of differently placed functional groups is one of the very bases for the widely divergent physiological properties of organic molecules. In recent years considerable progress has been made in the synthesis of metal-carbon bonds and methods have become available for the preparation of widely divergent types of functionally substituted organometal-

lic compounds. There is no doubt but that these developments will lead to a renewed interest into the biological implications of a thus widened organometallic chemistry. Nevertheless, there are again reasons not to be too optimistic in
this respect. For the transition metals this has already been
indicated. For the main group metals, in particular for tin, a
truly functional organometallic chemistry has been developed
by Noltes and van der Kerk (1958), but thus far the introduction of functional groups into fungitoxic organotin compounds
has had the effect of abolishing activity rather than modifying
it. A few examples will be given later on.

    In the following, I shall review the antimicrobial and in
particular the antifungal activity of organometallic compounds.
After some consideration, I have decided not to discuss the
organomercurials. At first sight, this may seem unjustified.
The historical significance of a great variety of organomercury
compounds as agricultural fungicides and as general purpose
biocides in the prevention of biodeterioration has been phenomenal. But everywhere a strong tendency exists to banish the
use of organomercurials because of the very serious environmental health hazards involved in their applications. There is
no doubt that their use will be forbidden altogether. But
let us not forget that in the past very modest amounts of
organomercurials have been extremely effective in the combat
or rather the prevention, of economically very important plant
diseases of cereals. And further, that no really satisfactory
substitutes have been developed so far. Whereas the indis-
criminate use of organomercurials is no longer justified, it
remains to be seen whether their total abolishment may be
considered a wise decision. However this may be, for the
time being the organomercurials are a part of history and not
of the present. In connection with what I have said before,
this leaves me with the organometallic derivatives of the
fourth and fifth main-group metals: silicon, germanium, tin,
lead, arsenic, antimony and bismuth. A further restriction is,
that the fourth group metal lead and the fifth group metal
arsenic are highly toxic in their inorganic forms and that the
applications of their organic forms pose lasting environmental
problems. On the basis of practical considerations my discussion will therefore be restricted to the fourth group elements silicon, germanium and tin, some data for lead being
nevertheless included, and with the fifth group elements antimony and bismuth.

Antimicrobial, in Particular Antifungal, Activity of Organometallic Compounds of Silicon, Germanium, Tin and Lead.

Among the fourth-main group elements, carbon, silicon,
germanium, tin and lead, carbon is so to say the "element
of life". It is worthy of note that silicon is the only other
fourth group element known to be utilized by living organisms.
Many monocotyledonous plants and lower animals and plants,
e.g. radiolaria and diatoms, use silica for building up their
structural elements. It is not known with certainty whether
the solubilization, transportation and deposition of silica is
a truly physicochemical process or whether enzymic processes
are involved as well. It would be tempting to deal here
with the remarkable results published during the past ten
years or so by Voronkov and his group (3) in the USSR on
the broad range of physiological effects shown by a great
variety of organosilicon coordination compounds. This is
beyond the scope of my paper, but one compound will be
mentioned later on. Apart from the observations of Voronkov,
organosilicon compounds had never exhibited any significant
physiological activity.

The antimicrobial, in particular the fungicidal and bactericidal effects of organogermanium, -tin and -lead compounds
were discovered in Utrecht and have been extensively studied
by our group (4).

The stable fourth main group organometallic compounds
all contain the metal in the oxidation state four. Since most
of the relevant compounds contain only one metal atom per
molecule the following basic types of compounds must be distinguished:

	R_4M	R_3MX	R_2MX_2	RMX_3
Type	I	II	III	IV

R represents a group attached to the metal atom by means of
a carbon atom. It is generally a hydrocarbon (alkyl, aralkyl,
or aryl) group. In one and the same compound the groups
R may be equal (symmetrical compounds) or different (unsym-
metrical compounds). In the special case in which one or
more R groups contain a functional substituent they are called
functionally substituted compounds. X denotes a group not
linked to the metal atom via carbon. It may stand for a
halogen, hydroxyl, oxygen, alkoxyl, sulfur, or an organic or
inorganic acid radical.

In these compounds the physical and chemical stability of the metalcarbon bonds decreases from silicon to lead, but all compounds may be considered stable to fairly stable under "physiological" conditions. The anionic groups X are less firmly bound and can be exchanged rather easily.

Our work started in 1950 with tin and was later extended to germanium and lead. For the series of ethyltin compounds Luijten and Kaars Sijpesteijn observed a dramatic influence on fungicidal activity of the number of direct tin-carbon bonds (Table I).

Table I

Antifungal Activity of Ethyltin Compounds

Minimum concentrations in mg/l (ppm) causing complete growth inhibition. Peptone glucose agar, pH 6.4; 24°; 3 days.

	Botr. allii	Pen. italicum	Asp. niger	Rh. nigricans
Et_4Sn	50	>1000	100	100
Et_3SnCl	1	10	2	2
Et_2SnCl_2	>1000	>1000	>1000	>1000
$EtSnCl_3$	>1000	>1000	>1000	>1000
$SnCl_2$ $SnCl_4$	>1000	>1000	>1000	>1000

It thus appeared that only triethyltin chloride exhibited high antifungal activity, the other types being much less active or inactive, like the inorganic tin compounds. Replacement of chloride by other anionic groups either inorganic or organic, in general had no significant effect on the in vitro activity*. Nevertheless some prudence should be exercised in this respect as will be shown later on.

Next, Luijten prepared a series of tri-substittuted organotin acetates, which were tested for antifungal activity by Kaars Sijpesteijn. (Table II)

---

* Such groups, which do not involve direct tin-carbon bonds, may, however, be of significance in practical formulations.

Table II

A ntifungal Activity of Triorganotin Acetates

Minimum concentrations in mg/l (ppm) causing complete
growth inhibition.   Peptone glucose agar, pH 6.4; 24°; 3 days.

$R_3SnOCOCH_3$ R =	Botr. allii	Pen. italicum	Asp. niger	Rh. nigricans
Methyl	200	500	200	500
Ethyl	1	10	2	2
n-Propyl	0.5	0.5	0.5	0.5
i-Propyl	0.1	0.5	1	1
n-Butyl	0.5	0.5	1	1
i-Butyl	1	1	10	1
n-Pentyl	5	2	5	5
Cyclo-pentyl	0.5	0.5	5	0.5
n-Hexyl	>500	>500	>500	>500
Cyclo-hexyl	20	20	50	20
n-Octyl	>500	>500	>500	>500
Phenyl	10	1	0.5	5

Here again, a dramatic effect, be it of a different kind,
became apparent.   Among the trialkyltin compounds, the propyl and butyl derivatives classified themselves at once
amongst the most powerful fungicides known.   Also the ethyl,
pentyl and cyclo-pentyl derivatives showed high activity.
The trimethyltin and in particular the tri-n-hexyl- and tri-n-
octyltin compounds were notably inactive.   Triphenyltin acetate exhibited moderate to high activity.

These results at once suggested a number of possibilities for practical applications, in the first place of course
as fungicides, but, on the basis, of anticipated wider biocidal, in particular antimicrobial effects, of quite different
biocidal applications as well.   These expectations have been
fulfilled remarkably well.   Later on in this paper I shall
briefly survey the present-day applications of organotin compounds as fungicides and as biocides in a more general sense.

This early explorative work was continued along three
lines:

1.   As has already been said before, no truly func-
       tionally-substituted organotin compounds - i.e.,

compounds carrying functional groups like OH, OR, NH_2, NR_2, COOH, COOR, etc. - were known. Since in organic compounds the presence of such groups is of outstanding significance for their physiological properties, it was decided to look for ways to synthesize functionally-substituted organotin compounds and to study their fungitoxicity.

2. The work was extended to the study of corresponding organo-germanium and -lead compounds and broadened to include a wider series of test fungi.

3. The work was extended to the study of the bactericidal effects of organogermanium, -tin and lead compounds.

A few words will be said about the results of each of these lines of approach.

ad   1. At Utrecht in the mid-fifties, Dr. J.G. Noltes (5) succeeded in finding an elegant solution for the synthesis of functionally-substituted organotin compounds. I discussed his early work at another session of this Centennial Meeting. Subsequently, his compounds were tested for fungicidal activity. Some of the results are shown in Table III.

Much to our surprise - and contrary to experience in general organic chemistry - the introduction of functional substituents in organic groups attached to tin did not modify antifungal activity - e.g., by causing shifts in specificity or changes in the mode of action - but instead abolished it. This was not only a disappointing observation but a challenging one as well. The disappointment is over, but the challenge has remained, since so far we have not been able to find a reasonable explanation (Table III).

ad   2. In Utrecht a tremendous amount of effort was spent on the preparation of representative series of organogermanium and -lead compounds and to the study of their antifungal and antibacterial properties. Only a few results will be mentioned here. Under this section some comparative figures will be given regarding the fungicidal activity. In the next section the bactericidal properties will be mentioned. Table IV summarizes the activities of the several types of organogermanium, -tin and -lead compounds containing ethyl, n-butyl and phenyl as the organic groups.

Table III

Antifungal Activity of Functionally-Substituted Organotin Compounds

Minimum concentrations in mg/l (ppm) causing complete growth inhibition. Peptone glucose agar, pH 6.4; 24°; 3 days.

Compounds	Botr. allii	Pen. italicum	Asp. niger	Rh. nigricans
R_4Sn				
$Ph_3SnCH_2CH_2COOMe$	>500	>500	>500	>500
$Ph_3SnCH_2CH_2COOH$	>100	>100	>100	>100
$Prop_3SnCH_2CH_2CH_2NH_2$	20	100	50	100
$Prop_2Sn(CH_2CH_2COONa)_2$	>100	>100	>100	>100
$PropSn(CH_2CH_2COONa)_3$	200	>500	>500	>500
R_3SnX				
$Ph_2(CH_2CH_2CN)SnI$	>50	50	>50	>50
$Ph_2Sn^+CH_2CH_2COO^-$	>100	100	50	>100
$Bu_2Sn^+CH_2CH_2COO^-$	>100	>100	>100	>100
$Bu_2SnCH_2CH_2COOMe(Br)$	5	50	50	50
R_2SnX_2				
$PhSnCH_2CH_2CN(Br_2)$	50	>50	>50	>50

Table IV

Antifungal Activity of Corresponding Organogermanium, -Tin and -Lead Compounds Against Aspergillus Niger

(Minimum concentrations in mg/l (ppm) causing complete growth inhibition)

Types	Ge			Sn			Pb		
	Et	Bu	Ph	Et	Bu	Ph	Et	Bu	Ph
R_4M	>500	>500	>500	>500	>500	>500	>500	>500	>500
R_3MX	50	>500	>500	2	1	0.5	20	0.5	2
R_2MX_2	>500	>500	>500	>500	>500	10	>500	20	50
RMX_3	>500	>500	>500	>500	>500	500	+)	+)	200

Here again, it appears that highest activity for germanium, tin and lead is connected with the structural type R_3MX. However, the activity of the germanium compounds is negligible and the activities of the tin and lead compounds of this type are high and of the same order of magnitude. For lead, but not for tin, also the dibutyl compound is fairly active. For phenyl, it is just the other way around.

In Table V a summary is given of the antifungal activities of compounds R_3MX for germanium, tin and lead and for different kinds of groups R (X being acetate throughout).

Table V

Antifungal Activity of Triorganogermanium,
-Tin and -Lead Acetates

(Minimum concentrations in mg/l (ppm) causing complete
growth inhibition)

R3MOAc M	R	Botr. allii	Pen. italicum	Asp. niger	Rh. nigricans
Ge	Methyl	>500	>500	>500	>500
	Ethyl	50	200	50	200
	n-Propyl	50	>500	50	100
	n-Butyl	>500	>500	>500	>500
	n-Pentyl	>500	>500	>500	>500
	Phenyl	>500	>500	>500	>500
Sn	Methyl	200	>500	200	>500
	Ethyl	1	10	2	2
	n-Propyl	0.5	0.5	0.5	0.5
	n-Butyl	0.5	0.5	1	1
	n-Pentyl	5	2	5	5
	n-Hexyl	>500	>500	>500	>500
	Phenyl	10	1	0.5	5
Pb	Methyl	100	200	200	>500
	Ethyl	20	20	20	50
	n-Propyl	2	5	10	5
	n-Butyl	0.1	0.5	0.5	0.5
	n-Pentyl	0.1	0.2	0.5	0.5
	n-Hexyl	0.5	2	2	100
	n-Heptyl	50	100	100	>500
	n-Octyl	>500	>500	>500	>500
	Phenyl	2	2	2	5

To make things a little bit better surveyable the results
for the alkyl compounds are given in a graphical form (Fig.1).

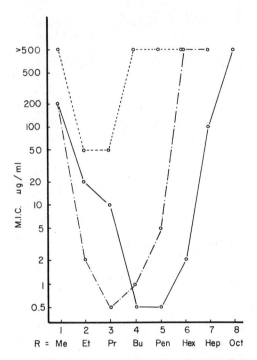

*Figure 1. Influence of chain length of trialkyl-
substituted germanium, tin, and lead acetates on
minimum concentration inhibitory to Aspergillus
niger. – – –, germanium; – · –, tin; ———, lead.*

The overall activity of the triorganotin and –lead compounds
is about the same, that of the germanium compounds is much
lower. Optimum activity for germanium occurs with ethyl and
propyl, for tin with propyl and butyl, and for lead with butyl and
pentyl substituents. There was little or no influence of the
composition of the nutrient medium nor of its pH on activity.
Later on it was found by Kaars Sijpesteijn (6) that certain fungi
are considerably more sensitive to trialkylgermanium compounds
(e.g. Debaryomyces nicotianae, Trichophyton mentagrophytes
and Glomerella cingulata). A few related organosilicon compounds (R = Ethyl, Butyl and Phenyl) were found to be completely inactive, even against a few fungi which had been found
to be highly sensitive to triethylgermanium acetate.

Later on our results were extended, in particular with
regard to phytopathogenic fungal species, by several other
workers. This extension has resulted in the present-day
practical applications of organotin compounds as biocides.
As a general conclusion, it can be stated that thus far, all
fungi tested, whether belonging to the Phycomycetes, the As-
comycetes, or the Basidiomycetes have been found to be susceptible to certain types of tri-substituted organotin compounds.

For more detailed information, also on mixed alkyl and
mixed alkyl-aryl compounds, I may refer to a review article
(4).

ad   3.   In this section results are summarized which have
            been obtained at Utrecht with the structural types
            R₃MX and R₂MX₂ against five characteristic bac-
            terial species. The following organisms were used:
            the gram-positive species Bacillus subtilis, Myco-
            bacterium phlei and Streptococcus lactis, and the
            gram-negative species Escherichia coli and Pseudo-
            monas fluorescens. Some data are given in Tables
            VI, VII and VIII.

Table VI

Antibacterial Activity of Compounds R_3GeX and R_2GeX_2
(min. concentrations in mg/l (ppm) causing complete growth inhibi.)

Compounds	Gram-positive			Gram-negative	
	B. subtilis	M. phlei	S. lactis	E. coli	Ps. fluorescens
Me_3GeOAc	>500	>500	>500	>500	>500
Et_3GeOAc	>500	>500	50	>500	>500
$Prop_3GeOAc$	>500	20	5	>500	>500
Bu_3GeOAc	>500	2	1	>500	>500
$Pent_3GeOAc$	>500	5	2	>500	>500
Hex_3GeOAc	>500	>500	20	>500	>500
Ph_3GeOAc	>500	>500	>500	>500	>500
Et_2GeCl_2	>500	>500	>500	>500	>500
Bu_2GeCl_2	>500	>500	>500	>500	>500
Ph_2GeCl_2	>500	>500	>500	>500	>500

Table VII

Antibacterial Activity of Compounds R_3SnX and R_2SnX_2

(Minimum concentrations in mg/l (ppm) causing
complete growth inhibition)

Compounds	Gram-positive			Gram-negative	
	B. subtilis	M. phlei	S. lactis	E. coli	Ps. fluorescens
Me_3SnOAc	>500	>500	>500	>500	>500
Et_3SnOAc	50	10	100	20	20
$Prop_3SnOAc$	2	0.2	5	50	20
Bu_3SnOAc	2	0.1	5	>500	100
$Pent_3SnOAc$	5	0.2	10	>500	>500
Hex_3SnOAc	50	10	50	>500	>500
Hep_3SnOAc	>500	>500	500	>500	>500
Ph_3GeOAc	0.5	0.1	5	>500	>500
Me_2SnCl_2	200	200	500	500	200
Et_2SnCl_2	50	100	200	100	100
$Prop_2SnCl_2$	20	50	50	50	50
Bu_2SnCl_2	20	20	20	20	>500
$Pent_2SnCl_2$	20	20	50	500	>500
Hex_2SnCl_2	50	100	>500	>500	>500
Hep_2SnCl_2	>500	>500	>500	>500	>500
Ph_2SnCl_2	20	5	50	>500	>500

Table VIII

Antibacterial Activity of Compounds R_3PbX and R_2PbX_2

(Minimum concentrations in mg/l (ppm) causing
complete growth inhibition)

Compounds	Gram positive			Gram-negative	
	B. subtilis	M. phlei	S. lactis	E. coli	Ps. fluorescens
Me_3PbOAc	100	100	200	200	100
Et_3PbOAc	50	50	50	50	20
$Prop_3PbOAc$	2	2	2	5	10
Bu_3PbOAc	0.5	0.2	1	20	20
$Pent_3PbOAc$	0.5	0.1	5	50	50
Hex_3PbOAc	5	0.2	10	>500	>500
Hep_3PbOAc	20	5		>500	>500
Oct_3PbOAc	50	20	200	>500	>500
Ph_3PbOAc	1	0.05	1	20	50
Me_2PbAc_2	0.2	0.2	1	50	50
Et_2PbAc_2	0.2	1	5	5	5
$Prop_2PbAc_2$	0.2	0.2	0.5	1	2
Bu_2PbAc_2	0.1	0.1	0.2	1	10
$Pent_2PbAc_2$	0.2	0.2	0.5	2	500
Hex_2PbAc_2	0.5	0.5	1	5	>500
Hep_2PbAc_2	2	2	10	100	>500
Oct_2PbAc_2	20	20	50	>500	>500
Ph_2PbAc_2	1	2	1	10	100

From tables VI-VIII, the following generalized conclusions can be drawn:

- with two exceptions the bacteria were insensitive to both types of germanium compound
- gram-positive species are more sensitive to the organotin and -lead compounds than gram-negative species
- for tin the dialkyl compounds are generally less active than the trialkyl compounds; for lead rather the reverse is true, in particular against the gram-negative species. In fact, certain dialkyllead compounds are surprisingly active and belong to the most potent antibacterial agents known.

A presentative triethylsilicon compound was found inactive against all bacterial species investigated. Here again, for details I must refer to the review article mentioned (4).

A few remarks may be made on the mode of antifungal action of tri- and disubstituted organotin and -lead compounds. Very little direct information is available in this respect. Early observations indicated that a profound difference does exist between the biochemical modes of action of triorganotin and -lead compounds on the one hand and diorganotin and -lead compounds on the other. Whereas the latter compounds are antagonized by thiol compounds, in particular by the dithiol compound 2,3-dimercaptopropanol (BAL), no single antagonist is known of the triorganotin and -lead compounds.

On the basis of studies by Aldridge (7) on the mammalion toxicity of triorganotin (and -lead) compounds it is now generally accepted (cf 4) that these compounds effectively interfere with oxidative phosphorylation and block a reaction step in the energy-transferring chain leading to ATP formation. The variations in antifungal activity within the series of homologous trialkyltin and -lead compounds may be due both to differences in intrinsic activity of the compounds at the enzymic site, and to permeability differences for the several compounds. In this latter respect the relation between water- and lipid-solubility of the compounds will be of importance.

According to Barnes and Stoner (8) dialkyltin (and -lead) compounds in mammalian systems are inhibitors of the enzymes α-keto acid oxidases by interference with the physiological function of a dithiol compound, the coenzyme α-lipoic acid. The same mechanism may apply for the antimicrobial activity of these compounds. It remains, however, remarkable that their antifungal activity is rather low, whereas in particular

certain dialkyllead compounds are extremely powerful bactericides. One possible explanation may be a considerable difference in the capacities for cell penetration. (c f 9).

In the early part of my paper, I referred to the work of
Voronkov (3) regarding the physiological effects observed by
him for a series of organosilicon compounds. A particularly
intriguing observation was the high mammalian toxicity of the
compound phenylsilatrane. This compound can easily be obtained from phenylsilicon trichloride and triethanolamine:

$$PhSiCl_3 + (HOCH_2CH_2)_3N \longrightarrow PhSi(OCH_2CH_2)_3N$$

Structurally the compound is highly interesting since it is a
tricyclic cage compound, containing one silicon-carbon bond,
three silicon-oxygen bonds and one silicon-nitrogen coordination bond, resulting in a very stable penta-coordinated organosilicon structure:

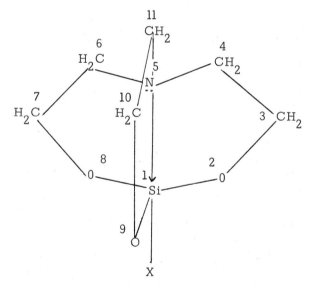

Voronkov also prepared the corresponding germanium compound
phenylgermatrane. For this compound he observed a very low
mammalian toxicity. Both phenylsilatrane and phenylgermatrane had negligible antimicrobial activity. Since at Utrecht
significant biological activity had never been observed for
any monoorganotin compound, we prepared the tin-analogue
phenylstannatrane and tested it on antifungal and antibacterial activity. To our surprise phenylstannatrane showed appre-

ciable fungitoxicity but was completely inactive again both gram-positive and gram-negative bacteria.

It is not possible to draw general conclusions from these observations, but it should be clear that biological activity of fourth main group (organo)metal compounds may depend as well on some factors which are as yet unknown and which are possibly related with the occurrence of certain types of coordination structures with very specific molecular geometries. Here, in my opinion, a field for further explorative research lies wide open.

Antimicrobial Activity of Organometallic Compounds of Antimony and Bismuth

Arsenic, antimony, and bismuth are the metallic representatives among the fifth main-group elements. Owing to early chemotherapeutic applications a tremendous number of organometal derivatives has been prepared, especially of arsenic. Both in their inorganic and their organic compounds these metals can occur in the trivalent or in the pentavalent state. Consequently the following types of organometallic compounds are known:

Trivalent	R_3M	R_2MX	RMX_2	
Pentavalent	R_5M	R_3MX_2	R_2MX_3	RMX_4

R and X have the same meaning as indicated before.

In these compounds the metal-carbon bonds are highly covalent and chemically rather stable. The chemical reactivity of the trivalent compounds, in particular those of the type R_3M is associated with an easy oxidizability to the pentavalent state rather than with rupture of metal-carbon bonds. Thus, the vigorous reaction of the trialkyl compounds R_3M with air depends on the following oxidative transformation:

$$R_3M \xrightarrow{\quad O_2 \quad} R_3MO$$

On the other hand, under reducing conditions the pentavalent compounds are easily converted into the trivalent ones. This is of importance since the biological properties within this group seem to be associated with the trivalent state.

For reasons mentioned before, only the antimicrobial activity of organoantimony and -bismuth compounds will be presented here. The results have been taken from a paper of Beiter and Leebrick (10) and are summarized in Table IX.

Table IX

Antimicrobial Activity of Organoantimony and -Bismuth Compounds

	Fungi			Bacteria		
				Gram +	Gram –	
	Pen.		Cand.		A.	Ps.
	funicu-	Asp.	albi-	Staph.	aero-	aerug-
Compounds	losum	flavus	cans	aureus	genes	inosa
Antimony						
R_3Sb						
$Prop_3Sb$	>500	>500	250	16	31	125
Bu_3Sb	125	250	63	5	31	63
Ph_3Sb	>500	>500	>500	>500	>500	>500
R_2SbCl						
Ph_2SbCl	125	250	31	2	4	4
$RSbCl_2$						
$PhSbCl_2$	250	250	63	2	8	4
R_3SbCl_2						
Ph_3SbCl_2	>500	>500	>500	63	>500	>500
Bismuth						
R_3Bi						
Bu_3Bi	250	250	63	0.5	4	2
Ph_3Bi	>500	>500	>500	>500	>500	>500
R_2BiCl						
Ph_2BiCl	>500	>500	63	0.5	4	2
$RBiCl_2$						
$BuBiCl_2$	500	>500	125	0.5	8	2
$PhBiCl_2$	>500	>500	63	0.125	2	2
R_3BiCl_2						
Ph_3BiCl_2	>500	>500	125	8	31	31

From this Table, it is evident that the antifungal activity of both organoantimony and -bismuth compounds is very low to negligible. As bactericides they are clearly more active, the structural types R_2MX and RMX_2 being even highly active. It should be noted that published information on the antifungal and antibacterial activity of organoantimony and - bismuth compounds is much less complete than that available for the fourth main group elements.

Although suggestions have been made for potential uses of organoantimony and -bismuth compounds as antimicrobial agents and undoubtedly much more extensive work has been done than has been published, it can be stated that no single compound has reached the market place. For that reason, I restrict my discussion of these compounds to the few facts mentioned.

In summary, it would seem that the evidence resulting from the fundamental studies of structure-activity relationships indicate only certain triorganotin compounds as biocides of potential practical significance. This, in fact, has become true in a remarkable way. In my paper "Organotin Chemistry. Past, Present and Future", presented during this same Centennial Meeting, I have reviewed all present-day practical applications of organotin compounds. To conclude my present paper, I will briefly summarize the applications of certain triorganotin compounds as fungicides.

Fungicidal Applications of Tributyltin and Triphenyltin Compounds*

Our original observations regarding the very high antifungal activity of the lower trialkyltin and of triphenyltin compounds raised the expectation that these compounds might be generally useful protectant agricultural fungicides. Because of their broad antifungal spectrum, it was anticipated that they would be suitable for the combat of a wide variety of fungal plant diseases. This broad expectation has not become true.

Independent work of Härtel (Farbwerke Hoechst, Germany) (12) showed that in the laboratory trialkyl- in particular tributyltins are better fungicides than triaryltin compounds, but that the reverse is true in the field. This has been ascribed

* For an extensive review on all present organotin applications, see Luijten (11).

to the lower stability and the higher volatility of the former.
Moreover, triaryltin compounds are less phytotoxic than trialkyltin compounds. The final result has been that now certain
triphenyltin formulations - containing either triphenyltin hydroxide or acetate - have become important agricultural fungicides. Their importance is not connected with their general
usefulness but with their specific effectivity against two
economically extremely important plant diseases, viz. late
blight of potatoes, caused by Phytophthora infestans, and
leaf spot in sugar beets, caused by Cercospora beticola. In
these applications, they have in Europe almost completely
ousted the formerly dominating inorganic copper compounds.
Later on it was found that also a number of important tropical plant diseases - viz. in coffee, rice, ground nuts, banam
and pecan - can be successfully controlled. A further extension of the triphenyltin compounds as agricultural fungicides
was found in their combination with manganese ethylenebisdi-
thiocarbamate (maneb). A particular advantage of triphenyltin
formulations is, that so far no development of field resistance
has ever been observed.

The problem of toxic residues from field sprays with triphenyltin compounds has been very thoroughly investigated.
An important feature is the relatively short half life of these
compounds on the foliage under field conditions (3-4 days).
Moreover the compounds do not penetrate into the plant and
their action is thus purely protective.

In summary, it may be said that the agricultural applications of organotin compounds as fungicides so far are restricted to a comparatively small, though very important, number
of plant diseases and pests. Moreover, on the basis of the
more recent developments and because tin compounds in
several cases are fully active against resistant varieties, it
may be expected that a further modest growth of the uses of
organotins in agriculture is likely to occur.

Another agricultural development of great potential   interest is based on the more recent observation that certain
rather unusual triorganotin compounds have considerable acari-
cidal activity. Well-known at present is the compound tri-
cyclohexyltin hydroxide (trade name "Plictran") developed by
Dow Chemical Company and M & T Chemicals. This compound is very effective against spider mites in fruit orchards
and has been found to act as well against varieties of spider
mites which had developed resistance towards the usual
acaricides based on organic phosphorous compounds and car-

bamates. Another promising compound with a similar application field is marketed by Shell. It is the compound trisneo-
phyltin acetate,

$$\left(\left\langle \bigcirc \right\rangle -\overset{\overset{\displaystyle CH_3}{|}}{\underset{\underset{\displaystyle CH_3}{|}}{C}}-CH_2 \right)_3 SnOAc$$

Whereas the trialkyltin compounds have not succeeded
as agricultural fungicides, one particular tributyltin compound,
viz. bis(tributyltin) oxide (TBTO):

$$(C_4H_9)_3SnOSn(C_4H_9)_3$$

has become notoriously successful as a general biocide, in
materials protection, in particular in wood and paint preservation, as an antifouling agent and as a surface disinfectant.
The origin of these applications stems entirely from the early
work at Utrecht by Luijten and Kaars Sijpesteijn, which I
already cited before.

Among the first publications on the preservation of wood
against fungal attack by means of triorganotin compounds were
those of Hof and Luijten (TNO) (13) and of Fahlstrom (14).
Since then, wood-preservation using TBTO as or among the
active ingredients has become common practice. Tributyltin
compounds are characterized by their high activity and broad
antifungal spectrum. Their leachability by water is extremely
low and they have the advantage of being colorless and non-
corrosive. Amounts of 0.5 - 2kg of TBTO per m^3 of wood are
quite effective not only against fungal decay but as well
against the attack by marine borers: shipworms (Teredo) and
gribble (Limnoria). Much higher concentrations are required
to protect wood against wood-boring insects such as the common furniture beetle and in particular termites, and here combinations with other active ingredients, in particular insecticides, are required.

An excellent review on TBTO-based wood preservatives
has been given by Richardson at the 1970 Annual Convention
of the British Wood preservers Association (15).

The low aqueous leachability of TBTO is due to its high
affinity in particular to cellulose. As a consequence, how-

ever, its penetration into deeper layers of the treated wood
poses some problems. To a certain extent these have been
solved by the use of special impregnation techniques and also
by combining organtins with other biocidal agents which have
better penetrating properties. During the past few years, our
group at Utrecht, in cooperation with the Wood Research Institute TNO at Delft, has developed a different approach. The
hydrocarbon-like compound hexabutylditin $Bu_3SnSnBu_3$, which is
very soluble in non-polar hydrocarbon solvents, was found to
have much better wood-penetrating properties than TBTO, but
to equal this compound in wood-preserving capacity. We
believe that hexabutylditin offers considerable promise as a
new wood-preserving agent, provided that a satisfactory method can be developed for its technical manufacturing.

Interesting and rather surprising is the claim, made in a
recent patent application (16) that monobutyl- and monoctyltin
compounds are effective wood preserving agents, notwithstanding their negligible in vitro fungitoxicity. It is suggested
that these compounds effectively block places within the wood
which are vulnerable to fungal attack.

Triorganotin compounds, in particular TBTO and tributyltin fluoride, are finding increasing use in marine antifouling
paints (cf 17). An interesting application where organotins
may substitute for organomercurials is paint preservation, although a few complications have to be solved. For instance, the
antimicrobial spectrum of triorganotins, though considerable, is
not so wide as that of the organomercurials. To reach an
equivalent degree of protection, new formulations have to be
developed which in certain cases must contain other active
ingredients as well. One notable deficiency of TBTO is its
modest activity against gram-negative bacteria. It has been
found in Utrecht that tripropyltin compounds have a wider antibacterial spectrum and are rather active against gram-negative
bacteria as well.

A modest but important use of certain tributyltin-contain-
ing formulations is in hospital and veterinary disinfectants.
Similar formulations are applied to protect textiles against
fungal and bacterial attack, both in the industrial and the
hygienic sector ("sanitizing").

In reconsidering the biocidal properties of organotin compounds, one cannot get away from the conclusion that the biocidal applications are likely to expand strongly in the future,
both as a result of an extension of the present possibilities
and of the development of new ones.

Much will depend here on the outcome of the present
study of the metabolic fate of organotin compounds under environmental conditions. It is generally accepted that the
basic types of organotin compounds are subject to the following generalized pattern of physical, chemical and/or biochemical degradation:

$$R_4Sn \rightarrow R_3SnX \rightarrow R_2SnX_2 \rightarrow RSnX_3 \rightarrow SnX\ 4 \quad \text{or} \quad SnX_2 \text{ resp.}$$

which ultimately leads to non-toxic inorganic forms of tin.
Until recently, there was very little evidence for the actual
course and rates of such degradation processes under environmental conditions. The overall toxicity picture for any compound is, however, dependent both on its own toxicity and on
the toxicity of the degradation products formed under the conditions of its application. To fill this gap, a joint programme
was started some years ago at the Institute for Organic Chemistry TNO at Utrecht under the final responsibility of the Tin
Research Institute. This programme - the Organotin Environmental Project, or ORTEP - is supported by about ten major
organotin-producing companies all over the world.

Conclusion

Among the 92 naturally-occurring elements listed in the
periodic table, 75 are considered metals. My review has
shown that on the basis of present knowledge and on that of
presently accepted standards only the organometallic compounds
of tin are likely to have a future as fungicides, and, in a
wider sense, as general biocides. This is a meagre conclusion which nevertheless is founded on a considerable amount
of evidence. Of course, a larger number of metals, in particular transition metals, is of practical significance in a number of fungicidal applications, either in inorganic forms -
like copper - or in combination with organic molecules known
to have fungicidal activity - like iron, zinc and manganese
in the dithiocarbamates. In the latter, the metals do not, as
far as we know, contribute to the intrinsic fungitoxicity of the
compounds in question, but their function is nevertheless important, so to say as built-in formulation factors which modify the chemical and biological characteristics of their ligand
molecules.

One particular aspect has not yet been discussed. In
organometallic compounds in the first instance, we must forget

about the underlying metal. I will illustrate this for tin.
Let us look again at the basic types of organotin compounds:

$$R_4Sn \qquad R_3SnX \qquad R_2SnX_2 \qquad RSnX_3$$

in which only the groups X are easily interchangeable. As
long as no tin-carbon bond ruptures occur, we are dealing
with the units R_4Sn R_3Sn^+ and RSn^{3+}. Whatever the properties of these units are, these are completely different from
those of Sn, Sn^{2+} or Sn^{4+}, i.e. from metallic or inorganic tin,
and, in fact, have very little to do with the latter. Ultimately, R_3Sn^+, R_2Sn^{2+} and RSn^{3+} must be considered as ions
of completely different "metals", not only mutually different
but also different from the ions Sn^{2+} and Sn^{4+}. Here lies
the ultimate clue to the understanding of both the tremendous
differences between the several basic types of organotin compounds and of the profound influence of the organic groups R
on the properties of the individual types. In organotin compounds, it is not tin which defines their ultimate properties,
but its combinations with different types and numbers of firmly
bound organic substituents.

What has been explained for tin is appropriate for all
organometallic compounds containing stable to reasonable
stable metal-carbon relations.

Literature Cited

1.(a) Janssen, M.J., and Kaars Sijpesteijn, A., S.C.I. Mono-
       graph, London, (1961), 15, 40.
  (b) Kaars Sijpesteijn, A., and Van der Kerk, G.J.M., Proc. 5th
       Brit. Insect and Fung. Conf., (1969), 724.
2.   Van der Kerk, G.J.M., Pluygers, C.W., and De Vries,G.,
       Rec. Trav. Chim. Pays-Bas, (1955), 74, 1262.
3.   Voronkov, M.G., Chemistry in Britain, (1973), 9, 411.
4.   cf Kaars Sijpesteijn, A., Luijten, J.G.A. and Van der
       Kerk, G.J.M., "Fungicides, An Advanced Treatise",
       chap. 7, II, Academic Press, New York and London(1969)
5.   Van der Kerk, G.J.M., and Noltes, J.G., J. App. Chem.,
       (1959), 9, 113. Ibid (1959),9, 176. Ibid.(1959), 9, 179.
6.   Kaars Sijpesteijn, A., Rijkens, F., Van der Kerk,G.J.M.,
       and Manten, A., Antonie van Leeuwenhoek J.Microbiol.
       Serol. (1964), 30, 113.

7. Aldridge, W. N. and Street, B. W., Biochem. J. and
    references cited therein, (1964), 91, 287.
8. Barnes, J. M. and Stoner, H. B., Pharmacol. Rev., (1959)
    11, 211.
9. Kahana, L., Kaars Sijpesteijn, A., Antonie van Leeuwenhoek
    J. of Microbiol. and Serol., (1967), 33, 427.
10. Beiter, C. B. and Leebrick, J. R., Chem. Specialties Mfrs.
    Assoc. (cf 4), (1963), 49, 132.
11. Luijten, J. G. A., "Organotin Compounds", chap. 12,
    Marcel Dekker, Inc., New York, 1972.
12. Härtel, K., Agr. Vet. Chem., (1962), 3, 19. (See also:
    Härtel, K., Tin and its Uses, (1958), 43, 9 and (1963), 61,
    7).
13. Hof, T. and Luijten, J. G. A., Timber Technology, (1959),
    67, 83.
14. Fahlstrom, G. B., Proc. Am. Wood - Preservers' Assoc.,
    (1958), 54, 178.
15. Richardson, B. A., British Wood Preservers' Assoc., Annual
    Convention, (1970).
16. Germ. Offenl. 2.351.188 to Albright & Wilson Ltd.
    (Oct. 13, 1972 - May 9, 1974).
17. Evans, C. J., Tin and its Uses, (1970), 85, 3 and (1973),
    96, 7. Evans, C. J. and Smith, P. J., J. Oil Col. Chem.
    Assoc. (1975), 58, 160.

9

The Sulfenimide Fungicides

GUSTAVE K. KOHN

Zoecon Corp., 975 California Ave., Palo Alto, Calif. 94304

Historical Introduction

Shortly after World War II, a research chemist at the Standard Oil Development Company (Esso) strolled into an oil additive laboratory and saw an interesting intermediate called perchloromethyl mercaptan (CCl_3SCl). A. F. Kittleson, spurred by visions of the trichloromethyl group in that then new miracle drug DDT, decided to try some reactions with the above described sulfenyl halide.

He synthesized a multiplicity of new compounds (1) (2) (3) and discovered a unique series which contained the N - S bond. Unfortunately these structures possessed no insecticidal potential whatsoever. Fortunately, however, certain of these compounds were directed to a plant pathologist at Rutgers University, <u>Dr. Robert H. Daines, (4) (5) (6) who noted exceptional fungistatic and fungicidal properties</u>.

If chance was involved in this discovery, let it be emphasized that it is a component in all inventions (7), and this one proved in time to be highly significant. Subsequent development and derivative invention (8) and discovery have provided biocides used in this country, in the agriculture of all the developed countries, in much of undeveloped Asia, Latin America and Africa, and in the Communist domains throughout the globe. The present installed capacity over the world for sulfenimide group fungicides is estimated as above 50 million lbs but less than 100 million lbs/year.

Thus the conception of this discovery; the gestation in the early period was difficult and troubled. In the beginning of this century, perchloromethyl mercaptan was considered (and had been given a brief trial as) a war gas. There was little experience with its use by industry. The cost projections and the

The content of this paper derives from thirty years association with the Research Department of Chevron Chemical Company, Richmond, California.

153

actual manufacturing costs for the early produced captan was
approximately five uninflated dollars per pound. The first production employed a DDT-like batch condensation. The product that
was obtained was odoriferous, corrosive, expensive and of quite
doubtful exploitable potential.

For two consecutive years, large areas of apple orchards in
New Jersey (apple scab, <u>Venturia inaequalis</u> infection was a primary
target at that time for these fungicides) were almost totally
defoliated and many favoured abandonment of the development project. No more names will be mentioned in this history but
chemists and chemical engineers found ways to make the intermediates, to purify the product and finally to produce captan, a
fungicide, at a cost comparable to the less expensive synthetic
pesticides of that period - all before the rise of crude oil
prices, shortage of intermediates and subsequent runaway infla-
tion distorted manufacturing economics.

Biologists discovered how and when to use these fungicides
and particularly the critical periods that defined and circum-
scribed their usefulness and practical safety. Finally, through
this long conception and gestation process, there were company
executives who had the vision and the courage to venture capital
and support all the necessary phases of the development, despite
considerable periods of discouragement. Since that period, new
series of compounds were discovered (eg. Difolatan Ⓡ (8) and
analogues) and compositions possessing practical fungicidal,
bactericidal, algicidal and medicinal properties (9) have found
a broad application throughout the world.

Structural Definition

The sulfenimide fungicides may be structurally defined as in
Figure 1. The formula given is quite general and provides for an
immense number of synthetic variants. R and R' may be rings
(homocyclic or heterocyclic, aromatic, or of various degrees of
saturation and unsaturation, substituted or unsubstituted) or
chains of multiple types. R and R' can be part of a single ring.
Whether ring or chain, at least one sulfonyl, phosphoryl or
carbonyl group (etc) is vicinal to the nitrogen. This affects
the character of the trivalent nitrogen so that the intermediate
R(R')NH is preferentially weakly acidic with pKa's frequently in
the phenolic range.

R'' is a short chain polyhaloalkyl or alkenyl group. Most
frequently the halogens are Cl, Br and F or mixtures of them.
Many other N-S compounds may be and have been prepared but the
formula in Figure 1 generalizes for those with useful and practical antifungal properties.

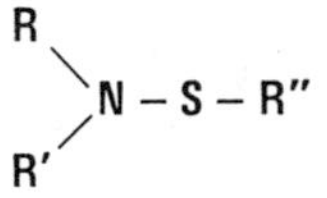

$$\begin{array}{c} R \\ \diagdown \\ \diagup N - S - R'' \\ R' \end{array}$$

R and R' may be cyclic including part of same ring or separate rings or chains. These contain at least one carbonyl, sulfonyl, phosphonyl etc. group.

$$\text{The intermediate} \qquad \begin{array}{c} R \\ \diagdown \\ \diagup N - H \text{ is preferably a weak acid.} \\ R' \end{array}$$

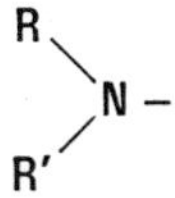

R" is a short chain polyhaloalkyl or alkenyl group.
Halogens = F, Cl, Br or mixed.

Figure 1. Sulfenimide fungicides: structural definition

There are constraints to this generic formula that relate to solubility. The implications of aqueous solubility will be later discussed. It must be low. High oil solubility, such as would result from long chain polyhaloalkyl groups, while providing inherent fungitoxic properties is excluded because it results in excessive phytotoxicity. R'' can only rarely exceed two carbons.

Figure 1 and the brief discussion now concluded summarizes quite briefly an extremely voluminous patent literature with contributions from all major chemical centers of the world and continually being supplemented to this very day.

Examples of these sulfenimide compositions are given in Figures 2 and 3. Although it is normally proper to utilize generic names, we will employ the usual names by which these compounds are best known throughout the world for the remainder of this paper. In these figures we have indicated some major areas of usefulness.

In addition to the compounds given in the figures, it is not an exaggeration to state that well over a thousand homologues of this series have been synthesized. This author has knowledge of upwards of 100 compositions that exhibit superior fungicidal properties. As is usually the case, however, simplicity and industrial and agricultural economics determine which compounds achieve broad agricultural usage. Of those synthesized captan, Phaltan and Difolatan dominate the market.

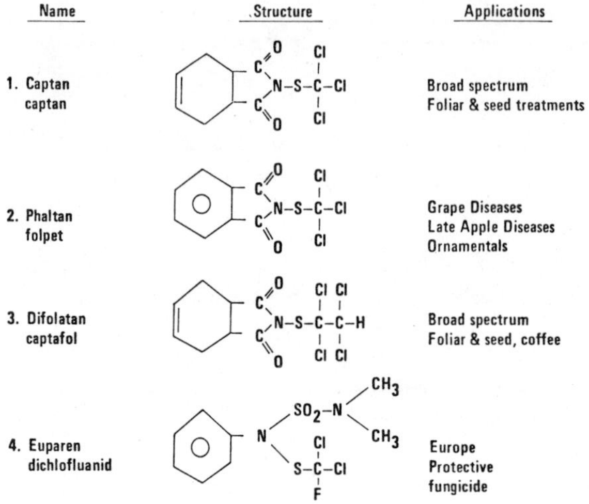

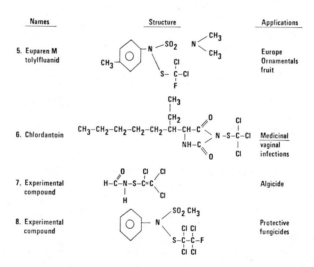

Figure 2. Some sulfenimide fungicides

Figure 3. Some sulfenimide fungicides

Nature of the N – S Bond

At the time of the discovery of captan (except perhaps where sulfur was in an oxidized state), very little was known about the nature and properties of this bond in organic structures. Even today, compilations of bond energies or bond distances or spectroscopic properties fail to include data for organic chemical

molecules with the N - S - linkage. Nevertheless, this is the
distinctive and definitive bond for this entire group of fungicides, and its properties both provide for and limit the usefulness of these therapeutic agents. In Table 1 are summarized some
values extracted from the literature for the subject linkage.
The N - S bond energy was calculated from the Pauling equation by
Dr. Philip Magee (10). There is, for example, an obvious anomaly
in the Raman and infra red frequencies (10) (11) (12) (13).

Table I. The $\diagdown \atop \diagup$ N—S— Bond

Bond Energy	53 K cal/Mol
Bond distance	1.686 Å
IR absorption	950 cm−1
Raman absorption	650 cm−1

The bond stability is greatly modified by the unusual substitutions on both the nitrogen and the sulfur (the dicarbonyl
attachment to the N and the trichloromethyl to the S). The
effect of these electron-withdrawing substitutions certainly
alters the bond strength and its susceptibility to attack. These
contribute further to the extraordinary chemical and biological
properties which we will subsequently examine.

Aqueous Solubility

Early in the history of plant chemotherapy the differential
toxicity of the therapeutic chemical was related to the limitation of its aqueous solubility. A case in point was the 19th
century discovery of the grape fungicide, Bordeaux mixture.
Soluble copper salts are extremely toxic both to higher plants
and to the lower groups such as algae as well as to the fungi and
bacteria that may attack them. The addition of lime to copper
sulfate to precipitate a relatively insoluble basic copper
sulfate provided among other properties an aqueous concentration
of cupric ion sufficient to combat the fungi but insufficient to
interfere with, except marginally, the normal metabolic processes
of the plant.

At Chevron and elsewhere a whole series of copper, zinc,
manganese, calcium, cadmium, lead and arsenic salts were manufactured as plant protection agents and micronutrients by the carefully pH controlled precipitation of insolubles where the active
cation or anion could only reach a small, plant-tolerable, maximum concentration. In such cases this maximum could be calculated

from the arithmetic of the solubility product relationship. Products containing these ions could be tested for effectiveness
against the pathogen and for tolerance by the host and would be
different for each product.

One of the highly significant properties of the sulfenimide
group and the purpose of this digression relates to the limited
aqueous solubility of its various members. Table II provides
the solubilities of three agriculturally significant members of
this class of sulfenimide fungicides.

These solubilities were quite carefully determined (14) and
some comment on the method employed is instructive. It was found
early in these determinations that if the time for the estimation
of the concentration of fungicide in the aqueous phase after
separation from the solid varied then the values for the solubility as determined by extraction also varied. Further, if one
plotted the time after separation against the assay results, a
smooth curve was obtained that could simply be extrapolated to
zero time. This value, of course, is the equilibrium concentration and is higher than any of the experimental values and is the
one quoted in Table II. My purpose in describing this portion of
the methodology is to provide a logical transition to the highly
significant property of these fungicides, and that is their
susceptibility to nucleophilic attack.

Table II. Aqueous Solubility of Captan, Phaltan, and Difolatan

FUNGICIDE	Sol. @ 25 deg. C ppm	T½ hrs.	$K_d \times 10^{-5}$ sec.$^{-1}$
CAPTAN	3.3	8.2	2.4
PHALTAN	1.25	6.6	2.9
DIFOLATAN	1.4	10.5	1.8

In fact this genus of useful sulfenimide fungicides requires
a low aqueous solubility to protect against its inherent appreciable hydrolytic instability (14).

Susceptibility to Nucleophilic Displacement and Biochemical
Interactions

The half-life of an equilibrium concentration of captan,
for example, in deionized water at 25 deg. C is 8.2 hrs. The
maximum concentration of OH$^-$ is 10^{-7} moles per liter and probably
approached 10^{-9} since the determinations were made in unbuffered,
deionized water. The significant point is that OH$^-$ is a weak to

moderate nucleophile participating in the destruction of the
fungicide at a very low concentration of ion and substrate. The
author wishes to avoid discussion as to the location of the
initial attack. Probably carbonyls but possibly halogens may be
involved prior to the ultimate scission of the N-S bond.

Whereas OH⁻ is a relatively weak nucleophile (15), biological fluids abound with highly active nucleophilic species,
particularly sulfhydryls and substituted nitrogen species. This
is indeed reflected in a series of measurements on the rate of
degradation of captan and other members of the sulfenimide group
in blood and Table III summarizes the rates of that degradation in
the whole blood of humans. This remarkable shortlivedness (and
the specific values may err on being on the higher side) again
justifies further comment. These measurements were made at
different periods and with somewhat varying concentrations and
techniques. The important point is not the absolute values but
the marked rapidity of the decomposition (16) (17) (18).

Table III. Decomposition of Blood at 25°C

Fungicide	T½ (minutes)
Captan	0.9
Phaltan	0.9
Difolatan	0.8

Certain toxicological investigations particularly in the
molecular biology area utilize the interaction of the chemical
with single cell organisms or the injection of the chemical into
chick eggs or isolated enzyme preparations. These investigations
provide interesting and significant information. At times such
information has been extrapolated to indicate hazard associated
with the chemical when ingested by man or higher mammals from
the residues remaining on the raw agricultural product. The
above susceptibility to nucleophilic attack and the shortlivedness of these fungicides in biological media suggests a low
hazard associated with their normal use for the intact mammal.

It accounts further for the very large number of biochemical
mechanisms that have been invoked to explain their therapeutic
efficacy, some of which are noted in Table IV (19) (20) (21) (22)
(23) (24).

Table IV. Recorded Biochemical Interactions

MECHANISMS

1. Inhibition of glyceraldehyde dehydrogenase

2. Alpha chymotrypsin inactivation

3. Oxidative phosphorylation uncoupler

4. Destructive membrane interactions

5. Destruction of mitochondrial systems

6. Inhibition of oxidation of $NADH_2$

7. Interaction with thiol enzymes

8. Inhibition of chitin biosynthesis

Field Usefulness and Specificity

In Table II we have shown that the two $SCCl_3$ homologues, captan and Phaltan have closely similar homogenous rates of hydrolysis although captan is appreciably more soluble. On the other hand, Difolatan and Phaltan have low solubility but the rate of hydrolysis of Phaltan is approximately twice that of Difolatan. Not in the tables is the fact that Difolatan generally has two to five times the in vitro antifungal activity.

These data can be correlated with field observation. For example, in viticulture in California, the grape grows and matures in a generally dry and almost infection-free environment, while in North and Central Europe and in much of the Mediterranean area the growing areas give rise to endemic infections e.g. by Plasmopara and Botrytis organisms. Further, in these areas, the grapes are largely cultivated for wine making. The yeasts that ferment the sugars are frequently sensitive in varying degree to small concentrations of fungicidal compositions.

One would like then to have a fungicide that protects close to harvest but where the residue is so reduced in concentration or disappears altogether at the time of crushing (and subsequently in the juice). Residues of Difolatan where the hydrolysis rate is low impair the fermentation by inhibiting the growth of yeasts. Phaltan ® and/or captan sprayed at the same time as Difolatan give almost as good plant disease protection, but as the chart reveals, are less persistent. Hence these are used in much of Europe for control of grape mildew. Fermentation proceeds at a practical rate and there are no residues of the parent fungicide in the wine.

Similar analysis can be made regarding the protection of the coffee plant and fruit. Here the activity of Difolatan plus its resistance to hydrolysis and greater persistence provides the more ideal combination of properties. Therefore, under the tropical, moist conditions of Kenya, Brazil, Central America and South India, particularly for Colletrichium infections, Phaltan and captan are mediocre and Difolatan is excellent. Incidentally, none of these compounds are systemic and the residue is entirely on the fruit, not on the bean.

Finally, the appreciable hydrolytic rate of all of these provide for the assurance that there will be no soil residues from one season to the next, a decidedly ecological plus.

Honesty requires the author to add that field trials and experience provided the choice of chemical both for viticulture and for coffee plant protection. These parameters provide a rationalization for the particular choice of compound and are an aid to the understanding of that choice.

Organism Resistance and the Sulfenimide Fungicides

There is a Piedmont farm area in Virginia where apple orchards dominate the agricultural landscape. Captan has been employed on many of these farms from the day of its introduction as a practical fungicide to the present. The spray schedules can require as many as 15 to 20 applications during the growing season, yet the same dosage is employed today as when the chemical was first utilized. It was customary to ask our plant pathologists over the years if, first, any evidence of field organism resistance was observed, and second, if not, why not. The answer to the first question is in fact negative. The answers to the second were many, different, varied, and sometimes contradictory. In the section of this paper that follows, we will explore this matter of practical resistance to fungicides.

It is now commonplace to recognize that resistance to chemotherapeutic agents is a normal and expected phenomenon and that the nonappearance of resistance is the abnormal. If one rereads the Journal of Economic Entomology of the early 50's and 60's, one is struck by a seeming disregard, or, at least, lack of appreciation and recognition of this fundamental law of biology and, incidentally, of chemistry (Le Chatelier's Principle). There were, of course, some exceptional scientists "crying in the wilderness" but they were very much the minority.

Now that flies in Denmark's dairies are resistant to all insecticides, that likewise are certain ticks in Australia, that Heliothis species of various types in the U.S., the Near East and elsewhere exhibit multiple resistance, that the Gonococcus in the U.S. has shown resistance to a series of sulfa drugs, to various penicillin homologues, and even now to the tetracyclines, that certain members of the Acaridae have successfully adapted to three or four different classes of chemical therapeutic agents,

that many fungal organisms manifest resistance to certain fungicides, etc., etc., we recognize, accept and expect this fundamental property of living organisms to adapt to unfavourable
environmental pressures -- to whit, foreign chemicals.

In fact this fundamental law of life guarantees that there
will be a bicentennial ACS meeting in the year 2076, and that
chemists, indeed, have a long and never totally successful future.

In the next few paragraphs we will briefly summarize some
recent experiences relating to practical resistance to fungicides.

Ten to fifteen years ago the two surfactant-type fungicides
in Figure 4, were considered among the most effective agents
against Venturia inaequalis and certain other organisms. Where
these substances were used intensively, observations of the need
for increased dosage were made, and today these fungicides have
a declining role in American agriculture.

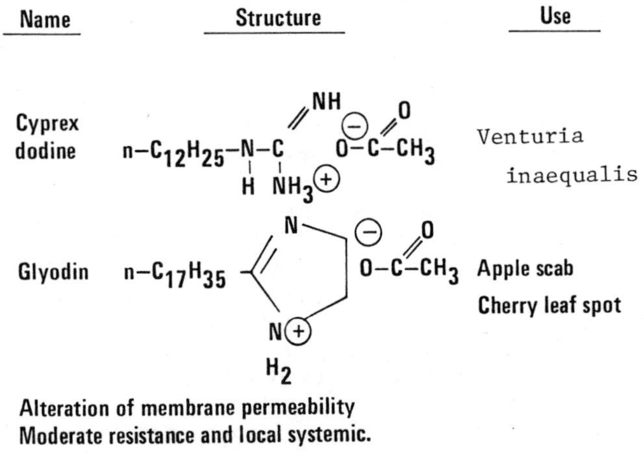

Figure 4.   Surfactant fungicides

The concept of plant 'immunity' to attacking organisms seemed and is an attractive hypothesis. The introduction of systemic
fungicides provided a sort of practical approach to 'immunity'
and was regarded as the solution to the problems of plant chemotherapy. Indeed, systemics are most valuable and useful agents.
They are not panaceas. They have limitations. The structures of
some of the more useful systemics of the Benzimidazole group are
provided for reference in Figure 5.

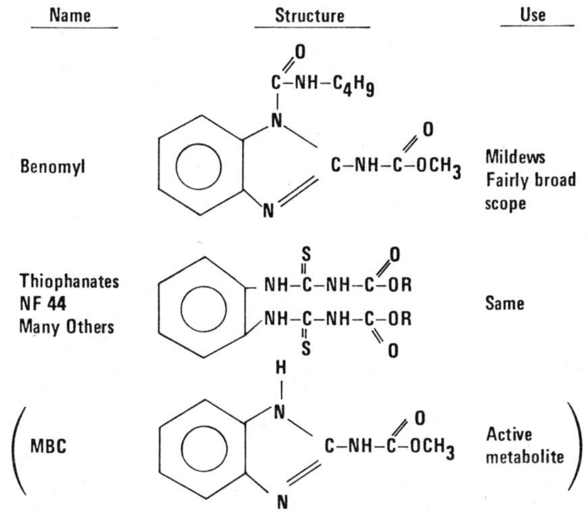

Figure 5.   Benzimidazole systemics

Another group of heterocycles has yielded valuable anti-fungal agents outstanding against certain infections of grain. In Greece (25), <u>Cercospora</u> infections of sugar beets were treated for two years with Benomyl. The first response was superb, but repeated applications revealed an increasing resistance and it was replaced after two years by a second systemic, Vitavax (Figure 6). The same sequence occurred and reports have been made that Greek agriculturists have had to return to a more conventional, albeit, a more toxic protective fungicide, Brestan (Figure 7).

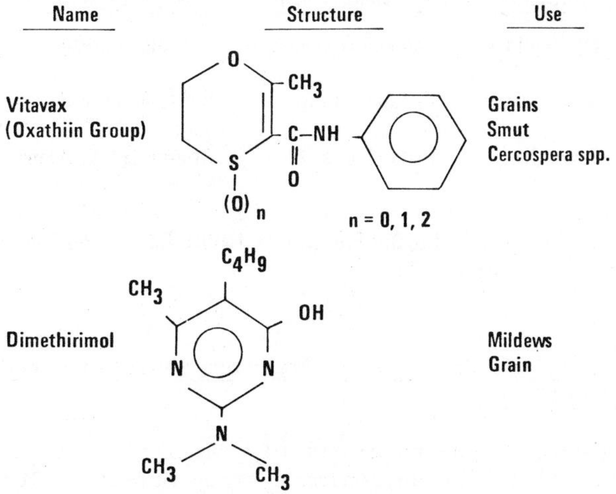

Figure 6.   Other systems

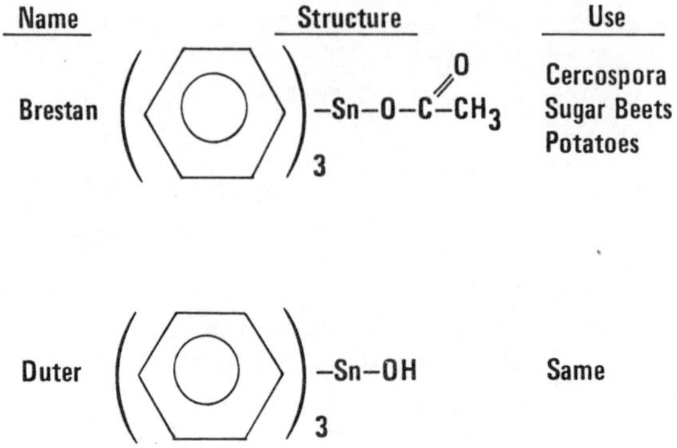

Name	Structure	Use
Brestan	$\left(\langle\bigcirc\rangle\right)_3-Sn-O-C\!\!\overset{O}{\underset{}{\diagup}}-CH_3$	Cercospora Sugar Beets Potatoes
Duter	$\left(\langle\bigcirc\rangle\right)_3-Sn-OH$	Same

Figure 7. Organotin fungicides

In Japan, a whole new generation of antifungal agents derived from fermentation processes provided great promise. In Table V, we record the experience of pathologists in Japan, who have noted resistance in laboratory, greenhouse and field in a relatively short period to structurally quite dissimilar antibiotic fungicides. Against the attack of <u>Alternaria kikuchiana</u> particularly on pears, Japanese orchardists have returned to a member of this sulfenimide group, Difolatan (26).

Table V. Resistance to Antibiotics

Antibiotic	Where Noted	Major Organism
Blasticidin S	Lab and Greenhouse	Pyricularia oryzae
Kasugamycin	Field (L and G)	Pyricularia oryzae
Polyoxins	Field (L and G)	Alternaria kikuchiana

T. Misato and K. Ko, 3rd Proceedings, IUPAC Conf. – Pesticides Helsinki, August 1974

Particularities and Features of Organism Resistance to Plant Protection Fungicides

This abnormal non-appearance of practical resistance of fungal organisms to the sulfenimide group merits exploration. This we shall do by examining some current explanations by

generalizing from the experience of resistance and the properties
of the chemical agents, and quite unashamedly by speculation.

In a recent book devoted to biochemical mechanism of pesticidal action, the author states (quoting primary sources) that
resistance to systemics is caused by "the high selection pressure
exerted by these fungicides on the fungal population with the
result that, in some circumstances only, resistant strains sur-
vive. Older fungicides seem to have been less effective as
fungicides than the new compounds"(27) This means that most of the
chemical protectants such as the sulfenimides left both resistant
and sensitive strains and presumably, and as is usual, the
sensitive population adapts better to the total environment.

It is possible that with systemics "because they have a more
specific mode of action than most of the older compounds,...there
may be less chance of their undergoing a multiplicity of non-
lethal reactions within the fungal cell" (27). This implies an
ease of detoxification of the classical protectants which permitted a larger population of survivors.

There are further generalizations that should be stressed.
The first of these also relates systemic activity to specificity
of biochemical mechanism. An effective fungitoxic systemic must
not react and be detoxified or interfere with <u>plant</u> enzymes.
Were this not the case, either a phytotoxic effect would result
(as for 2,4-D) or an ineffective fungicide would result. Exactly
these effects are achieved when through synthesis the solubility
of the sulfenimides is increased. This author has, alas, quite
frequently converted good fungicides into mediocre herbicides by
such synthetic effort on the solubility modifications of the
sulfenimide generic structure. A systemic must then be preferably a chemically relatively stable substance and not a highly
reactive nucleophile or electrophile.

A further implication of this relates to one way in which
resistance may be acquired. A single site chemical creates a
lesion in some highly essential biochemical pathway. Organisms
can however create a 'shunt' where they can accomplish their
metabolism by altering that pathway. This may be possible for
a single site toxicant. It is mathematically most unlikely for
the multisite chemicals. They presumably may be lethal by
reacting with a number of vital enzyme systems. In fact, it is
very difficult with a multisite chemical to be entirely certain
as to its mode of action. The experimental procedure may pre-
determine the conclusion (Table IV). A sort of biochemical
'uncertainty principle' is here involved. It is possible that
different fungi are killed by different biochemical interactions by these multisite toxicants. Again the mathematical
probability for resistance is reduced. Further, these plant-
fungus-chemical interrelationships enable us to particularise
in a manner that differentiates our experience and conclusions
from that of the insecticide field.

The generalizations, then, in Figure 8 refer exclusively to the subject matter at hand. Single site substances, with appreciable aqueous solubility, which are translocatable, will for the reasons mentioned with high probability develop resistance in the organisms which are their targets. Multisite chemicals, non water soluble and non systemic, show if not no tendency, at least a highly reduced probability for the induction of resistance.

Fungicides	Activity Spectrum	Biochem Sites	Translocation (Aq.Solubility)	Resistance
Benzimidazoles (Benomyl, thiophanates etc.)	+ +	− −	+ + +	+ +
Oxathiins (Vitavax)	+	− − −	+ + +	+
Antibiotics (Polyoxin etc.)	+	− − −	+ + +	+ +
Surfactant type (glyodin, cyprex)	±	− −	±	+
Dithiocarbamates (maneb,thiram etc.)	+ + +	+ +	− −	− − −
Sulfenimides (captan, Difolatan)	+ + +	+ + +	− − −	− − −

Tentative & Arbitrary
Values vary between + + + for highest to − − − for absent or lowest.

Figure 8.   Resistance and properties of fungicidal groups

In an article on the <u>Biochemical Mode of Action of Fungi-cides</u> (28) the authors generalized on fungicidal resistance on the basis of whether their biochemical mode of action involved electron transport and fundamental energetics or involved interference with metabolic changes. Our point of view differs somewhat, emphasizing organic chemical reactivity and avoiding specific biochemical mechanism which is sometimes clouded by doubt and some controversy.

Obviously, one can not precisely quantify the elements of Figure 8. It is nevertheless highly indicative. Resistance of a practical nature is rarely, if ever, encountered in normal field practice by the sulfenimides (or for example, the dithiocarbamates, Figure 9) - insoluble, multisite protectives. The water soluble single site and variably translocatable antibiotics, benzimidazoles, oxathiins, etc., etc., all exhibit degrees of field resistance. As far as this author knows, this analysis can be extended over the whole class of plant protection fungicides.

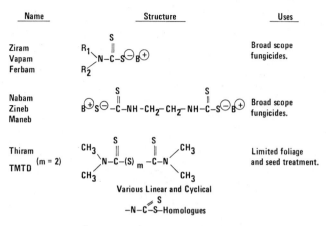

Name	Structure	Uses
Ziram / Vapam / Ferbam		Broad scope fungicides.
Nabam / Zineb / Maneb		Broad scope fungicides.
Thiram / TMTD (m = 2)		Limited foliage and seed treatment.

Various Linear and Cyclical
−N−C−S−Homologues

Figure 9. Dithiocarbamate fungicides

Summary

In summary, we have attempted to cover briefly (Table VI) the history of the development of this group of fungicides. The sulfenimides are a broad genus providing opportunities for much synthetic modification. The compounds presently exploited, particularly captan, Phaltan and Difolatan, are characterized by the relative simplicity of their structures.

Table VI. The Sulfenimide Fungicides

Outline

1. Introduction   a) Brief History
                b) Chemical Definition
                c) Examples

2. On the nature of the $= N - S -$ bond

3. Aqueous solubility of useful compounds

4. Susceptibility to Neucleophilic Displacement
                a) Hydrolytic Instability
                b) Instability in Biological Media

5. Attributed Biochemical Mechanisms

6. Correlations between chemical properties and field efficacy — Examples

7. Organism Resistance and the Sulfenimides.

The particular feature that defines the class, and contributes to useful characteristics and to limitations is the N - S bonds, a linkage which within the constraints of the generic formula is particularly susceptible to nucleophilic attack. This requires that useful members of the class possess low solubility, particularly aqueous, so that hydrolytic destruction may be maintained at a low practical limit. We have correlated field usefulness of members of this class to their chemical and physical properties as above discussed.

Many biochemical interactions of the sulfenimides with enzyme systems and biological structures have been described in the literature and can be amply demonstrated with isolated systems. At this stage, we must conclude that the sulfenimides are involved in biochemical multisite attack, most likely with the sulfhydryl associated enzymes and co-enzyme systems.

Finally, we have surveyed particularities that pertain to the fungicide resistance field. From this survey we have presented some generalizations. These all point to the low probability of organism resistance in the future to these sulfenimide fungicides and to fungicides that possess similar physical and biochemical characteristics.

In contrast to the problems of field entomology, one can feel optimistic about the present status and the future for plant disease chemotherapeutants. We have the opportunity for reasonable pest management and with proper precautions, can avoid gross manifestations of practical fungus resistance. This includes the avoidance of excessive dependence on the systemics and the joint employment in a felicitous manner of protectants and systemics.

In the mid 1970's, the avoidance of resistance is a social responsibility involving all of us, in government, in education, in industry and in agriculture.

From the particularities above outlined, we know which chemicals can be utilized with minimal probabilities of resistance development. Among these compositions are the subject fungicides of this paper - the sulfenimides.

Literature Cited

1. Kittleson, A.R., Science (1952), 115, 84.
2. Kittleson, A. R., J. Agr. Food Chem. (1953), 1, 677.
3. Kittleson, A. R., U.S.P. 2,553,770-2,553,778.
4. Loc. cit. (2) above gives a description of Dr. Daines' technique and his demonstration of significant antifungal activity.
5. Daines, R. H., Plant Disease Reporter (1956), 40, 335.
6. Daines, R. H., Plant Disease Reporter (1955), 39, 739.
7. Van der Kirk, G. J. M., Abstract of Proc. Third Int. Conf. of Pest. Chem., Helsinki (1974) Abstract M 182.
8. Kohn, G. K., U.S.P. 3,178,447.
9. U.S.P. 2,533,773.

10. Calculations by Dr. Philip Magee, Res. Dept., Chev. Chem. Co. By the same method, values for related bonds are N-O = 38, N-Cl = 42, Cl-Cl = 57 (K cal).
11. Torok, F., et al, Acta Chim (Budapest) (1970), 63(4), 417.
12. Hargittai, I., et al, Magy Kem. Foly (1970), 76(2), 63.
13. Goehring, M., Chem. Ber. (1947), 80, 219.
14. Abell, J., The Water Solubility of Difolatan, Captan and Phaltan, Unpublished - Internal Co. File, Chev. Chem. Co. dated January 5, 1968.
15. Streitweiser, A., Chem. Reviews (1956), 56, 571.
16. Crossley, J., The Stability of Captan in Blood and similar studies. Unpublished Chev. Chem. Co. Files.
17., Very recent studies reflect on the ease of formation and
18. stability characteristics of the free radical N-S derived from model compounds. Whether such a radical species is involved in the biochemistry of the sulfenimides is not known. See:
Pannen, W. C., Newkirk, D. O., J.A.C.S., (1976), 98, 516.
Maillard, R. A., Ingold, K. U., J.A.C.S. (1976), 98, 520.
19. Lukens, R. J., Phytopathology (1962), 52, 740.
20. Siegel, M. R., Pest. Biochem. Physiol. (1971), 1, 225.
21. Siegel, M.R., Pest. Biochem. Physiol. (1971), 1, 234.
22. Nelson, B. D., Biochem. Pharmacol. (1971), 20, 749.
23. Nelson, B. D., Biochem. Pharmacol. (1971), 20, 737.
24. Marks, E. P., Sowa, B. A., Personal Communications, to be published.
25. Georgopoulos, S. G., The Third Inter. Cong. of Pest. Chem. Helsinki (1974).
26. Misato, T., Ko, K., The Third Inter. Cong. of Pest. Chem. Helsinki (1974) and Personal Communications.
27. Corbett, J. R., The Biochemical Mode of Action of Pesticides. Academic Press, London and New York (1974) pp. 230-231; discussion of Evans, E., Pest Science (1971), 2, 192.
28. Sijpersteijn, K., Van der Kirk, G. J. M., Proc. 5th Br. Insect. and Fung. Conf. Brighton (1969). Vol. 3, pp. 724 et. seq.

10

The Development of Agricultural Antibiotics

TOMOMASA MISATO

The Institute of Physical and Chemical Research, Wako-shi, Saitama 351, Japan

Introduction

The successful use of antibiotics against bacterial diseases of human beings has led to a large scale screening of antibiotics effect for plant disease control in the world. Many antibiotics developed for medical purposes were investigated for activity against plant pathogens. Furthermore screening of soil organisms for production of antibiotic substances was started with the prime purpose of plant disease control. However, the results obtained with antibiotics and antibiotic containing culture broth did not fulfil the high expectations. Many of them were too unstable under field conditions or showed toxic side effects on plants. Most antibiotics were rather expensive, even when used as a crude product. In western countries only a few antibiotics have been developed for practical use. These are streptomycin, tetracycline, cycloheximide and griseofulvin. Streptomycin, the first antibiotic introduced in agriculture, was used in the United States for the control of pear fire blight. This antibiotic and a mixture of streptomycin and tetracycline have been used for the control of bacterial plant diseases, while cycloheximide and griseofulvin have been used for the control of fungal plant diseases. Cycloheximide is a very powerful fungicide, but unfortunately, highly toxic to plants, which restricts its use against plant diseases. Griseofulvin is a much less phytotoxic systemic fungicide, but its use is also restricted, because the relation of its manufacturing cost to its performance under field condition is not quite satisfactory. In Japan, these four antibiotics had been used only on a very limited scale for practical control of plant diseases, until the curative effect of blasticidin S on rice blast was discovered by the author's research group in 1958. The successful application of blasticidin S against rice blast has stimulated the development of agricultural antibiotics and led to the discovery of several excellent antibiotics, such as kasugamycin, polyoxins and validamycin, etc. Nowadays, blasticidin S and kasugamycin have been in practical use for rice blast control instead of mercuric fungicides, and polyoxins and validamycin have

Table I. Agricultural Antibiotics used in Japan

Registration	Antibiotics	Diseases	Amounts used in Japan (1974)	
			(ton)	(10³ yen)
ANTIFUNGAL ANTIBIOTICS				
1959	Cycloheximide (Wettable Powder)	Onion Downy Mildew / Shoot Blight of Japanese Larch	17	35,020
1959	Griseofulvin (Paste)	Fusarium Wilt of Melon	2	4,700
1961	Blasticidin S (Dust) (Wettable Powder) (Solution)	Rice Blast	1,250 / 3 / 152	75,000 / 2,547 / 102,426
1965	Kasugamycin (Dust) (Wettable Powder) (Solution)	Rice Blast	7,930 / 265 / 10	507,762 / 221,805 / 8,820
1967	Polyoxins (Dust) (Wettable Powder) (Solution)	Rice Sheath Blight / Fungal Diseases of Fruits and Vegetables	387 / 418 / 34	32,121 / 960,982 / 38,216
1970	Ezomycin (Wettable Powder)	Stem Rot of Kidney Bean	0	0
1972	Validamycin (Dust) (Wettable Powder)	Rice Sheath Blight	3,893 / 94	513,876 / 143,256
ANTIBACTERIAL ANTIBIOTICS				
1957	Streptomycin (Wettable Powder)	Bacterial Diseases of Fruits and Vegetables	349	692,086
1964	Cellocidin (Wettable Powder)	Rice Bacterial Leaf Blight	0	0
1964	Chloramphenicol +Basic copper (Wettable Powder)	Rice Bacterial Leaf Blight	10	33,130
1968	Novobiocin (Solution)	Bacterial Canker of Tomatoes	0	0
Insecticidal Antibiotics				
1974	Tetranactin	Insects Carmine Mite of Fruits and Tea	—	—

been used to control the sheath blight of rice plant instead of
arsenic fungicides. The amount of antibiotics used in Japan is
shown in Table I. The development of agricultural antibiotics
has not been limited only for controlling plant diseases, but has
extended wider and more actively over various areas such as
utilization of insecticides, herbicides and plant regulators in
Japan. As shown in Table II, many compounds of microbiological
origin are already used as pesticides or show promise for
practical application. Blasticidin S, etc. as antifungal antibiotics, streptomycin, etc. as antibacterial antibiotics,
tetranactin as a miticide, and gibberellins as plant growth regulators are practically used. Aabomycin as an antiviral antibiotic, a product of <u>Bacillus</u> <u>thuringensis</u> as a insecticidal antibiotic and anisomycin derivatives as herbicides have been tested
for practical use in the fields.

Table II. Pesticidal compounds of microbiological origin

[Fungicide]
* Antifungal antibiotics   : Blasticidin S, etc.
* Antibacterial antibiotics   : Streptomycin, etc.
  Antiviral antibiotics   : Aabomycin, etc.
[Insecticide]
* Miticidal antibiotic   : Tetranactin
* Bacterial toxin   : <u>Bacillus</u> <u>thuringensis</u>
[Herbicide]
  Herbicidal antibiotic   : Anisomycin
[Growth regulator]
* Fungal product   : Gibberellins

---

      * Practically used as pesticides

Reviews on many antibiotics including cycloheximide,
griseofulvin and streptomycin tested for the purpose of agricultural use in western countries have been published (1-6). It is
the purpose of this paper to discuss the present status of antibiotics as plant disease control agents. The discussion will
mainly be limited to antibiotics which are practically used as
new pesticides in Japan. For the other literature, the reader may
refer the reviews mentioned above.

Antifungal antibiotics

Blasticidin S. Blasticidin S is the first successful agricultural antibiotic developed in Japan. It was isolated from the
culture filtrates of <u>Streptomyces</u> <u>griseochromogenes</u> by Takeuchi
et al. (7), and the potent curative effect of blasticidin S on
rice blast was found by Misato et al. (8). Thereafter the benzyl-
aminobenzene sulfonate of blasticidin S was reported to be least
phytotoxic to the host plant without reducing antifungal activity
against <u>Pyricularia</u> <u>oryzae</u>, the pathogen of rice blast (9), and

this salt has been industrially produced for agricultural use.

1) Chemistry and mode of action: The chemical structure of
blasticidin S has been studied extensively by Yonehara and his
co-workers and the final structure assigned blasticidin S is 1-
(1'-cytosinyl)-4-[L-3'-amino-5'-(1"-N-methylguandidino)-valeryl-
amino]-1,2,3,4-tetradeoxy-β-D-erythro-hex-2-eneuronic acid as
shown in Figure 1 (10,11). Seto et al. (12,13) studied the biosynthesis of blasticidin S by the producing organism using ^{14}C-
labeled suspected precursors. The results obtained were that the
pyrimidine ring of the antibiotic came from cytosine directly and
sugar moiety from glucose; arginine served as the precursor for
blastidic acid, and the N-methyl group of blastidic acid arose
from methionine. Misato and his co-workers have studied the
biochemical properties of blasticidin S on P. oryzae. They found
the curative effect of blasticidin S on rice blast due to a strong
inhibitory action on mycelial growth of the pathogen, and reported
that the antibiotic markedly inhibited the incorporation of ^{14}C-
labeled amino acid into protein in the cell-wall system of P.
oryzae (14), while metabolic pathways including glycolysis,
succinic dehydrogenase system, electron transport system, and
oxidative phosphorylation system or incorporation of ^{32}P into the
nucleic acid were not inhibited by blasticidin S (15,16). The
mode of action of this antibiotic on the molecular basis in detail is not known so far with any certainty,but certain processes
related to peptidyl transferase activity are inhibited by blasticidin S (17,18).

2) Biological properties: Blasticidin S has a wide range
of biological activities. Besides its significant inhibitory
effects on the growth of P. oryzae, it also exhibits other antimicrobial (7), and anti-viral (19) as well as anti-tumor activities (20), though the medicinal applications are impeded by its
toxic properties. In the case of spraying in the field to protect rice blast, the effective concentration of blasticidin S is
usually 10 to 20 ppm (1 - 3 g blasticidin S / 10a), but it
occasionally causes chemical injury on rice leaves when sprayed
beyond the concentration described above. The application by
dusting occasionally causes conjunctivitis if it accidentally
contacts the eyes, although no accident has been reported in the
case of the spray of wettable powder or solution. Such toxic
effect on mammals is the most unfavorable characteristic of
blasticidin S. Many attempts have been made to remedy this de-
fect of blasticidin S. Sugimoto (21) found a simple method to
alleviate eye irritation caused by blasticidin S; the addition of
calcium acetate to blasticidin S dust (5% addition) specifically
reduced the eye trouble without influence on antiblast effect,
though other mammalian toxicity or phytotoxicity of the antibiotic are also not affected. This improved dust is now used
practically for agricultural use. The behavior and fate of
blasticidin S in the environment were investigated using radio-

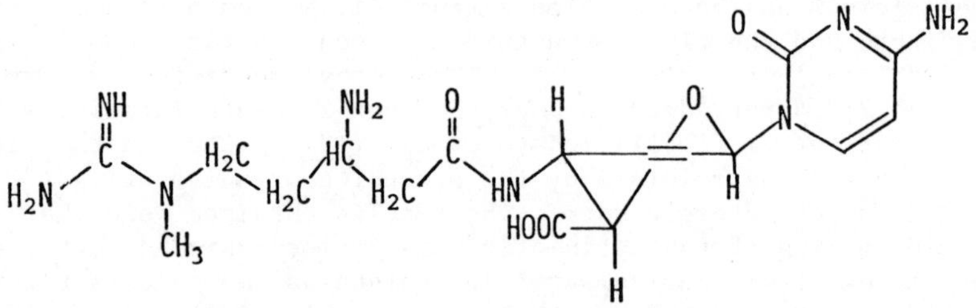

Figure 1.   Structure of blasticidin S

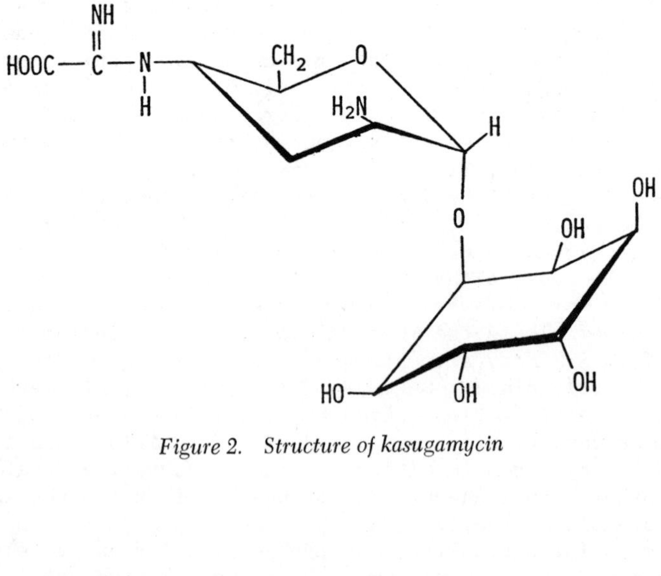

Figure 2.   Structure of kasugamycin

active compounds prepared biosynthetically from ^{14}C-cytosine and
^{14}C-L-methionine (22). The sprayed antibiotic was located on the
surface of the rice plant and little was diffused or transported
into the tissue. From the wound or infected part, however, the
compound was incorporated and translocated mainly to upper part.
The compound located at the plant surface was decomposed by sunlight and gave rise to cytosine as the main degradation product.
A considerable quantity of blasticidin S sprayed fell to the
ground and was adsorbed on the soil surface tightly. Furthermore, significant generation of ^{14}C-carbon dioxide from the ^{14}C-
blasticidin S treated soil was observed, and several microbes
usually inhabiting the paddy field were found to make the biological activity of blasticidin S lower. From the results obtained,
Yamaguchi et al. supposed that after application to the crop at
very low concentration, the antibiotic might be rapidly broken
down in the environment, so that there may be no danger of environmental pollution and food contamination.

Kasugamycin. Kasugamycin is a water-soluble and basic antibiotic produced by Streptomyces kasugaensis (23). Following the
development of blasticidin S, kasugamycin has been used as an
agricultural antibiotic for rice blast control in Japan since
1965. This antibiotic controls rice blast disease at a concentration as low as about 20 ppm. It can be safely used without any
toxicity on crops, and with very low toxicity to mammals. These
advantages are the main reasons that blasticidin S is losing
ground to kasugamycin. However, recently, the virulence of
kasugamycin-resistant strain in paddy field has raised a serious
problem in rice blast control by kasugamycin.

1) Chemistry and mode of action: The chemical structure of
kasugamycin was studied by Suhara et al. (24,25) by chemical
methods and by Ikekawa et al. (26) by X-ray diffraction analysis.
As shown in Figure 2, the molecule of kasugamycin consists of
three moieties which are D-inositol, kasugamine (2,3,4,6-tetra-
deoxy-2,4-diaminohexopyranose) and an iminoacetic acid side chain.
Nakajima and his associates studied the synthesis of kasugamycin,
and succeeded in synthesizing kasuganobiosamine and related compounds (27,28); that means the total synthesis of kasugamycin by
the introduction of the oxalimidyl group into kasuganobiosamine.
Kasugamycin enters into the plant tissue, and shows both
protective and curative action. It does not inhibit spore germination even at a concentration of 120 µg/ml. Its effect against
P. oryzae comes only to expression in the plant and in vitro at
low pH (29). Tanaka et al. (30) reported that kasugamycin inhibited protein synthesis in cell free systems of P. oryzae.
Kasugamycin inhibits protein synthesis in Escherichia coli by
interfering with the binding of aminoacyl-tRNA to mRNA-30 S
ribosomal subunit complex. The compound does not cause miscoding.

2) Biological properties : Kasugamycin selectively inhibited
the growth of *P. oryzae* and some bacteria including *Pseudomonas*
species, and showed little or no activity against other fungi
tested. The antibiotic did not show acute or chronic toxicity to
mice, rats, rabbits, dogs, monkeys and human beings. The oral
LD_{50} for mice was 2 g/kg. At a concentration of 1,000 ppm there
was no toxicity to fish.   Kasugamycin is now used in a large
scale against rice blast. It controls rice blast when sprayed at
about 20 - 40 ppm aqueous solution. For practical disease control
kasugamycin is mainly applied as a dust, containing 0.3 % of
active ingredient. No injury was observed to many other plants.
        The development of resistance in fungi to kasugamycin has
been reported from laboratory experiments, but not in the fields
for some years after application of the antibiotic. However,
since 1971, the development of a kasugamycin-resistant strain of
rice blast fungus in the fields has become a serious problem (31).
After kasugamycin resistant strains had been detected in the field,
the combined formulations of kasugamycin and chemicals with
different action mechanisms have been practically used.

        Polyoxins. The polyoxins, a new group of peptidyl-pyrimidine
nucleoside antibiotics, are produced by *Streptomyces cacaoi* var.
asoensis (32,33). Polyoxins are composed of thirteen components
(A - M) of some closely related "peptidic nucleosides" as referred
by Isono and Suzuki (34). They can be safely used with no
toxicity to man, livestock, fish and plant. Such excellent
characteristics may be due to the fact that polyoxins selectively
inhibit the synthesis of cell wall chitin of sensitive fungi, as
was reported by Misato and his co-workers (35-38). Polyoxins have
been widely used for the protection against some pathogenic fungi
such as *Alternaria kikuchiana*, *Pellicularia sasakii* and *Cochlibolus
miyabeanus* in Japan since 1967.

        1) Chemistry and mode of action : Structures of all polyoxins
were given by Isono *et al.* (39) as depicted in Figure 3. Among
polyoxins, C component is the smallest, and though it lacks antifungal activity it was a key compound to elucidate the structure
of polyoxins since hydrolytic degradation of all the polyoxins
afforded polyoxin C or its analogues. Isono and Suzuki (40)
assigned the structure, 1-β-(5'-amino-5'-deoxy-D-allofuranuronosyl)
-5-hydroxymethyluracil to polyoxin C by chemical and physical
techniques, and a single-crystal X-ray diffraction analysis of N-
brosylpolyoxin C confirmed the structure (41). This prompted the
total synthesis of polyoxin J by Kuzuhara *et al.* (42).   In
studying the mechanism of fungicidal action of polyoxins, Eguchi
et al. (43) observed a specific physiological action against
Alternaria spp. in inhibiting its growth ; polyoxins caused marked
abnormal bulbous phenomenon on germ tubes of spore and hyphal tips
of the pathogen at low concentration, and this abnormally swollen
spore became non-infectious. It was also reported that the

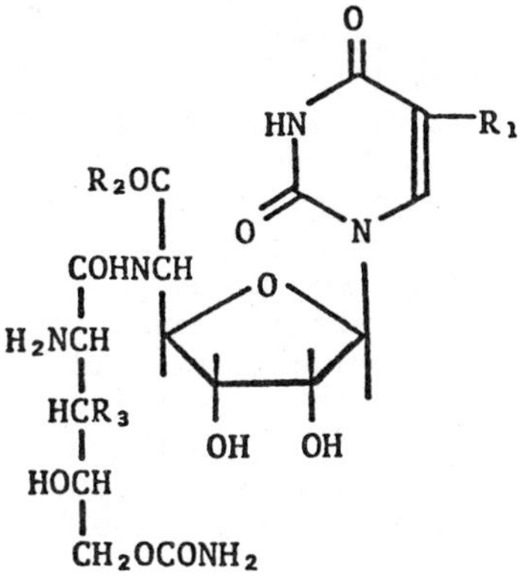

Polyoxin	R_1	R_2	R_3
A	CH_2OH	*	OH
B	CH_2OH	HO	OH
D	COOH	HO	OH
E	COOH	HO	H
F	COOH	*	OH
G	CH_2OH	HO	H
H	CH_3	*	OH
J	CH_3	HO	OH
K	H	*	OH
L	H	HO	OH
M	H	HO	H

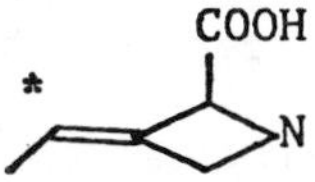

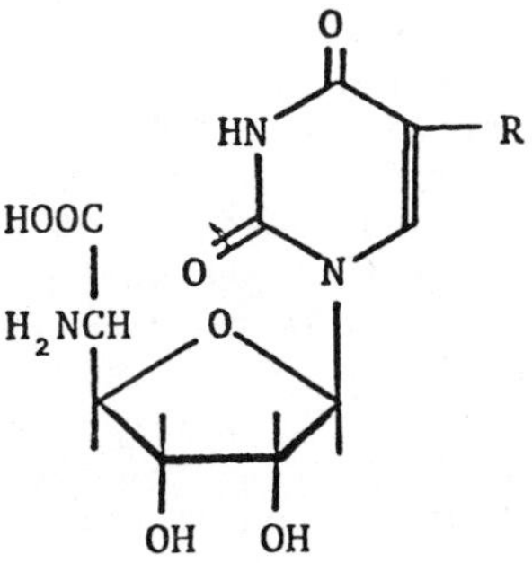

	R
C	HO
I	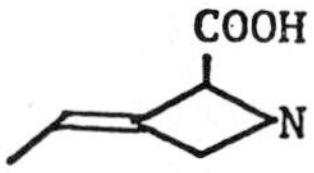

Figure 3.   *Structure of polyoxins*

incorporation of ^{14}C–glucosamine into cell wall chitin of
Cochliobolus miyabeanus was markedly inhibited by polyoxin D,
without inhibitory effect on respiration and synthesis of macro-
molecules such as protein or nucleic acids (44). Endo and Misato
(36) showed in their kinetic studies of the cell-free system of
Neurospora crassa that polyoxin D strongly inhibits the incorporation of N-acetylglucosamine (GlcNAc) into chitin in competitive
manner between UDP-GlcNAc and polyoxin D. More recently Hori *et
al.* (38) reported the relation between polyoxin structure and
inhibitory activity on chitin synthetase. According to their
kinetic analysis, the carbamoyl polyoxamic acid moiety of
polyoxins would help to stabilize the polyoxin enzyme complex and
the pyrimidine nucleoside moiety of the antibiotics would also fit
into binding site of the protein.   Therefore the excellent
characteristics of polyoxins may be due to the fact that the
antibiotics inhibit the cell wall synthesis of sensitive fungi but
have no influence on other organisms including mammals, since
there exist no cell walls in animal cells.

   2) Biological properties : Polyoxins inhibit the growth of
some fungi but are inactive against bacteria and yeast. All the
polyoxins except C and I showed selective antifungal activity
against various plant pathogenic fungi (45). Among polyoxins,
polyoxin D was most effective for rice sheath blight pathogen,
Pellicularia sasakii, whereas B and L were effective for pear spot
fungus and apple cork spot fungus at 50 to 100 ppm. Polyoxin
complex has been used in practice in duplicate forms ; polyoxin D
rich fraction for the sheath blight control, and B rich fraction
               for diseases caused by *Alternaria* spp. As for its
toxicity, oral administration at 15 g/kg and injection at
800 mg/kg to mice did not cause any adverse effect, nor is it
toxic to fish during 72 hours period of exposure at 10 ppm.
Moreover, foliar sprays of 200 ppm polyoxins have produced no
phytotoxicity on most crops, and especially on rice plant no
injury was observed even at 800 ppm application (33,46).
Recently, Nishimura *et al.* (47) have reported the discovery of
polyoxin resistant strains of *A. kikuchiana* in some orchards of
Tottori Prefecture, Japan. Hori *et al.* (48) suggested that the
resistance is caused by a lowered permeability of the antibiotic
through the cell membrane into the site of chitin synthesis.
   Mitani and Inoue (49) found that the inhibition of mycelial
growth of *P. sasakii* by polyoxins was protected by glycyl-L-
alanine, glycyl-D,L-valine and D,L-alanylglycine. Therefore, the
peptides may act as antagonists to the incorporation of polyoxins
into the cell of the fungus.

   Validamycin. Validamycin A (VM-A) is a new antifungal antibiotic recently developed in Japan for the control of rice sheath
blight (50–52). It was isolated from the culture filtrate of
Streptomyces hygroscopicus var. *limoneus*, which also produced five

additional components designated validamycin B to F, together with
validoxylamine A and B (52,53). VM-A can be used without injury
to plants, and with very low toxicity to mammals (54). Almost no
toxicity was also observed for birds, fish and insects.

  1) Chemistry and mode of action : The chemical structure of
validamycin A was determined by Horii, Kameda and their co-workers
to be N-[(1s)-(1,4,6/5)-3-hydroxymethyl-4,5,6-trihydroxycyclohex-2-
enyl][O-β-D-glucopyranosyl-(1→3)-(1s)-(1,2,4/3,5)-2,3,4-tri-
hydroxy-5-hydroxymethyl cyclohexyl] amine as shown in Figure 4
(53,55,56,57).   As for mode of action of validamycin A, Wakae
and Matsuura (58) showed that VM-A inhibits biosynthesis of
inositol in *P. sasakii*, and they supposed that inositol may be
indispensable for the normal growth and pathogenic activity of the
fungus. Although reduction of pathogenicity induced by VM-A was
remarkably recovered by the premixing of inositol in their experiment, further investigation will be required to sort out the
specific site and type of action of VM-A.

  2) Biological properties : Antimicrobial activity of VM-A
against about 3,000 species of fungi and bacteria was not detected
with ordinary methods (51,59), and also disturbance of microflora
on rice plant and crop field was not observed (58). Wakae and
Matsuura (60) found no phytotoxicity on over 150 species of plants
sprayed with VM-A even at a concentration of 1,000 ppm. Furthermore, acute and subacute toxicities to mammals were markedly low ;
in oral administration of validamycin A at the dose of 10 g/kg to
mice and rats, or in subcutaneous and intravenous administration
at the dose of 2 g/kg to mice, all animals examined survived without any change for 7 days (51).   VM-A is a main component of
validamycin complex and is specifically effective against certain
plant diseases caused by *Rhizoctonia* spp., such as web blight, bud
rot, damping-off seed decay, root rot and black scurf of several
crops and southern blight of vegetables as well as sheath blight
of rice plant (58). Though the antibiotic showed neither cidal
nor static action of *Rhizoctonia* spp., it caused an abnormal
branching at the tips of hyphae of the pathogen, followed by
cessation of further development (51). When it was applied in the
early logarithmic phase of lesion expansion on rice plant,
sufficient control was achieved by one spraying of 30 ppm VM-A
solution (60). VM-A has been commercially used upon sheath blight
disease since 1973.   Validamycins have been shown to be
susceptible to microbial attack and their addition to soil resulted in complete loss of biological activity by soil microbes.
Its half-life in soil was less than 4 hours. Microbial degradation of VM-A by *Pseudomonas denitrificans* gave rise to D-glucose
and validoxylamine A, which was further decomposed into
valienamine, validamine and other lower compounds (61).
Validamycin A has been practically used to protect sheath blight
of rice plant in the formulations of 3 % solution or 0.3 % dust.

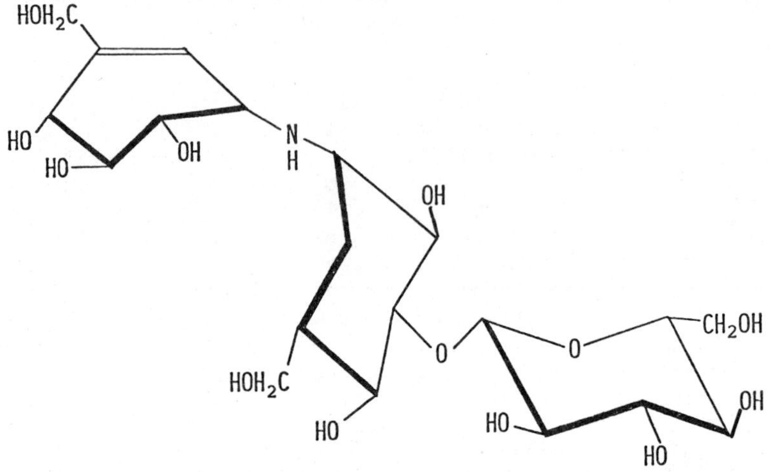

Figure 4.   Structure of validamycin

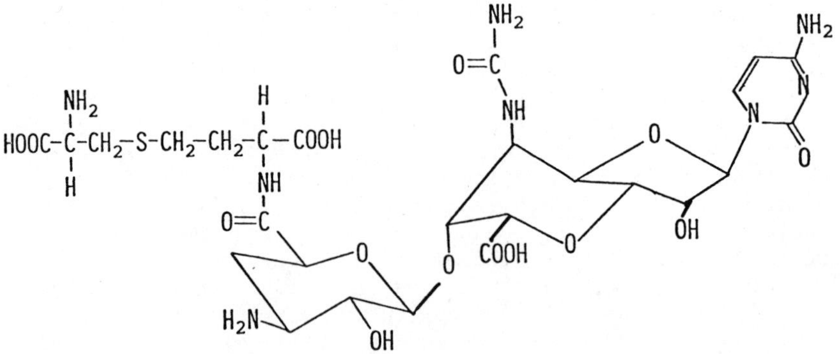

Figure 5.   Structure of ezomycin

Residues in rice grains and straws were less than each detectable
limit by gas chromatography (62).

   Ezomycins. Ezomycins are antifungal antibiotics produced by
a strain of *Streptomyces* very similar to *S. kitazawaensis*.
Takaoka *et al.* (63) isolated a complex of the antibiotics from
the culture filtrate of the producing organism and reported that
the complex has unique biological activity in suppressing the
growth of very limited species of phytopathogenic fungi, such as
Sclerotinia and *Botrytis* spp. Since the complex showed remarkable
antimicrobial activity against *Sclerotinia sclerotiorum* de Bary
that causes stem rot in kidney bean plants (*Phaseolus vulgaris* L.),
isolation and characterization of each component of ezomycins
were carried out by Sakata *et al.* (64).   According to Sakata
et al., ezomycins are new pyrimidine nucleosides, and the presence
of L-cystathionine in ezomycin molecule is responsible for
specific antifungal activity. Recently they elucidated the
chemical structure of all the ezomycins (65-67) ; Figure 5 shows
the chemical structure of ezomycin A. This antibiotic was
registered as an agricultural antibiotic for the control of stem
rot of kidney bean in 1970, but has scarcely been on the market
since then.

Antibacterial antibiotic

   Cellocidin. Cellocidin is an antibiotic produced from
Streptomyces chibaensis (68,69). It is an acetylenedicarboxyamide
containing only four carbon atoms as shown in Figure 6. As its
chemical structure is so simple, it is easy to synthesize
chemically. Technical grade cellocidin for commercial formulations is now synthesized from fumaric acid or butynediol.
Cellocidin shows an excellent preventive effect against rice
bacterial leaf blight when sprayed on rice plants at 100 to 200
ppm (70). Its toxicity when injected intravenously is high (LD_{50}
to mice, 11mg/kg), but in oral administration and skin application
it is not so highly toxic (LD_{50} to mice, 89.2 - 125 mg/kg and LD_{50}
to mice, 667 mg/kg respectively). Cellocidin has been practically
used since 1964. However, its consumption has been remarkably
decreased due to its phytotoxicity. The antibacterial action of
cellocidin was antagonized by cysteine or glutathione, which
indicates interaction with SH-groups. A study of several metabolic systems from *Xanthomonas oryzae* revealed that cellocidin
selectively inhibited NAD-requiring dehydrogenase, and especially
in the pathway from α-ketoglutamic acid through succinyl Co A to
succinic acid at the minimum growth inhibitory concentration of
10 ppm (71).

Insecticidal antibiotic

   Tetranactin. Tetranactin, a new miticidal antibiotic, was

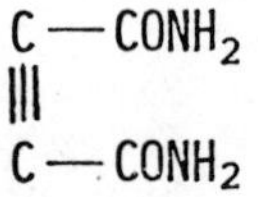

$$C - CONH_2$$
$$\text{|||}$$
$$C - CONH_2$$

Figure 6. Structure of cellocidin

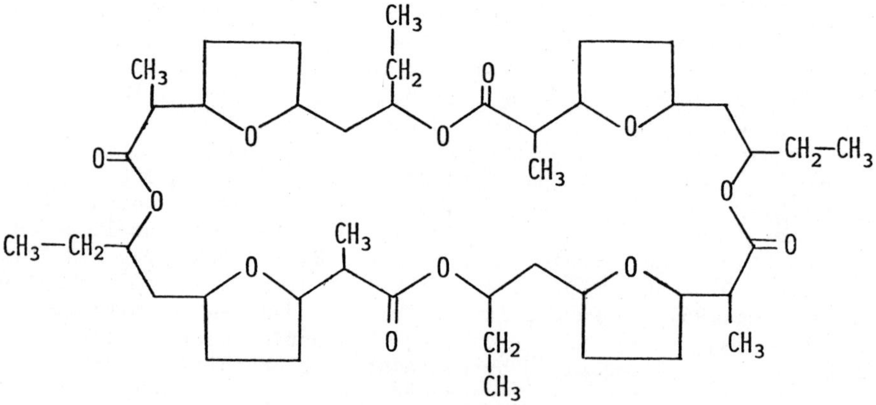

Figure 7. Structure of tetranactin

isolated as crystalline rhombic prisms from the filter cake of the
fermented broth of *Streptomyces aureus* strain S-3466 (72). The
antibiotic exerted remarkable pesticidal activity specifically
against the adults of carmine mite and showed very weak toxicity
to a warm-blooded animal. Also it showed no phytotoxicity to
apple, mandarin orange and tea, when sprayed at high concentration
(73). The miticidal property of tetranactin in the fields of
apple and tea had been evaluated in Japan since 1968, and
tetranactin has been used as a miticide for plants since 1974.

1) Chemistry and mode of action : Ando *et al.* (72) isolated
the active principle in crystalline form by extracting the
mycelial cake of *S. aureus* with acetone followed by silicagel
column chromatography. They also showed that *S. aureus* produces,
along with tetranactin, two other structurally related macrotetrolide antibiotics, i.e., dinactin and trinactin, in minor
amount.   From the studies on the chemical characteristics of
tetranactin, it was found that the antibiotic also belongs to the
class of macrotetrolide antibiotic and is a cyclic polyester
composed of four units of homononactic acid, as shown in Figure 7
(74). The stereochemical structure was clarified with the use of
X-ray crystallography by Iitake *et al.* (75).   As for mode of
action of tetranactin, Ando *et al.* (76) observed that tetranactin
is an uncoupler in cockroach mitochondria and supposed that the
antibiotic caused the leakage of alkali cations such as K^+ through
the lipid layer of the biomembrane in mitochondria, followed by
uncoupling.

2) Biological properties : Specificity in biological
activity is a unique property of tetranactin ; it exerted potent
pesticidal activity against the adults of a carmine spider mite
alone, LD_{50} for which is 4.8 μg/ml with the spray method (77).
Azukibean weevil and larva of mosquito were moderately sensitive
to the antibiotic, while other pests such as house fly and
cockroach were insensitive. In addition, it was observed that the
ovicidal activity of the antibiotic against the sensitive mites is
not so significant, which appeared to be one of the weak points of
tetranactin. The miticidal activity, however, was confirmed in
the trials. Tetranactin suspensions were sprayed on apple trees
on which leaves *Kanzawa* spider and European red mite were naturally parastic ; proliferation of both mites were completely retarded
during 32 days of the experiment.   Another characteristic of
tetranactin is its safety. Ando *et al.* (72) reported that mice
tolerated an intraperitoneal administration of 300 mg/kg and an
oral administration of 15 g/kg. They also observed that acute
toxicity of the antibiotic is very low ; the oral LD_{50}'s are more
than 2 g/kg to rats, guinea pigs, quails and rabbits (76). They
suggested that the low toxicity is partly attributable to the
poor absorption by animals. When ^{14}C-tetranactin prepared by
biosynthesis was administered orally to mice, it was revealed that

the antibiotic is little absorved so that the distribution in
various organs was negligible and almost all radioactivity was
recovered in feces 72 hours after administration (76).

Other promising antibiotics

1. Herbicidal antibiotic

Methoxyphenone (An anisomycin analogue). Yamada *et al.* (78)
found a strain of *Streptomyces* to produce two plant-regulating
substances, which were later identified as anisomycin (79) and
toyokamycin (80). They observed that anisomycin exerted strong
growth-inhibitory activity on the roots and shoots of all the
plants tested (rice, barnyard grass, crab grass, lucerne and
tomato) at 12.5 and 50 ppm, respectively. These results led to
the investigation of compounds having p-methoxyphenyl groups (p-
anisole derivatives) on plant growth-regulating activity, and many
anisole derivatives were synthesized and their activities were
tested (81). This resulted in the finding of interesting plant
growth-regulating activities of p-methoxy diphenylmethanes and
p-methoxybenzophenones. Especially, remarkable herbicidal
activity was confirmed for 3,3'-dimethyl-4-methoxybenzophenone
(methoxyphenone) in the paddy field tests. Methoxyphenone
completely induced chlorosis in barnyard grass and provided a
satisfactory herbicidal effect at 4 kg/ha application, although
weak chlorosis was occasionally observed in rice stem at 6 kg/ha
(82). According to Ishida *et al.*, methoxyphenone is quite a
stable substance, but is gradually decomposed by sunlight. In
paddy field, it also seems to be susceptible to microbial attack;
concentration of methoxyphenone in the soil reached a max 2.16
ppm 7 days after application, but decreased to 0.018 ppm after
30 days and to below 0.004 ppm after 60 days. While the metabolic
fate of methoxyphenone in the environment is presently under
investigation, thirteen metabolities have so far been identified
; the methoxy group was transformed into the hydroxy group and
the benzophenone skeleton was decomposed to m-toluic acid and
4-hydroxy-m-toluic acid. In addition, the acute toxicity of
methoxyphenone to mice and rats was found to be more than 4 g/kg
independent of the administration routes (82). Therefore,
methoxyphenone is considered to be a promising herbicide with a
high level of safety for use in the environment.

2. Antiviral antibiotics

One of the most serious problems on plant disease control is
the virulence of virus diseases. Trials to develop antiviral
antibiotics have been enthusiastically conducted by many workers.
Consequently, many antibiotics have been revealed to be effective
on inhibiting the multiplication of several plant viruses by *in
vitro* test and pot test. They are blasticidin S, laurusin,
bihoromycin, miharamycin, citrinin and aabomycin A etc. However,

there is no antibiotic   used practically for controlling any plant virus diseases.

Aabomycin A.   Aabomycin A was isolated from culture broth of *Streptomyces hygroscopicus* var. *aabomyceticus* by Aizawa *et al.* (83).   By Yamaguchi *et al.* (84) with leaf disc dipping method, aabomycin A showed about 80 % inhibition on TMV multiplication in tobacco tissues.   Aabomycin A is not only effective to inhibit the disease development of TMV, but also effective to inhibit that of CMV and AMV etc., with pot test.

Future prospects
One of the greatest needs in the present world is production of food for billions of people.   At present, such production requires the use of pesticides, but in turn, this use brings about the possibility of environmental pollution.   Environmental hazards caused by conventional agricultural chemicals are classified into two categories ; a. non-selective toxicity (parathion) and b. concentration and accumulation of toxic compounds in the environment (DDT and BHC).   Pollution free pesticides, therefore, should have selective toxicity to target organisms and be sensitive for photolysis and degradation by soil microorganisms.   From these viewpoints, antibiotics may be presumed to be useful biodegradable pesticides.   As is true for every scientific technique, the use of agricultural antibiotics also has its advantages and limitations.

The advantages.

1) Selective toxicity to target organisms :   Since most antibiotics have selective toxicity to target organisms and low toxicity to mammals as shown in Table III, they can be safely used without harming man, livestock, fish and crops.   Mode of action of agricultural antibiotics are summarized in Table IV.

Table III.   Toxicity of antibiotics to animals

Antibiotic	Animal	Acute oral toxicity (LD_{50} mg/kg)
Blasticidin S	Rat	53.3
Kasugamycin	Mouse	20,900
Polyoxins	Mouse	15,000
Validamycin	Mouse	10,000
Tetranactin	Mouse	15,000

Table IV. Mode of action of antibiotic

Antibiotic	Primary action site
Polyoxins	Chitin synthesis of cell wall
Tetranactin	Cation leakage from mitochondria
Validamycin	Biosynthesis of inositol
Blasticidin S	
Kasugamycin	
Cycloheximide	Protein synthesis
Streptomycin	
Cellocidin	DNA synthesis
Griseofulvin	

   2) Easy degradation by soil microorganisms : Antibiotics
produced by microorganisms would be rapidly degraded by soil
microorganisms. After application to the crop, antibiotics might
be rapidly broken down in the environment, so that there may be
no danger of environmental pollution and food contamination.

   3) Small amount of compound used in a unit area : Since
agricultural antibiotics are sprayed at very low concentration as
shown in Table V, the amount of compounds sprayed in a unit area
is far less (1/10 - 1/100) than that of other conventional
pesticidal chemicals. Also antibiotics would be rapidly degraded
by soil microorganisms. Therefore, it is expected that the use of
agricultural antibiotics does not bring about the possibility of
environmental pollution.

Table V. The concentration of antibiotic for application

Antibiotic	Concentration (ppm)
Cycloheximide	2 - 3
Blasticidin S	10 - 20
Kasugamycin	20 - 40
Validamycin	30 - 50
Tetranactin	100 - 130
Polyoxins	100 - 200
Streptomycin	100 - 200
[Other fungicides]	
Organic phosphorus compounds	500
Organic sulfur compounds	1,000 - 1,500
Inorganic sulfur compounds	2,000
Bordeaux mixture ($CuSO_4$)	4,000

4) Manufacture of bio-active compounds with complex chemical structures :   Novel bio-active compounds with very complex chemical structures which are outside the domain of organic synthesis, can be isolated and manufactured on a commercial basis.

5) Favorable investment in equipment :   Various antibiotics can be produced by using a single set of equipment and facilities. This advantage brings about low initial cost of antibiotics.

6) Utilization of solar energy :   Antibiotics are produced by utilizing agricultural products which are obtained from biological photosynthetic conversion of solar energy.   The production of antibiotics does not much consume the stored energy such as oil and coal.

The limitations.

1) Difficulty for analysis in micro-scale :   Antibiotics are generally mixtures of various structurally related components like polyoxins.   This complexity is a difficulty for analysis in micro-scale and safety evaluation of compounds.

2) Resistant of plant pathogens to antibiotics :   Tolerance or resistance of pathogenic microorganisms to antibiotics has occurred shortly after application of antibiotics for the control of plant diseases as shown in Table VI.   In order to reduce or avoid the emergence of tolerant fungi and bacteria in the fields, the alternate or combined application of chemicals with different mechanisms of action is recommended.

Table VI.   Resistance to antibiotic

Antibiotic	Where noted	Major organism
Blasticidin S	Laboratory	*Pyricularia oryzae*
Kasugamycin	Field and lab.	*Pyricularia oryzae*
Polyoxins	Field and lab.	*Alternaria kikuchiana*
Streptomycin	Field and lab.	*Xanthomonas oryzae*

Public health aspects.   A limited number and a relatively small quantity of medical antibiotics have been introduced in agricultural use as shown in Table I.   Most agricultural antibiotics have been used only for plant protection purposes and not used in medical treatment.   Therefore, the public's concern for the environmental problem of antibiotics must be different in the two areas where antibiotics are used.   Agricultural antibiotics do not involve primarily the health of the individual, but their use has macroenvironmental consequences.   Most human infectious diseases are caused by bacteria and viruses, while plant pathogens

are mostly classified as fungi. Accordingly, most medical antibiotics are effective against bacteria, whereas agricultural
antibiotics are generally fungicidal. Selectivity of agricultural
antibiotic action can eradicate fungi responsible for the
target   plant disease without harming other microorganisms such
as bacteria parasitic on humans. Application of antibiotics for
the control of plant pests is never concerned in the development
of resistant microorganisms to medical antibiotics.   Some
antibiotics can be synthesized chemically. In this respect there
is no difference between antibiotics and synthetic chemicals. The
problem is whether an antibiotic is used in agricultural or in
medical use. It makes no difference whether it is produced by
microorganisms or synthesized chemically.

       In this article the present status of agricultural anti-
biotics has been described. Their development in Japan has
brought about successful discoveries of blasticidin S, kasugamycin,
polyoxins and validamycin. Recently, studies on agricultural
antibiotics have not been limited only to controlling plant
pathogenic microorganisms, but extended wider and more actively
over the various subjects such as utilization as antiviral agents,
insecticides, herbicides and plant regulators. It is expected
that many potential antibiotics will be developed and applied in
agriculture in the near future.

Literature cited
   (1) Dekker, J. "Fungicides" Vol. II, 579-635. Academic Press,
       New York (1969)
   (2) Dekker, J. (1971), *World Rev. Pest. Control* 10, 9-23.
   (3) Thirumalachar, M. J. (1968), *Adv. Appl. Microbiol.* 10,
       313-337.
   (4) Woodbine, M. (ed.), "Antibiotics in Agriculture",
       Butterworths, London (1962).
   (5) Zaumeyer, W. J. "First International Conference on
       Antibiotics in Agriculture" (National Academy of Sciences-
       National Research Council pub. 397), pp. 171-196.
       Washington (1956).
   (6) Woodcock, D. "Systemic Fungicides", pp. 42-54, Longman,
       London (1972).
   (7) Takeuchi, S., Hirayama, K., Ueda, K., Sakai, H., and
       Yonehara, H. (1958), *J. Antibiot.*, 11A, 1-5.
   (8) Misato, T., Ishii, I., Asakawa, M., Okimoto, Y., and
       Fukunaga, K. (1959), *Ann. Phytopath. Soc. Japan* 24, 302-306.
   (9) Asakawa, M., Misato, T., and Fukunaga, K. (1963), *Pesticide
       and Technique* 8, 24-30.
  (10) Ōtake, N., Takeuchi, S., Endō, T., and Yonehara, H. (1966),
       Agr. Biol. Chem. 30, 132-141.
  (11) Yonehara, H., and Ōtake, N. (1966), *Tetrahedron Letters*,
       pp. 3785-3791.

(12) Seto, H., Yamaguchi, I., Ōtake, N., and Yonehara, H. (1966), *Tetrahedron Letters*, pp. 3793-3799.

(13) Seto, H., Yamaguchi, I., Ōtake, N., and Yonehara, H. (1968), *Agr. Biol. Chem.* 32, 1292-1298.

(14) Huang, K. T., Misato, T., and Asuyama, H. (1964), *J. Antibiot.* 17A, 65-74.

(15) Misato, T., Ishii, I., Asakawa, M., Okimoto, Y., and Fukunaga, K. (1961), *Ann. Phytopath. Soc. Japan* 26, 19-24.

(16) Misato, T., Okimoto, Y., Ishii, I., Asakawa, M., and Fukunaga, K. (1961), *Ann. Phytopath. Soc. Japan* 26, 25-30.

(17) Coutsogeogopoulos, C. (1969), *Fed. Proc.* 28, 844.

(18) Yukioka, M., Hatayama, T., and Morisawa, S. (1975), *Biochim. Biophys. Acta* 390, 192-208.

(19) Hirai, T., and Shimomura, T. (1965), *Phytopathology* 55, 391-395.

(20) Tanaka, N., Sakagami, Y., Yamaki, H., and Umezawa, H. (1961), *J. Antibiot.* 14A, 123-126.

(21) Sugimoto, T. (1972), *Nihon Noson Igakukai Zasshi* 21, 316-317.

(22) Yamaguchi, I., Takagi, K., and Misato, T. (1972), *Agr. Biol. Chem.* 36. 1719-1727.

(23) Umezawa, H., Okami, Y., Hashimoto, T., Suhara, Y., Hamada, M., and Takeuchi, T. (1965), *J. Antibiot.* 18, 101-108.

(24) Suhara, Y., Maeda, K., and Umezawa, H. (1966), *Tetrahedron Letters*, pp. 1239-1244.

(25) Suhara, Y., Sasaki, F., Maeda, K., Umezawa, H., and Ohno, M., (1968), *J. Am. Chem. Soc.* 90, 6559-6560.

(26) Ikekawa, T., Umezawa, H., and Iitaka, Y. (1966), *J. Antibiot.* 19, 49-50.

(27) Nakajima, M., Shibata, H., Kitahara, K., Takahashi, S., and Hasegawa, A. (1968), *Tetrahedron Letters*, pp. 2271-2274.

(28) Kitahara, K., Takahashi, S., Shibata, H., Kurihara, N., and Nakajima, M. (1969), *Agr. Biol. Chem.* 33, 748-754.

(29) Ishiyama, T., Hara, I., Matsuoka, M., Saito, K., Shimada, S., Izawa, R., Hashimoto, T., Hamada, M., Okami, Y., Takeuchi, T., and Umezawa, H. (1965), *J. Antibiot.* 18, 115-119.

(30) Tanaka, N., Yamaguchi, H., and Umezawa, H. (1966), *J. Biochem.* 60, 429-434.

(31) Miura, H., Ito, H., and Takahashi, S. (1975), *Ann. Phytopath. Soc. Japan* 41, 415-417.

(32) Suzuki, S., Isono, K., Nagatsu, J., Mizutani, T., Kawashima, Y., and Mizuno, T. (1965). *J. Antibiot.* 18A, 131.

(33) Isono, K., Nagatsu, J., Kawashima, Y., and Suzuki, S. (1965), *Agr. Biol. Chem.* 29, 848-854.

(34) Isono, K., and Suzuki, S. (1968), *Tetrahedron Letters*, pp. 1133-1137.

(35) Sasaki, S., Ota, N., Eguchi, J., Furukawa, Y., Akashiba, T., Tsuchiyama, T., and Suzuki, S. (1968). *Ann. Phytopath. Soc. Japan* 34, 272-279.

(36) Endo, A., and Misato, T. (1969), *Biochem. Biophys. Res. Commun.* 37, 718-722.

(37) Ohta, N., Kakiki, K., and Misato, T. (1970), *Agr. Biol. Chem.*
     34, 1224–1234.
(38) Hori, M., Kakiki, K., and Misato, T. (1974), *Agr. Biol. Chem.*
     38, 691–698.
(39) Isono, K., Asahi, K., and Suzuki, S. (1969), *J. Am. Chem.*
     Soc. 91, 7490–7505.
(40) Isono, K., and Suzuki, S. (1968), *Tetrahedron Letters*,
     pp. 203–208.
(41) Asahi, K., Sakurai, T., Isono, K., and Suzuki, S. (1968).
     Agr. Biol. Chem. 32, 1046–1047.
(42) Kuzuhara, H., Ohrui, H., and Emoto, S. (1973), *Tetrahedron*
     Letters, pp. 5055–5058.
(43) Eguchi, J., Sasaki, S., Ota, N., Akashiba, T., Tsuchiyama, T.,
     and Suzuki, S. (1968), *Ann. Phytopath. Soc. Japan* 34,
     280–288.
(44) Sasaki, S., Ohta, N., Yamaguchi, I., Kuroda, S., and
     Misato, T. (1968), *J. Agr. Chem. Soc. Japan* 42, 633–638.
(45) Suzuki, S., Isono, K., Nagatsu, J., Kawashima, Y., Yamagata,
     K., Sakai, K., and Hashimoto, K. (1966), *Agr. Biol. Chem.*
     30, 817–819.
(46) Isono, K., Nagatsu, J., Kobinata, K., Sakai, K., and Suzuki,
     S. (1967), *Agr. Biol. Chem.* 31, 190–199.
(47) Nishimura, M., Kohmoto, K., and Udagawa, H. (1973), *Rept.*
     Tottori Mycol. Inst. (Japan) 10, 677–686.
(48) Hori, M., Eguchi, J., Kakiki, K., and Misato, T. (1974), *J.*
     Antibiot. 27, 260–266.
(49) Mitani, M., and Inoue, Y. (1968), *J. Antibiot.* 21, 492–496.
(50) Iwasa, T., Yamamoto, H., and Shibata, M. (1970), *J. Antibiot.*
     23, 595–602.
(51) Iwasa, T., Higashide, E., Yamamoto, H., and Shibata, M.
     (1971), *J. Antibiot.* 24, 107–113.
(52) Iwasa, T., Kameda, Y., Asai, M., Horii, S., and Mizuno, K.
     (1971), *J. Antibiot.* 24, 119–123.
(53) Horii, S., and Kameda, Y. (1972), *J. Chem. Soc. Comm.*,
     pp. 747–748.
(54) Hosokawa, S., Ogiwara, S., and Murata, Y. (1974), *J. Takeda*
     Res. Lab. 33, 119–131.
(55) Horii, S., Iwasa, T., and Kameda, Y. (1971), *J. Antibiot.* 24,
     57–58.
(56) Horii, S., Iwasa, Y., Mizuta, E., and Kameda, Y. (1971), *J.*
     Antibiot. 24, 59–63.
(57) Kamiya, K., Wada, Y., Horii, S., and Nishikawa, M. (1971),
     J. Antibiot. 24, 317–318.
(58) Wakae, O., and Matsuura, K. (1974), *Proc. 1st Intersectional*
     Congress of IAMS (Science Council of Japan) 3, 620–627.
(59) Iwasa, T., Higashide, E., and Shibata, M. (1971), *J.*
     Antibiot. 24, 114–118.
(60) Wakae, O., and Matsuura, K. (1973), *Abstr. 2nd International*
     Congress of Plant Pathology, No. 129 (U.S.A.)

(61) Kameda, Y., and Horii, S. (1972), *J. Chem. Soc. Comm.*, pp. 746-747.
(62) Kameda, Y., and Yamamoto, K. (1970), *Abstr. Ann. Phytopath. Soc. Japan* 36, 356.
(63) Takaoka, K., Kuwayama, T., and Aoki, A. (1971), Japanese Patent, 615332.
(64) Sakata, K., Sakurai, A., and Tamura, S. (1974), *Agr. Biol. Chem.* 38, 1883-1890.
(65) Sakata, K., Sakurai, A., and Tamura, S. (1974), *Tetrahedron Letters*, pp. 4327-4330.
(66) Sakata, K., Sakurai, A., and Tamura, S. (1975), *Agr. Biol. Chem.* 39, 885-892.
(67) Sakata, K., Sakurai, A., and Tamura, S. (1975), *Tetrahedron Letters*, pp. 3191-3194.
(68) Suzuki, S., and Okuma, K. (1958), *J. Antibiot.* 11, 84-86.
(69) Suzuki, S., Nakamura, G., Okuma, K., and Tomiyama, Y. (1958), *J. Antibiot.* 11, 81-83.
(70) Okimoto, Y., and Misato, T. (1963), *Ann. Phytopath. Soc. Japan* 28, 209-215.
(71) Okimoto, Y., and Misato, T. (1963), *Ann. Phytopath. Soc. Japan* 28, 250-257.
(72) Ando, K., Oishi, H., Hirano, S., Okutomi, T., Suzuki, K., Okazaki, H., Sawada, M., and Sagawa, T. (1971), *J. Antibiot.* 24, 347-532.
(73) Hirano, S., Sagawa, T., Takahashi, H., Tanaka, N., Oishi, H., Ando, K., and Togashi, K. (1973), *J. Econ. Entomol.* 66, 349-351.
(74) Ando, K., Murakami, Y., and Nawata, Y. (1971), *J. Antibiot.* 24, 418-422.
(75) Iitaka, Y., Sakamaki, T., and Nawata, Y. (1972), *Chemistry Letters*, pp. 1225-1230.
(76) Ando, K., Sagawa, T., Oishi, H., Suzuki, K., and Nawata, Y. (1974), *Proc. 1st Intersectional Congress of IAMS* (Science Council of Japan) 3, 630-640.
(77) Sagawa, T., Hirano, S., Takahashi, H., Tanaka, N., Oishi, H., Ando, K., and Togashi, K. (1972), *J. Econ. Entomol.* 65, 372-375.
(78) Yamada, O., Kaise, Y., Futatsuya, F., Ishida, S., Ito, K., Yamamoto, H., and Munakata, K. (1972), *Agr. Biol. Chem.* 36, 2013-2015.
(79) Nishimura, H., Katagiri, K., Sato, K., Mayama, M., and Shimaoka, N. (1956), *J. Antibiot.* 9A, 60-62.
(80) Sobin, B. A., and Tanner, F. W. Jr. (1954), *J. Am. Chem. Soc.* 76, 4053.
(81) Yamada, O., Ishida, S., Futatsuya, F., Ito, K., Yamamoto, H., and Munakata, K. (1974), *Agr. Biol. Chem.* 38, 1235-1240.
(82) Ishida, S., Yamada, O., Futatsuya, F., Ito, K., Yamamoto, H., and Munakata, K. (1974), *Proc. 1st Intersectional Congress of IAMS* (Science Council of Japan) 3, 641-650.

(83) Aizawa, S., Nakamura, Y., Shirato, S., Taguchi, R.,
     Yamaguchi, I., and Misato, T. (1969). *J. Antibiot.* 22,
     457-462.
(84) Yamaguchi, I., Taguchi, R., Huang, K. T., and Misato, T.
     (1969), *J. Antibiot.* 22, 463-466.

Insect Growth and Behavior Regulators

Introduction

JULIUS J. MENN

Stauffer Chemical Co., Biochemistry Dept., Mountain View, Calif. 94042

A part of the centennial symposium on Pesticide Chemistry in the Twentieth Century was devoted to four presentations on the state of the art of insect growth and behavior regulators including: pheromones, insect hormones and synthetic analogs, inhibitors of chitin synthesis, and anti-juvenile hormones.

As a result of heightened social and environmental awareness on the part of scientists and society as a whole, there have been intensified efforts towards discovery and implementation of more selective methods of insect control; particularly in those areas mentioned above.

Among the scientific milestones which provided major advances in this field was the discovery by C.M. Williams of "Cecropia Golden Oil", a rich source of juvenile hormone, and the advent of gas chromatography-mass spectrometry which facilitated the identification of the three endogenous juvenile hormones (I, II, and III) and many pheromones.

This portion of the symposium brings together four distinguished and eminently qualified scientists to report on the chemicals which regulate and control the external behavior and internal organization of insects: Professor Murray S. Blum of the University of Georgia, an internationally recognized authority on the chemistry and action of pheromones; Dr. John B. Siddall, Vice President of Scientific Affairs, Zoecon Corporation, who pioneered much of the chemistry of the ecdysones and insect juvenile hormones and their analogs; Dr. A. Verloop, Head of the Biochemical Research Department of Phillips Duphar, The Netherlands, a discoverer of the benzoyl phenyl ureas, a new class of chitin synthesis inhibitors; and Professor William S. Bowers, Cornell University, well known for his fundamental contributions to the identity of the endogenous

juvenile hormones, plant-derived juvenile hormone analogs, synthetic juvenile hormone analogs, and the
discoverer of the precocenes, the first compounds
known with antijuvenile hormone activity.

Although the impact of these selective approaches
to insect control and management has been relatively
small thus far, their impact in the applied field is
beginning to be realized. Furthermore, they already
serve as useful models in developing chemical control
tools for the future.

Perspectives of Hormonal Control of Insect Development

J. B. SIDDALL

Zoecon Research Laboratories, 975 California Ave., Palo Alto, Calif. 94304

In keeping with the symposium theme of pesticide chemistry in the Twentieth Century, this paper will discuss chemical perspectives of insect development which have provided both a proven method of insect control and a number of promising avenues for further research into new strategies for selective pest control. Bearing in mind that another 24 years of Twentieth Century pesticide chemistry are still untouched, it would seem appropriate at this symposium to try to look ahead into some areas of insect chemistry which remain to be explored. In so doing, it will be necessary to reexamine continually whether such areas of research on chemical pest control will lead to selectivity on the one hand for a limited number of insect families, or on the other hand for all insects as a class with safety to higher animals. Because the hormonal regulation of insect development is so fundamentally different from that of higher animals, the latter kind of selectivity has been inherent in chemical pesticides which interfere with this regulation, and it would seem wise to continue the search for class selective pesticides of this type.

Among such avenues which are relatively unexplored, are the control of molting in larvae, the mechanism of regulation of molting hormone synthesis and secretion and the pathway of molting hormone biosynthesis. The mechanism of C-20 hydroxylation of α-ecdysone and the involvement of cofactors remain unknown, even though this is a crucial step in the genesis of the active hormone β-ecdysone. What is almost certain is that larval development without ecdysones would be impossible. It is likely that the higher centers controlling the timing and the rate of synthesis of the known hormones will exert their action through small peptide neurohormones associated with complex protein

carriers, in addition to electrical control through
direct innervation. Even the direct nervous control of
endocrine glands by electrical means will probably
involve conversion of nervous impulses into chemical
transmitters which inhibit glandular activity. Although
the accumulation for isolation and structure elucidation of such neurohormones and transmitters is a formidable task, the potential for the use of such knowledge
in pest control is surely no less formidable. With the
future in mind it is this writer's hope to gain some
perspectives of insect development and its hormonal
control as a guide to future research, by reviewing a
brief selection of events which have punctuated the
spectacular development of hormonal pesticides as
insect growth regulators.

Hormone Isolation

     Between the discovery of insect juvenile hormone
(JH) some forty years ago (1) and the beginning of work
on chemical structure elucidation, over twenty years
elapsed for the major reason that there was simply no
usable source of the hormone until Williams discovered
a rich depot in the abdomens of male silkmoths (2,3) in
which about 3 micrograms was apparently stored in 10
grams of tissue. Without careful experimentation (3)
it was generally assumed that the unstable hormone was
protected in a large quantity of oily lipids present in
the abdomens. However, in 1976 it was discovered that
the accessory sex glands of the male Cecropia moths
have the exclusive ability to sequester JH (4). Quite
apart from the implications for the study of insect
sexuality, the possession of such knowledge of
accessory gland storage in 1956 would almost certainly
have revolutionized the tedious process of JH isolation
and purification which was not accomplished until 1966
(5). In connection with the future isolation of the
rare neurohormones of insects, one may usefully recall
this localization of JH. No doubt the surgical isolation of accessory sex glands would have been much
simpler as a purification scheme than the numerous
column and gas chromatographic procedures employed.
Closely related to these events in its implications was
the discovery that JH could be isolated, albeit in
minute quantities, from in vitro cultures of the endocrine organs (6). Because culture medium is relatively
free of extractable organic impurities, the higher
state of purity of hormones obtained through organ
culture by solvent extraction of the medium more than
compensates for the smaller quantities obtainable.

These simple considerations led to the discovery (7)
of JH III (Figure 1) by culture of organs from Manduca
sexta and to the elucidation of important elements of
hormone biosynthesis from propionate, acetate, and
mevalonate (8). It seems likely therefore that the

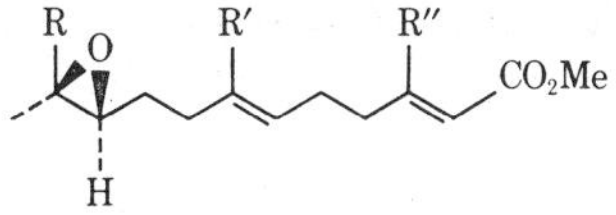

R = Me; R′ = Me; R″ = Me   (JH III)
R = Et; R′ = Me; R″ = Me   (JH II)
R = Et; R′ = Et; R″ = Me   (JH I)
R = Et; R′ = Et; R″ = Et   (JH 0)

Figure 1.

techniques of organ and tissue culture will play a
major role in the isolation of workable quantities of
insect neurohormones. The original isolation of
molting hormones from insects and crayfish was certainly no less laborious than work on JHs, and recent
advances in organ culture of prothoracic glands have
been reported (9,10). These advances not only verify
the original hypothesis that α-ecdysone is secreted by
prothoracic glands, but also provide an invaluable tool
for the future investigation of ecdysone biosynthesis.
To date, the definitive conversion of cholesterol to
α-ecdysone by these glands in vitro has not yet been
reported, and without such evidence neither the
detailed study of ecdysone biosynthesis nor its inhibition by chemicals as potential pesticides can be
expected to progress rapidly.

During the events leading to the isolation of JH I,
a notable paper of W. S. Bowers and co-workers (11)
predicted most accurately all the structural features
of the now known JHs (Figure 1) with the sole exception
of the unprecedented ethyl branches on the terpenoid
chains of JH I and II. On examining the basis of this
prediction, it seems that Bowers carefully pieced
together small items of information from the literature
and the laboratory bench even though none of these
taken alone would have sufficed to elucidate the structure of natural JH I, which was accomplished two years
later in 1967 by Röller and co-workers (5). Both of
these publications of discrete chemical structures with
hormone activity undoubtedly opened the door to the
numerous chemists whose skills lay in synthesis and
structure optimization for maximum biological activity.
From these events one may conclude that the long and
hard labor of hormone isolation was clearly worthwhile,

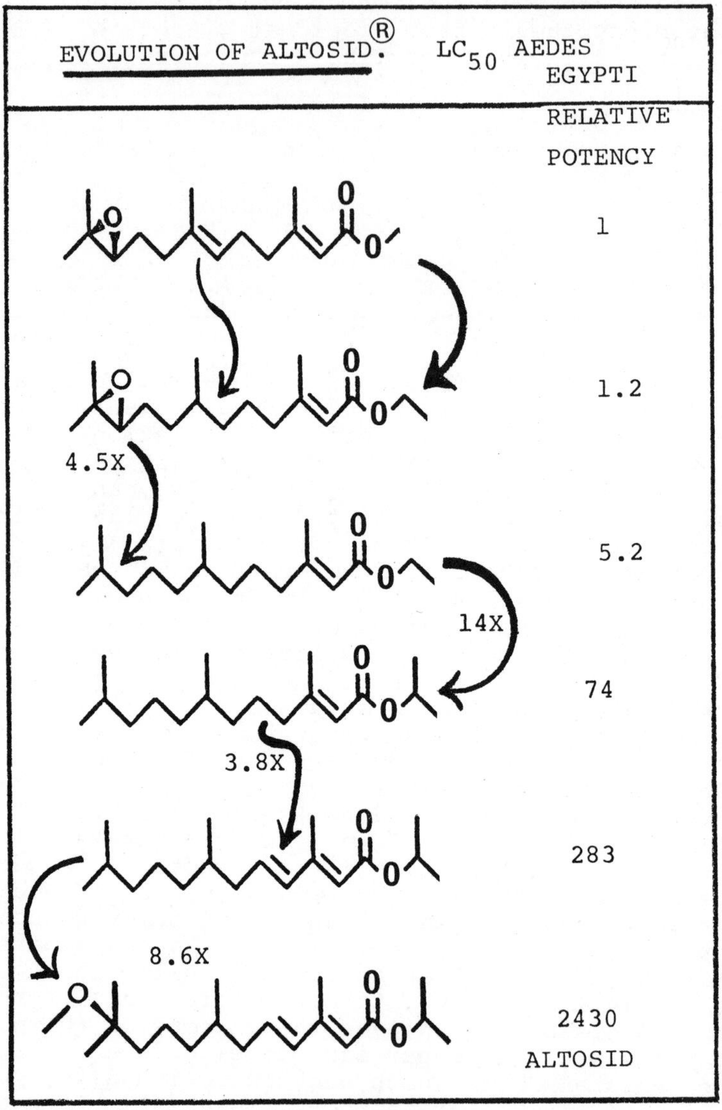

Figure 2.

and that the skillful application of new techniques of
the past decade could shorten considerably the isolation of new insect hormones and physiologically active
substances for research in pest control.

Juvenile Hormone Analogs as Insecticides

The possibility of using insect hormones as insecticides arose as a by-product of studies of insect
physiology in 1956 and the concept is attributed to
Williams (2,12). In chemical terms the discovery of JH
activity in farnesol and farnesal from feces of meal
worms by the late P. Schmialek, could be regarded as
the beginning of JH analog chemistry (13). Although it
soon became clear that farnesol was not identical with
natural JH, the important fact of its possession of
demonstrable JH activity probably formed the basis for
Bowers and co-workers' (11) elaboration of (E,E)-10,11-
epoxymethylfarnesoate. From this latter compound there
has emerged a large class of potent analogs, mostly
esters, which are based on the 15 carbon skeleton of
farnesane, and these have been reviewed in detail by
Staal (14). Since this class of compound contains the
only two chemicals which have so far received government
approval for use as insect growth regulators (Altosid
or methoprene, Figure 2, and kinoprene, Figure 3), their
discovery will be examined in more detail. The hypothetical evolution of Altosid from epoxymethylfarnesoate

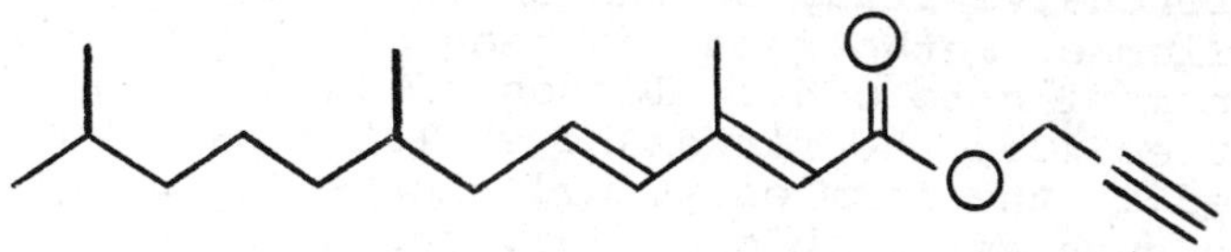

Figure 3.

is illustrated schematically in Figure 2, where curved
arrows indicate molecular structural changes and the
nearby notations such as 4.5X and 14X denote the
increases in biological potency associated with each
change. By late 1971 these changes had been reported
(15) as leading to an increase in relative potency of
1900 fold compared with JH III (Figure 2, top), in
laboratory mosquito bioassay. More recent assay data
indicate an increase of 2,430 times, resulting in laboratory activity sufficient to prevent emergence of adult

mosquitoes with 0.1 parts per billion in water. Of the
six molecular changes in Figure 2 perhaps the most
important are replacement of the 10,11 epoxide by a
tertiary methoxyl group and the introduction of a conjugated dienoic ester system, both of which contribute
markedly to increased stability in the field. Clearly,
several hundred changes were explored during this
process of structure optimization and several of these
have been reported in detail (14,16). The chemical and
biological properties of the geometrical isomers of a
related ethyl ester have been reported (17) and a
general rule for this class is that the 2E,4E isomer
(all trans) is the most biologically active of the four
possible. Several approaches to their synthesis have
been explored (16,17,18) but the method of choice is a
stereoselective synthesis (19) involving the condensation of dialkyl 3-methylglutaconates with 7-methoxy-
citronellal, in turn manufactured from the pinenes
present in oil of turpentine.

At this point the history of the concept of hormonal control of insects should be recalled, since the
major reasons for the selection of JH as a rational
lead for pesticide design were the beliefs that JH
occurred only in insects and not in other animals. The
implication was that JH would therefore be selectively
active in insects with no significant effects on other
forms of life. In the cases of JH analogs of the
farnesane skeleton, extensive studies of comparative
toxicology have largely verified these beliefs. Toxicological results have been reviewed in detail (20) and
a comprehensive study of the environmental fate and
metabolism of methoprene has been completed (21).

In moving to other classes of JH analogs, major
departures from the farnesane skeleton have been
reported in the form of phenyl ethers (22,23,24), cyclo-
hexenes such as juvabione (25), and small peptides (26)
as an extreme case of completely selective action on
one family of bugs. The latter compounds are most
remarkable for the pronounced differential activity of
their optical enantiomers, in which one antipode is
several thousand times more active biologically than
the other (27). In connection with the peptides, it
should be noted that there is no formal proof that
these compounds exert their action as true mimics of
juvenile hormones at the target tissue level. One may
well ask whether these peptides act directly on the
corpora allata glands as allatotropins.

Biosynthesis of Juvenile Hormones

Studies of the biosynthesis of the unique ethyl
branched JH are important not merely for the sake of
gaining knowledge, but for the major reason that a
detailed knowledge of the pathway should assist in the
design of irreversible inhibitors as new insect control
agents. Despite the major difficulties of work with
nanogram quantities of materials produced by organs of
fluctuating synthetic capacity, considerable progress
has been made since the introduction of organ culture
techniques as a tool. In 1970 this author wrote that
"advances in organ culture technique may later simplify
such work and presently provide an avenue for fruitful
research" (28). By 1973 the use of in vitro cultures
led to the elucidation by Schooley and co-workers (8) of
the role of propionate as a precursor of the ethyl
branches, and current work in several laboratories is
divided between whole organ culture systems and
homogenate systems summarized most recently in a comprehensive book entitled "The Juvenile Hormones" (29).
At the present time the candidacy of homomevalonic acid
as a precursor of JH I and JH II is still attractive
even though this compound has never been isolated from
any living system.
        In looking ahead to future methods of insect con-
trol based on biosynthetic inhibition, it would seem
that a few years of hard work will be necessary to
elucidate the individual steps of the pathways, as a
basis for synthesis of substrate analog inhibitors.
These inhibitors would be classified as anti-juvenile
hormones and could be expected to show selective action
on insects as a class. Such analogs are by no means
just around the corner since at least two important
properties that they should possess may be difficult to
build into small organic molecules suitable for pest
control. These properties are the ability to withstand
general metabolic inactivation while retaining the
ability to inhibit irreversibly the target enzymes of
the corpus allatum and the property to accumulate selectively in corpora allata, a physically small target, so
as to offset dilution in the general body cavity.

Anti-juvenile Hormones

        Despite the testing of several thousand JH analogs
in many laboratories between 1961 and 1975, no confirmed report of JH antagonism appeared. Part of the
reason for this may well have been the use of inappro-
priate bioassays, such as the classical Tenebrio test or

Galleria wax wound assay; however, several laboratories
maintained lengthier bioassays using early larval
instars in which JH-antagonistic activity would most
likely be detected. The expected symptoms of anti-JH
activity in a test chemical would be similar to those
caused by surgical removal (allatectomy) of the corpora
allata glands, which leads to premature metamorphosis of
early stage larvae into pupae. Although the expression
of premature metamorphosis at the time of a molt may lag
behind allatectomy by several days or by an intervening
larval instar, the surgery usually shortens the feeding
stages of the larvae of moths and beetles, which are
the damaging stages of the major pests of crops.
    The search for defined chemical structures which
will duplicate the effects of surgical allatectomy will
most likely continue and intensify in the next few
years, but in order for the search to be of any practical value it must focus upon the holometabolous insects
which are the major pests of agriculture and the major
insect vectors of disease. From the practical view-
point, the recent discovery by W. S. Bowers (30) that
the bedding plant Ageratum houstonianum contains two
chemicals which possess anti-JH activity on milkweed
bugs but not on larvae of moths or beetles, is both
intriguing and disappointing. Both chemicals showed a
very narrow spectrum of activity on larvae, and the
more potent named precocene-2 (Figure 4) produced
effects which could be counteracted by JH III (31).

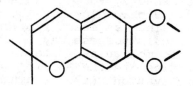

Figure 4.   Precocene 2

Consequently, it will be important for future research
to examine at least two aspects of this work; to elucidate the mechanism of action of precocenes on larvae of
bugs, and to find whether the reported sterilization of
adult female insects and the reported induc tion of
diapause in Colorado potato beetles (31) involve a
similar mechanism of action.

In contrast with the present limited range of
applications for insect growth regulators with JH
activity, Bowers states that "a hormone antagonist or
anti-hormone would be a more efficacious insecticide"
(31). This statement is based on the idea that JH is
necessary throughout most stages of insect life, and
the expectation that an anti-JH which tends to reduce
the insect's JH level would be able to act on the
insect throughout most stages of its life with the
result of disruption of development. These oversimplified ideas would lead to the bright prospect of an
anti-JH insecticide which could be used to control most
larval stages of insects. However, these ideas over-
look two vitally important factors. The developmental
stage which will emerge at the molt from a given larval
instar is decided only during a brief critical period
in the early part of that instar, and the decision or
determination for what will emerge as the next stage
depends on whether the biologically effective titer of
JH is above or below a critical level during the brief
critical period. Thus for normal development involving
five larval instars there would be five critical
periods, four of which could be influenced by chemical
reduction of JH titer to disrupt development. It is not
yet understood why three JHs are present during certain
stages of larval development, nor is it known whether
the ratios of the hormones are important in the determination of the next molt. The very presence of three
hormones having different morphogenetic potencies
suggests a buffer system which stabilizes the biologically effective level of JH. The effective level of JH
may prove to be only the portion which is bound to
hypothetical target tissue receptors and not the
portions bound to carrier protein or in free circula-
tion, though each level will influence the others and
all will contribute to whole body titers measured by
recently available techniques (32,33,34).

    There emerges a very complex picture of three hor-
mones synthesized and secreted at variable rates, competing for carrier binding proteins, presumed receptor
proteins, epoxide hydratase and carboxyl esterase
enzymes (35,36). It is possible experimentally to
measure the timing of critical periods for larval determination and to measure total levels of JH at these
critical periods although both measurements involve
extreme difficulty. Approaches to this were described
recently by G.B. Staal (37) using third instar larvae
of the tobacco hornworm moth, Manduca sexta, which were
allatectomized and raised on JH impregnated diets as
an experimentally reproducible method of JH therapy.

One striking result of Staal's work was the very low
morphogenetic potency of JH III relative to JH I or II,
measured as the ability to maintain normal larval-larval
molting in the allatectomized insects.

Since the effects of precocene-2 can be abolished
by addition of JH III (31), it may turn out that the
precocenes are selective antagonists for JH III but not
for the more potent JH I and II. If so, the narrow
spectrum of activity of precocene-2 may be further
limited to those insects which lack the ability to biosynthesize JH I or JH II. The presence of JH I has
been reported in larval cockroaches which are very
primitive insects (38). Work in this laboratory to be
reported in detail elsewhere (39) failed to detect any
activity whatsoever of precocene-2 on nymphs of the
cockroach, Blattella germanica, or Schistocerca vaga,
or larvae of Aedes aegypti mosquitoes, or of the bug
Pyrrhocoris apterus which is most surprising in view of
its closer relationship to the milkweed bug. Similarly
no effects on larval development or on egg maturation
in Manduca sexta could be found. However, precocene-2
was reported (31) to induce diapause behavior in adult
Colorado potato beetles which were independently found
(40) to contain JH III as the only hormone present (280
picogram/animal). Adult females of Manduca sexta however contain JH II (34,40) and traces of JH I (34) and
are insensitive to the action of precocene-2. Although
corpora allata of the grasshopper Schistocerca vaga
were found (41) to synthesize only JH III in vitro, the
hormones present in larvae (which are insensitive to
precocene-2) have not been investigated. The analytical
measurement of which hormones occur at what levels in
larvae of various families of insects assumes added
importance even though it remains to be seen whether
precocenes act by changing the circulating titer of JHs.

The negative implications for pest control by precocenes themselves are clear, but it remains to be seen
whether the expansion of their spectrum of activity is
limited merely by the chemical structural features of
precocenes or, more problematically, by the hormonal
mechanisms which control insect development. In either
case the JH antagonist approach to the control of larval
insect pests presents a major challenge to chemical and
physiological research.

Literature Cited

1.   Wigglesworth, V.B., Quart. J. Microscop. Sci.
     (1934), 77, 191.

2. Williams, C.M., Nature (1956), 178, 212.
3. Williams, C.M., Biol. Bull. (1963), 124, 355.
4. Shirk, P.D., Dahm, K.H., and Röller, H., Z. Natur-
    forsch. C. (1976), 31, 199.
5. Röller, H., Dahm, K.H., Sweeley, C.C., and Trost,
    B.M., Angew. Chem. (1967), 79, 190. Angew. Chem.
    Int. Ed. (1967), 6, 179.
6. Röller, H., and Dahm, K.H., Naturwissenschaften
    (1970), 57, 454.
7. Judy, K.J., Schooley, D.A., Hall, M.S., Bergot,
    B.J., and Siddall, J.B., Proc. Nat. Acad. Sci. USA
    (1973), 70, 1509.
8. Schooley, D.A., Judy, K.J., Bergot, B.J., Hall,
    M.S., and Siddall, J.B., Proc. Nat. Acad. Sci. USA
    (1973), 70, 2921.
9. King, D.S., Bollenbacher, W.E., Borst, D.W.,
    Vedeckis, W.V., O'Connor, J.D., Ittycheriah, P.I.,
    and Gilbert, L.I., Proc. Nat. Acad. Sci. USA
    (1974), 71, 793.
10. Chino, H., Sakurai, S., Ohtaki, T., Ikekawa, N.,
    Miyazaki, H., Ishibashi, M., and Abuki, H., Science
    (1974), 183, 529.
11. Bowers, W.S., Thompson, M.J., and Eubel, E.C., Life
    Sci. (1965), 4, 2323.
12. Williams, C.M., Scientific American (1967), 217 (1),
    13.
13. Schmialek, P., Z. Naturforsch. B. (1961), 16, 461.
14. Staal, G.B., Annu. Rev. Entomol. (1975), 20, 417-
    460.
15. Chem. Eng. News. (1971), 49 (49), 33.
16. Henrick, C.A., Staal, G.B., and Siddall, J.B., J.
    Agr. Food Chem. (1973), 21, 354.
17. Henrick, C.A., Willy, W.E., Garcia, B.A., and
    Staal, G.B., J. Agr. Food Chem. (1975), 23, 396.
18. Henrick, C.A., Willy, W.E., McKean, D.R.,
    Baggiolini, E., and Siddall, J.B., J. Org. Chem.
    (1975), 40, 8.
19. Henrick, C.A., Willy, W.E., Baum, J.W., Baer, T.A.,
    Garcia, B.A., Mastre, T.A., and Chang, S.M., J.
    Org. Chem. (1975), 40, 1.
20. Siddall, J.B., Environ. Health Perspec. (1976) 14,
    119-126.
21. Idem., Ibid., references 20-31 therein.
22. Bowers, W.S., Science (1969), 164, 323.
23. Pallos, F.M., Menn, J.J., Letchworth, P.E.,
    Miaullis, J.B., Nature (1971), 232, 486.
24. Hangartner, W., Suchý, M., Wipf, H.K., and
    Zurflueh, R., J. Agr. Food Chem. (1976), 24, 169.
25. Bowers, W.S., Fales, H.M., Thompson, M.J., Uebel,
    E.C., Science (1966), 154, 1020.

26. Hlavacek, J., Poduska, K., Sorm, F., and Slama, K.,
    Collect. Czech. Chem. Commun. (1976), 41, 1257 and
    references therein.
27. Poduska, K., Sorm, F., and Slama, K., Z. Natur-
    forsch. B. (1971), 26, 719.
28. Siddall, J.B., in "Chemical Ecology," Ed: E.
    Sondheimer and J.B. Simeone, page 289. Acad.
    Press, New York, N.Y., 1970.
29. "The Juvenile Hormones," Ed: L.I. Gilbert; Plenum
    Press, New York, N.Y., 1976.
30. Bowers, W.S., in "The Juvenile Hormones," page 397.
    Ed: L.I. Gilbert; Plenum Press, New York, NY (1976).
31. Bowers, W.S., Science (1976), 193, 542.
32. Dunham, L.L., Schooley, D.A., and Siddall, J.B.,
    J. Chromat. Sci. (1975), 13, 334.
33. Bergot, B.J., Schooley, D.A., Chippendale, G.M.,
    and Yin, C-M., Life Sci. (1976), 18, 811.
34. Peter, M.G., Dahm, K.H., and Röller, H., Z.
    Naturforsch C. (1976), 31, 129.
35. Kramer, K.J., Dunn, P.E., Peterson, R.C., and Law,
    J.H., in "The Juvenile Hormones," page 327. Ed.:
    L.I. Gilbert; Plenum Press, New York, NY (1976).
36. Slade, M., and Zibitt, C.H., Proc. II Int. IUPAC
    Congr. Pest. Chem. (1971), 3, 45.
37. Staal, G.B., presented at the International JH
    Symposium, Lake Geneva, Wisc. USA; Nov. 10, 1975.
38. Lanzrein, B., Hashimoto, M., Parmakovich, V.,
    Nakanishi, K., Wilhelm, R., and Lüscher, M., Life
    Sci. (1975), 16, 1271.
39. Staal, G.B., Cerf, D.A., and Ludvik, G., Manuscript
    in preparation (1976).
40. Peter, M.G., Biessels, H.W.A., Seshan, K.R.,
    Röller, H., Bhaskaran, G., and Dahm, K.H. (1976),
    Abs. Papers, 172nd Amer. Chem. Soc. Mtg. Pest. Div.
    No. 040.
41. Judy, K.J., Schooley, D.A., Hall, M.S., Bergot,
    B.J., and Siddall, J.B., Life Sci. (1973), 13,
    1511.

Insect Pheromones

MURRAY S. BLUM

Department of Entomology, University of Georgia, Athens, Ga. 30602

That exocrinological chemistry is a relatively neoteric field is indicated by the fact that the first insect pheromone was identified only fifteen years ago (1). Since that time, chemical releasers of insect behavior have been characterized at a dizzying rate, and investigations of both the chemistry and functions of these compounds have become commonplace in laboratories all over the world. Pheromonally speaking, we have gone from "rags to riches," but our comprehension of the modus operandi of these compounds is far from adequate, and the utilization of pheromones in pest management has only recently shown indications of being economically feasible (2). If chemical studies of pheromones have considerably outstripped the complementary behavioral investigations, they have nevertheless made it possible to analyze many of the nuances of insect behavior in ways never before possible. This chemical-behavioral interface promises to have major implications in fields as patently diverse as stereochemistry and ecology.

As a prerequisite to adumbrating the significant chemical discoveries relating to insect pheromones, it will be necessary to exercise considerable selectivity, and, unfortunately, exclude many contributions. However, several excellent reviews treating specific aspects of this field are available (3, 4, 5, 6, 7, 8, 9), and the reader is invited to consult these for appropriate background material.

Evolution of Exocrinological Chemistry

Identification of the structure of the sex attractant of the silkworm, Bombyx mori, by Butenandt et al. (1) must be regarded as a landmark in the field of the chemistry of insect signaling compounds. Characterization of the sex pheromone, bombykol, as (E,Z)-10,12-hexadecadien-1-ol was particularly significant, since this compound bears the main structural features of most of the sex pheromones subsequently identified from female

Lepidoptera. Bombykol, representing an unsaturated normal alcohol, is typical of all but a few moth sex pheromones in being a medium-chain length compound with sites of unsaturation and a terminal polar group. Since this theme recurs so frequently in moth sex pheromones, it appears that these chemical releasers have been evolved independently in several unrelated lines of moths (10).

However, whereas the silkworm female appears to attract males with a single sex pheromone, many other insects use blends of pheromones as chemical releasers of behavior. This phenomenon is strikingly illustrated in the case of males of the bark beetle Ips paraconfusus (=Ips confusus) which utilize three monoterpene alcohols as an aggregation pheromone (11). Maximum attraction of beetles in the field was exhibited in the presence of a mixture of all three compounds, whereas single or pairs of compounds were considerably less active (12). Similarly, in laboratory bioassays, mixtures of compounds were vastly superior to single constituents as attractants (13).

Whereas these terpene alcohols were strongly synergistic for I. paraconfusus, they were inhibitory for a second Ips species which was attracted to a binary mixture but not to the normal tertiary mixture (13). Furthermore, predators of I. paraconfusus utilized the pheromonal blend as a beacon to locate the bark beetles in the trees (12). In this case the highly adaptive aggregation pheromone constituted an evolutionary boomerang. The result of this research on Ips was particularly significant, since it emphasized that pheromones could be composed of blends of compounds that acted intra- and interspecifically as either inhibitors or attractants. Ultimately I. paraconfusus served as a seminal paradigm for the conclusion that the specificity is the blend (14).

A major development in the identification of many lepidopterous sex pheromones was the use of a neurophysiological assay to detect both the polar functionality as well as the geometry and location of the double bonds in the molecule. This method, which measures the electroantennogram (EAG) response of the male antennae, takes advantage of the fact that the sex attractant chemoreceptors display maximum sensitivity to compounds that are structurally closest to the natural sex pheromone (10, 15). Even when a sex pheromone possesses two sites of unsaturation, the EAG will accurately monitor the location of only one double bond, provided that it is present in a homologue which possesses the appropriate geometry. Testimony to the value of the EAG method was provided by the identification of (E,E)-8,10-dodecadien-1-ol as the sex attractant of the codling moth Laspeyresia pomonella (16). Employing conventional chemical techniques, McDonough et al. (17) had reported that (Z,E)-7-methyl-3-propyl-2,6-decadien-1-ol was one of the major pheromones produced by females of L. pomonella, but this claim was subsequently withdrawn (18). Ultimately, employing gas chromatography-mass spectrometry,

Beroza et al. (19) identified (E,E)-8,10-dodecadien-1-ol in
extracts of female abdominal tips of the codling moth.
    The critical importance of both concentration and mixtures
of geometric isomers of sex pheromones was illuminated in an
investigation of the responses of three species of male moths to
the same sex pheromone, (Z)-11-tetradecenyl acetate (20). Attraction of males of the European corn borer, Ostrinia nubilalis,
decreased as the concentration of the acetate was increased,
whereas the opposite effect resulted with males of the oblique-
banded leafroller. On the other hand, males of the redbanded
leafroller, Argyrotaenia velutinana, responded uniformly to all
concentrations of (Z)-11-tetradecenyl acetate. Furthermore, it
was demonstrated that males of the smartweed borer, Ostrinia
obumbratalis, were attracted to a 1:1 mixture of the (E)- and
(Z)-isomers of this ester, but were unresponsive to 1:2 and 2:1
ratios of the isomers of this compound. These results clearly
emphasize the abilities of male moths to selectively respond to
sex pheromones based on either the concentration of single
pheromones or pheromonal blends containing both geometric isomers
of a compound. When viewed as a species-isolating mechanism,
the implications of a response spectrum predicated on great
olfactory sensitivity to pheromonal concentration are considerable.
    The ability of male moths to perceive mixtures of geometric
isomers with extraordinary acuity was further documented in an
investigation of the responses of males of the redbanded leafroller and two populations of the European cornborer to isomers
of 11-tetradecenyl acetate (21). Redbanded leafroller males
were essentially unresponsive to pure preparations of their
reported sex pheromone, (Z)-11-tetradecenyl acetate, but were
strongly attracted to lures containing up to 8% of the (E)-isomer.
Similarly, European cornborer males from Iowa responded
maximally when 4% of the (E)-isomer was added to the (Z)-isomer,
whereas the New York population was attracted to an isomeric
mixture containing about 4% of the (Z)-isomer. Enhanced attraction by a small proportion of the opposite geometric isomer was
also demonstrated with males of the oriental fruit moth,
Grapholitha molesta (22). Females of this species emit (Z)-8-
dodecenyl acetate as a major sex pheromone component, along with
a synergist, dodecyl alcohol (23). Addition of the (E)-isomer
of 8-dodecenyl acetate increased male catches about 25-fold;
maximum attractiveness occurred with about 8% of this isomer.
The olfactory basis for the great discriminatory abilities of
male moths vis-a-vis geometric isomers is unknown, but its
presence provides an elegant mechanism for developing a highly
specific sex pheromonal blend.
    These pheromonal developments clearly demonstrate that
insects are remarkable odor specialists, but it would be inappro-
priate to lose track of the fact that this olfactory prowess is
predicated on their ability to biosynthesize a plethora of
volatile chemical stimuli. It seems appropriate at this juncture

to examine insects as the versatile natural product chemists that have reduced communication to a pheromonal art.

Chemistry of Insect Pheromones

Although pheromones are probably ubiquitous among species in the Insecta, serious chemical investigations of these compounds have been limited to species in about only one-fourth of the orders. Pest species, particularly those in the orders Lepidoptera and Coleoptera, have been subjected to considerable pheromonal scrutiny, and our knowledge of the chemistry of sex pheromones is primarily derived from compounds isolated from moths and beetles. On the other hand, the ants and bees (Hymenoptera) have proven to be an especially rich source of chemical releasers of social behavior, and chemisociality is now being explored more and more frequently in terms of identified signal molecules.

The availability of pure pheromones has made it possible to analyze some aspects of insect behavior with far greater incisiveness than was ever previously possible (24). The fruits of the interphase between chemistry and animal behavior may be soon available for agricultural use (2).

Dictyoptera. Notwithstanding the economic importance of termites and cockroaches, relatively few pheromones have been identified in species in this order. In the case of termites, most of the chemical research has been undertaken on trail pheromones, which are utilized for a variety of critical social functions, such as emigration and recruitment to nest breaks or food finds.

Matsumura et al. (25) identified (Z,Z,E)-3,6,8-dodecatrien-1-ol in extracts of the termite Reticulitermes flavipes and reported that this compound was a powerful releaser of trail following for workers. However, this compound is also produced by the fungus Lenzites trabea which infects the wood fed upon by R. flavipes. The significance of the dodecatrienol in the biology of this termite has recently been examined in considerable detail (26).

A diterpene hydrocarbon, assigned the trivial epithet nasutene, has been reported to be the trail pheromone of Nasutitermes exitiosus (27). This compound, which contains an unusual 14-membered ring structure, has been assigned the structure of neocembrene-A (I). Neocembrene can be derived from $C_1 \rightarrow C_{14}$ cyclization of geranylgeranyl pyrophosphate.

I

Although this compound has not yet been identified in the Eucalyptus wood fed upon by N. exitiosus, it has been isolated from Indian incense cedar Commiphora mokul (28). Thus, as in the case of R. flavipes, the compound reported to be the trail pheromone of N. exitiosus may represent a plant natural product.

Cephalic alarm pheromones are secreted by soldiers of termites in the genera Drepanotermes and Amitermes (29). These compounds have been identified as limonene and terpinolene, two of several monoterpene hydrocarbons forming part of the defensive battery of these insects.

Among the cockroaches, two chemical releasers of sexual behavior have been recently characterized. Females of Blattella germanica produce two sex pheromones, both of which appear to be active by contact chemoreception. One of these compounds, 3,11-dimethyl-2-nonacosanone, produces wing raising in the male and is perceived through antennal chemoreceptors (30). The absolute configuration of this diastereomeric ketone has not been determined.

A tentative structure has been presented for one of the two sex pheromones emitted by females of the American cockroach, Periplaneta americana. This compound, previously assigned the trivial name periplanone-B (31), contains a ten-membered alicyclic ring and a germacrane-type skeleton (32). Based on detailed NMR analyses and biogenetic considerations, a germacrene derivative containing a non-conjugated ketone and two epoxide groups is postulated (II). Significantly, germacrene-D has been previously demonstrated to possess considerable activity as a sex pheromone for males of P. americana (33). Proof of

II

structure, based on unambiguous synthesis, will be awaited with great interest by the scientific community, especially since this compound has constituted a real will-of-the-wisp among insect sex pheromones.

Orthoptera. The phase transformation of the locust Locusta migratoria from a solitary to a gregarious (migratory) form is pheromonally triggered during aggregations of these insects. One of the compounds responsible for inducing morphometric, melanic, and behavioral changes is 2-methoxy-5-ethylphenol, a guaiacol derivative which has been termed locustol (34). This compound may be produced in the crops of grasshopper larvae from lignin-derived guaiacol and subsequently excreted in

the feces. Whether locustol is synthesized de novo by the
insect or produced by the microbial flora of the crop has not
been determined.

Homoptera. Many species of aphids, whose aggregations are
especially susceptible to predation by a multitude of predators,
secrete alarm (dispersive) pheromones from the cornicles when
attacked. This pheromone, which is a minor constituent in the
cornicular secretion, has been identified as (E)-β-farnesene
in a wide range of aphid species (35, 36). Alarm behavior, which
results in aphids dispersing from the emission source either by
walking or falling from the leaf, is highly adaptive since it
reduces the probability that a predator will encounter other
aphids after the initial attack. However, ant-attended aphids
show less of a dispersive propensity than non-myrmecophilous
species, indicating that the presence of ants increases the thresh-
old for dispersion of aphid species (37). Interestingly, ants respond aggressively to (E)-β-farnesene, thus providing one of the
few examples of a pheromone being highly adaptive to both the
emitter and receiver individuals.

Recently, germacrene-A (III) has been identified as the
alarm pheromone of the sweet clover aphid Therioaphis trifolii
(38). This alarm releaser, which has often been proposed as
the progenitor of cyclic sesquiterpenes, constitutes the second
compound with a germacrane-type skeleton to be identified as an
insect pheromone.

III

Hemiptera. As in the case of aphids, hemipterous larvae
often form dense aggregations which can serve as a real bonanza
for voracious predators. However, when tactually stimulated,
larval hemipterans such as Dysdercus intermedius liberate the
contents of their dorsal abdominal glands, a response that results in the bugs dispersing (39). This alarm pheromone has been
identified as (E)-2-hexenal, a compound which is utilized de-
fensively by many species of true bugs. Adults of the bedbug
Cimex lectularius also respond dispersively to their main
defensive compounds, (E)-2-hexenal and (E)-2-octenal (40). The
simultaneous utilization of a defensive compound as an intra-
specific chemical releaser of behavior emphasizes the adaptiveness
resulting from a single exocrine compound subserving multiple
functions.
In many hemipterous families, long-distance attraction of

the sexes results from the emission of sex pheromones by the
males. In the coreid Leptoglossus phyllopus the sex pheromones
have been identified as a series of aromatic compounds that are
released from a pair of abdominal glands opening through the
7-8th abdominal intersegmental membrane (41). The main constituents present in the secretion are benzyl alcohol (IV),
guaiacol (V), and syringaldehyde (VI). In addition, vanillin
(VII), methyl p-hydroxybenzoate (VIII), and acetosyringone (IX)

IV   V   VI   VII   VIII   IX

occur as concomitants. Since males of L. phyllopus initially
colonize new habitats, this aromatic-rich secretion is probably
utilized as a long-range attractant in order to draw females to
newly-invaded areas.

Diptera. Cuticular hydrocarbons derived from females have
been reported to function as short range sex attractants for all
the species of flies that have been examined. (Z)-9-Tricosene was
identified as the sex pheromone of the house fly, Musca domestica,
whereas C_{27} and C_{29} cuticular monoolefins were only weakly active
(42). Furthermore, (Z)-9-tricosene was reported to function as
a sexual excitant as well, since the incidence of copulatory
attempts by male flies was reported to be increased in the
presence of this compound. It was subsequently suggested that
(Z)-9-heneicosene was an orientation pheromone for male flies,
and a 7:3 ratio of the C_{23} and C_{21} alkenes was optimal in terms
of orientation and mating behavior (43). However, neither
hydrocarbon increased the attraction of male flies to moving
dummies (44), and it was eventually concluded that these long-
chain (Z)-9-alkenes functioned primarily as psychedelics with
regard to visually stimulated sex attraction and aggregation (45).
A large series of (Z)-9-alkenes enhanced the releasing effect in
conjunction with the optical stimuli of sex attraction resulting
from the presence of dummy flies. By themselves, the monoolefins
showed little promise for the control of houseflies (45).
Several monoolefins were reported to function as short-range
sex attractants for male face flies, Musca autumnalis (46). In
order of decreasing activity, (Z)-14-nonacosene, (Z)-13-nonacosene,
and (Z)-13-heptacosene were demonstrated to increase the incidence of male strikes at females. These cuticular constituents
were present in both sexes, as were nonacosane and heptacosane,
two alkanes reported to attenuate the activity of the monoolefins.

However, since males contain a much higher proportion of
saturated and unsaturated hydrocarbons than females, it has
been suggested that sexual discrimination may be based on the
proportions of the alkanes and alkenes (46).

A large series of cuticular hydrocarbons extracted from the
female stable fly, Stomoxys calcitrans, is reported to function
as a sex pheromone (47). (Z)-9-Hentriacontene, (Z)-9-
tritriacontene, and methyl-branched hentria- and tritriacontenes
possessed activity as sexual releasers. In addition, mono- and
dimethyl-substituted hentria- and tritriacontanes were also
demonstrated to induce mating-strike behavior in male flies.
However, these compounds may actually function as psychedelics,
as does (Z)-9-tricosene for the housefly (45).

Coleoptera. At this juncture, beetles appear to be the
most versatile sex attractant chemists in the Insecta. The
structures of sex attractants from coleopterous species in six
families have been determined, and there are scant grounds for
generalizing about the exocrine chemistry of the species in this
large order. Lacking any thread of chemical continuity among
beetles in different taxa, it seems appropriate to examine their
natural product idiosyncracies as a family quality.

1. Elateridae. Females of the sugar beet wireworm,
Limonius californicus, utilize n-pentanoic acid (valeric) as a
long-distance sex pheromone (48). Each female synthesizes in
excess of 100 μg. of this acid, which is presumably stored in the
sex attractant gland in an inactive form. Isomeric C_5 acids
possess no demonstrable activity as sex pheromones.

2. Bruchidae. Males of the dried bean beetle,
Acanthoscelides obtectus, produce (-)-methyl (E)-2,4,5-
tetradecatrienoate, the only allenic sex pheromone identified in
insects (49). Each beetle produces 10-20 μg. of this compound,
which may be accompanied by a closely-related ester, possibly
methyl (E)-2,4,6-tetradecatrienoate. The role of this compound
as a sex pheromone has not been unambiguously established.

3. Scarabaeidae. Phenol is reported to be the sex attractant for males of the grass grub beetle, Costelytra zealandica,
a major economic pest of pastures in New Zealand (50). It was
subsequently reported that phenol was synthesized in the
colleterial glands, not by the female beetle, but rather by the
bacterial flora which was housed therein (51). However, it has
not been established whether or not phenol is also synthesized
de novo by the female scarab. If this were the case, the presence
of the bacteria in the colleterial glands would simply demonstrate
the ability of these microorganisms to resist the bacteriocidal
properties of phenol, a characteristic common to many species in

the Enterobacteriaceae.

Females of the Japanese beetle, Popilla japonica, synthesize one of the few lactonic sex pheromones that have been identified in insects (52). Tumlinson et al. (52) have recently identified the powerful sex pheromone of this insect as (R,Z)-5-(1-decenyl)dihydro-2(3H)-furanone (X). In addition to the Z-isomer, the E-isomer is also present as well as the saturated

X

homolog. The ratio of Z-, E-, and saturated isomers in the female is about 84/13/3, respectively. It was also demonstrated that mixtures of eugenol and phenylethyl propionate, which constitute a good attractant for both male and female beetles (53), synergized the attractiveness of the pheromone for both sexes. The availability of this potent sex pheromone should now make it possible to both monitor beetle infestations and control these insects through the use of a rational trapping program.

4. Curculionidae. The boll weevil, Anthonomus grandis, that great despoiler of cotton in the southern U. S., synthesizes a quaternary blend of sex pheromones that have been collectively labeled grandlure. Four compounds that interact synergistically have been identified as (+)-2-(cis-isopropenyl-1-methylcyclobutyl) ethanol (XI), (Z)-2-(3,3-dimethylcyclohexylidene)ethanol (XII), (Z)-2-(3,3-dimethylecyclohexylidene)acetaldehyde (XIII), and (E)-2-(3,3-dimethylcyclohexylidene)acetaldehyde (XIV) (54). Traps baited with a mixture of these male-derived terpenoids attract females from distances of at least ten meters.

XI   XII   XIII   XIV

5. Dermestidae. The sex pheromones of the so called carpet beetles appear to be generally identified with unsaturated normal or monomethyl-substituted alcohols, acids, or esters. Females of the black carpet beetle, Attagenus megatoma, utilize

(E,Z)-3,5-tetradecadienoic acid as a sex attractant (55). The
sexual releaser emitted by females of the furniture carpet beetle,
Anthrenus flavipes, has been identified as (Z)-3-decenoic acid
(56). The (Z)-isomer is about 20X more active than the (E)-
isomer.
      Two of the sexual releasers secreted by females of
Trogoderma inclusum have been identified as (Z)-(-)-14-methyl-
8-hexadecen-1-ol and (-)-methyl (Z)-14-methyl-8-hexadecenoate (57).
Each of these compounds is active by itself and in addition, two
unidentified pheromones are present in the sex attractant blend.
The alcohol is attractive to five other species of Trogoderma,
making it seem likely that similar compounds are utilized as sex
pheromones by many species in this genus. Indeed, Yarger et al.
(58) identified methyl (E)-14-methyl-8-hexadecenoate and (E)-14-
methyl-8-hexadecen-1-ol in extracts of females of T. glabrum.
In addition, n-hexanoic acid, methyl (Z)-7-hexadecenoate and
4-hydroxyhexanoic acid lactone (γ-caprolactone) (XV) have been
identified as part of the sex attractant blend. All of these
compounds are individually active.

XV

      6. Scolytidae. The worldwide ranges of bark beetles have
made them ideal candidates for research directed toward the isolation and identification of pheromones that can be used for
population monitoring and regulation. A decade ago, the aggregative pheromone liberated by males of Ips paraconfusus
(=confusus) was identified as a mixture of (-)-2-methyl-6-
methylene-7-octen-4-ol (ipsenol) (XVI), (+)-cis-verbenol (XVII),
and (+)-2-methyl-6-methylene-2,7-octadien-4-ol (ipsdienol) (XVIII).

XVI   XVII   XVIII

Maximum attraction of beetles required the presence of all three
compounds, although pairs of compounds were weakly active (12).
Other Ips species employ these pheromones in combination with
host volatiles as aggregative chemical tocsins (59, 60).

The frass of females of the western pine beetle Dendroctonus
brevicomis is enriched with endo- (XIX) and exo-7-ethyl-5-methyl-
6,8-dioxabicyclo[3.2.1]octane (XX), which are assigned the trivial
epithets endo- and exo-brevicomin (61). Males of D. brevicomis
synthesize 1,5-dimethyl-6,8-dioxabicyclo[3.2.1]octane (frontalin)
(XXI) in their hind guts (62), and this compound, in combination
with the brevicomins and host-derived myrcene, constitutes a
potent attractant for both sexes of D. brevicomis (63). Frontalin, also produced by females of D. frontalis (62), is reported
to function as a powerful aggregative pheromone when combined
with host monoterpenes such as α-pinene (64). D. pseudotsugae

XIX   XX   XXI

is also reported to produce frontalin (65) in combination with
3-methyl-2-cyclohexen-1-one (66) and 3-methyl-2-cyclohexen-1-ol
(67). A potpourri of functions have been assigned to these
Dendroctonus exocrine products, and the reader is referred to the
excellent review by Borden (68) for an analysis of these findings.
    A population aggregation pheromone has been identified from
males of the scolytid, Gnathotrichus sulcatus (69). A 65/35 mixture of the (S)-(+) and the (R)-(-) enantiomers of 6-methyl-5-
hepten-2-ol (sulcatol) was isolated from the boring dust and
shown to attract both females and males in a ratio of 2.65:1,
respectively.
    The terpenoid-exocrine theme emphasized by scolytid beetles
was again evident when the chemical constitution of the secondary
attractant for the smaller European elm bark beetle, Scolytus
multistriatus, was elucidated. The aggregation pheromone was
identified as a mixture of (-)-4-methyl-3-heptanol, 2,4-dimethyl-
5-ethyl-6,8-dioxabicyclo [3.2.1]octane (multistriatin) (XXII),
and (-)-α-cubebene (XXIII), a host-derived synergist (70). All
three compounds are required for the maximum attraction of
beetles. The inactive diastereomers of 4-methyl-3-heptanol and
multistriatin did not inhibit the responses of airborne beetles.

XXII   XXIII

Lepidoptera.
     Lepidopterous sex pheromones, particularly those produced by
female moths, have been primarily determined to be unsaturated
normal aliphatic alcohols, esters, or aldehydes (3, 10, 71). In
the present review, emphasis will be placed on the sex pheromones
that either are structurally distinctive or representative of
the general classes of compounds that are identified with lepidopterous species. Notwithstanding the terminological inexacti-
tude that characterizes the research on lepidopterous exocrine
products (72), these compounds will be referred to as sex
attractants or pheromones unless otherwise indicated.
     The sex attractant of the eastern spruce budworm,
Choristoneura fumiferana, is (E)-11-tetradecenal (73). A probable
precursor, (E)-11-tetradecen-1-ol, is produced in the sex
attractant gland (74), but this compound, which inhibits the
male response to the aldehyde, does not appear to be released by
the calling female. The (Z)-isomer of tetradecenal has been
identified as one of the sex pheromones of the tobacco budworm,
Heliothis virescens; it is accompanied by (Z)-11-hexadecenal
(75, 76). Similarly, the female of the striped rice borer
secretes two alkenals--(Z)-11-hexadecenal and (Z)-13-octadecenal--
as its sex pheromone blend (77).
     Females of the lymantriid, Porthetria dispar, the gypsy
moth, liberate cis-7,8-epoxy-2-methyloctadecane (disparlure) as a
sex pheromone (78). The probable precursor of the epoxide, (Z)-
2-methyl-7-octadecene, is present in the gland in large quantities, and it has been demonstrated that the olefin is epoxidized
in vivo (79). Disparlure is rapidly adsorbed on the male
antennae and quickly converted to two more polar metabolites (80),
probably as a consequence of hydrolysis of the epoxide group.
     Arctiids in the Holomelina aurantiaca complex utilize 2-
methylheptadecane as part of their sex pheromone complex (81).
This compound attracted males of at least eight species in this
complex, but in the case of at least some of these species, the
presence of ancillary pheromones was indicated. Although
homologous 2-methylalkanes were inactive as attractants, 2,15-
dimethylheptadecane was about one tenth as active as
2-methylheptadecane.
     The sex pheromone of the Douglas fir tussock moth, Orgyia
pseudotsugata, constitutes the only ketonic sex pheromone that
has been identified in a species of moth. This compound,
(Z)-6-heneicosen-11-one, is a powerful attractant for males both
under laboratory and field conditions, as is the (E)-isomer (82).
     Although acetate esters are commonly encountered as
lepidopterous sex pheromones, the occurrence of other esters has
proven to be a very unusual phenomenon. This fact renders the
sex pheromone of the pine emperor moth, Nudaurelia cytherea,
highly distinctive, since this compound, (Z)-5-decenyl 3-
methylbutyrate (83), represents an ester containing a C_5 acid.
That other saturniid moths produce unusual sex pheromones is

demonstrated by the report that females of another silkmoth, Antheraea polyphemus, secrete a sex pheromone consisting of a 9:1 mixture of (E,Z)-6,11-hexadecadienyl acetate and (E,Z)-6,11-hexadecadienal (84). This is the only example of a sex attractant composed of both an aldehyde and ester.

It now seems evident that the specificity of sex pheromones is predicated on the utilization of relatively exact blends of compounds. For example, Hummel et al. (85) identified (Z,Z)-7,11-hexadecadienyl acetate and (Z,E)-7,11-hexadecadienyl acetate as the sex pheromones of the pink bollworm, Pectinophora gossypiella. The pheromonal mixture, gossyplure, was highly active when evaluated in the field, and finally provided a reliable tool for challenging this pernicious pest of cotton. Similarly, Tamaki et al. (86) reported that the sex pheromone of Adoxophyes fasciata was composed of two geometric isomers, (Z)-9-tetradecenyl acetate and (Z)-11-tetradecenyl acetate. The closely related summer fruit tortrix, Adoxophyes orana, also utilized the same compounds as sex pheromones, but quantitative differences in the male response to the different proportions of these acetates produced by these two species appears to maintain species isolation (87). Sensitivity of males to different ratios of these two compounds is also reported to be responsible for the sexual isolation of A. orana from Clepsis spectrana (88).

Tertiary pheromonal blends have been identified in two noctuid moths. The red bollworm, Diparopsis castanea, emits dodecyl acetate, (E)-9-dodecenyl acetate, 11-dodecenyl acetate, and (E)-9,11-dodecadienyl acetate as a sex pheromone, whereas Spodoptera littoralis utilizes a blend made up of tetradecyl acetate, (E)-9-tetradecenyl acetate, (E)-11-tetradecenyl acetate, and (Z,E)-9,11-tetradecadienyl acetate (89). For both species, the conjugated dienes are the most potent olfactory stimulants. On the other hand, the sex pheromones of both S. littoralis and S. litura were reported to consist of binary mixtures of (Z,E)-9,11-tetradecadienyl acetate and (Z,E)-9,12-tetradecadienyl acetate (90, 91). The presence of additional compounds in the sex pheromone blend is believed to be responsible for the sexual isolation of these two Spodoptera species from each other.

Both the Indian meal moth, Plodia interpunctella, and the almond moth, Cadra cautella, utilize (Z,E)-9,12-tetradecadienyl acetate as a primary sex pheromone (92, 93). In addition, (Z)-9-tetradecen-1-ol has been identified as part of the sex pheromone of C. cautella (94). Significantly, attraction of almond moth males to their females is strongly inhibited in the presence of Indian meal moth females (95). These results emphasize the probable presence of secondary components in the sex pheromone blend that may play key roles in jamming the olfactory responses of closely-related and sympatric species.

On the other hand, Tumlinson et al. (96) demonstrated that two sympatric species of moths were reproductively isolated, based on the utilization of different geometric isomers of the same compound to which the males exhibited selective olfactory responses. The female of the lesser peachtree borer, Synanthedon pictipes, secretes $(\underline{E},\underline{Z})$-3,13-octadecadienyl acetate, whereas the peachtree borer, Sanninoidae exitiosa, utilizes the $(\underline{Z},\underline{Z})$-isomer as a sex pheromone. Furthermore, whereas low concentrations of the $(\underline{E},\underline{Z})$-isomer did not interfere with the response of males of S. exitiosa, the presence of low concentrations of the $(\underline{Z},\underline{Z})$-isomer inhibited the response of S. pictipes males to their own sex pheromone.

An interesting case of geographical variation in sex attractant sensitivity was illuminated by Roelofs et al. (97). Females of the fruittree roller, Archips argyrospilus, secrete a sex pheromone containing dodecyl acetate, $(\underline{E})$- and $(\underline{Z})$-11-tetradecen-1-ol, and $(\underline{E})$- and $(\underline{Z})$-11-tetradecenyl acetate. However, males from a population in British Columbia responded to a wide range of $(\underline{E})$- and $(\underline{Z})$-11-tetradecenyl acetate ratios with dodecyl acetate acting as a synergist, whereas a New York population required a much more precise ratio of isomeric acetates in conjunction with the acetate synergist. Presumably, the New York population of A. argyrospilus has been under greater selective pressure to develop a more precise discriminatory system for the $(\underline{E})$- and $(\underline{Z})$-isomers than the British Columbia population.

Male moths and butterflies have proven to be an especially rich source of interesting natural products. The sex pheromone produced in the wing glands of the lesser waxmoth, Achroia grisella, is composed of $\underline{n}$-undecanal and $(\underline{Z})$-11-octadecenal (98), whereas that of the greater waxmoth also contains $\underline{n}$-undecanal (99) but is dominated by $\underline{n}$-nonanal (100). The scent brushes of male noctuid moths produce large amounts of aromatic compounds and terpenes which are believed to function as aphrodisiacs (101). Benzaldehyde, 2-phenylethanol, benzyl alcohol, 6-methyl-5-hepten-2-one, pinocarvone, and isobutyric acid have been identified in the secretions of different noctuid species (102), and it appears that these pheromones may possess some chemotaxonomic value.

Structural investigations on the sex pheromones of male butterflies have yielded several unique insect exocrine products. The major components in the hair pencils of the danaid Lycorea ceres ceres are cetyl acetate, $(\underline{Z})$-vaccenyl acetate, and 2,3-dihydro-7-methylpyrrolizin-1-one (XXIV) (103). The dihydro-pyrrolizinone, as well as $(\underline{E},\underline{E})$-3,7-dimethyldeca-2,6-dien-1,10-diol, have been identified from the hair pencils of the queen butterfly, Danaus gilippus (104), and the former compound possesses pheromonal activity when evaluated electrophysiologically (105) and behaviorally (106). The hair pencils of the monarch butterfly, Danaus plexippus, have yielded $(\underline{E},\underline{E})$-10-hydroxy-3,7-dimethyl-2,6-deca dienoic acid (107) and $(\underline{E},\underline{E})$-3,7-dimethyl-2,6-decadien-1,10-dioic acid (108). On the other hand, the Old World monarch, Danaus chrysippus, contains $(\underline{E})$-3,7-dimethyloct-2-en-1,8-diol as well as the pyrrolizinone (XXIV) (109). Recently, Edgar et al. (110) identified two new dihydropyrrolizines in the

hair pencils of danaid butterflies. Several species of Danaus
and Euploea yielded either 1-formyl-7-hydroxy-6,7-dihydro-5H-
pyrrolizine (XXV) alone or in combination with the dihydropyrrili-
zinone (XXIV). The hair pencils of one species, Danaus affinis
albistriga, contained in addition to the dihydropyrrolizine
(XXIV), 1-formyl-6,7-dihydro-5H-pyrrolizine (XXVI). The
diversity of alkaloids found in danaid hair pencils was further
emphasized by the identification of lycopsamine (XXVII) from
Danaus hamatas hamatus and Euploea toilus toilus (111). The scent

XXIV   XXV   XXVI   XXVII   XXVIII

brushes (coremata) of arctiid moths in the genus Utetheisa also
contain dihydropyrrolizines (XXV) and (XXVI). Like the danaids,
the males feed on plants containing pyrrolizidine alkaloids and
it seems certain that the species in both families derive their
dihydropyrrolizines from their host plants (112).

The scent scales on the wings of a male lycaenid, Lycaeides
argyrognomon, secrete a mixture of n-nonanal, hexadecyl acetate,
and a sesquiterpene alcohol, tentatively identified as torreyol
(δ-cadinol) (XXVIII) (113); the absolute configuration of the
sesquiterpene has not been determined. These male-derived
pheromones appear to play an important role in the courtship
behavior of this species.

Hymenoptera

Chemical communication reaches its apogee in the social insects. Whereas the exocrine repertoire of gregarious or solitary
insects is essentially limited to aggregative and/or sex pheromones, that of the true social insects is characterized by a
dazzling variety of signal compounds that mediate a diverse con-
course of behavioral reactions (5). The evolution of a multitude
of exocrine glands (114) in combination with an extraordinary
natural product chemistry (115) have provided the ants, bees, and
wasps with the potential for exploiting chemisociality to its
fullest. These hymenopterans have evolved a variety of idio-
syncratic behavioral reactions which are now known to be triggered
by pheromonal stimuli, and it seems probable that most, if not all,
levels of insect sociality will ultimately be determined to
possess exocrine bases.

Hymenopterous species can modulate the informational content
of the signal by simultaneously evacuating the contents of two
glands, often resulting in blends of synergistic pheromones (116).
In addition, there are cogent grounds for concluding that the

development of complex societies in the Hymenoptera resulted, in
part, from the capacity of these insects to evolve the ability to
exhibit a variety of behavioral responses to a single chemical
stimulus. Pheromonal parsimony (116), the ability of an exocrine
compound to subserve multiple functions, has made it possible for
hymenopterans to expand the dimensions of sociality far beyond
what would have been possible with a finite number of chemical
releasers of behavior. In order to examine the chemisocial panor-
ama as a function of volatile information-bearing agents, the won-
drous world of the Hymenoptera will be analyzed in terms of
specific behavioral reactions and their exocrine mediators.

     1. Alarm Pheromones. Ants utilize a wide variety of methyl
and ethyl ketones to generate alarm signals (5). These compounds,
which are present in relatively large quantities, are produced by
species in most of the major subfamilies of ants. 2-Alkanones
such as 2-heptanone, 6-methyl-5-hepten-2-one, and 4-methyl-2-
hexanone are primarily produced by dolichoderine species (117,
118, 119) as products of the capacious anal glands. Myrmicines,
on the other hand, primarily synthesize ethyl ketones, and seven of
these compounds have been identified in their secretions. In
addition to 3-octanone, 3-nonanone, and 3-decanone, the methyl-
branched ketones 4-methyl-3-hexanone, 4-methyl-3-heptanone,
6-methyl-3-octanone, and 4,6-dimethyl-4-octen-3-one have been
identified as releasers of alarm behavior (120, 121, 122).
     Citral (123), formic acid (124), and n-undecane (125) are
among a host of other compounds identified as formicid alarm pheromones. Recently, Wheeler and Blum (126) reported that alkylpyrazines were secreted by Odontomachus spp. in response to foreign
stimuli. Some species produced 2,5-dimethyl-3-isopentylpyrazine
(XXIX) whereas 2,5-dimethyl-3-pentylpyrazine (XXX) and related
compounds were produced by others. Although these compounds are
attractants that release attack behavior in Odontomachus workers,
ponerine species that form small colonies utilize one of the
alkylpyrazines to release escape behavior (127).

                XXIX   XXX

     In addition to acyclic ketones, dolichoderine ants in the
genus Azteca generate an alarm signal with 2-methylcyclopentanone
(XXXI),cis-1-acetyl-2-methylcyclopentane (XXXII), and 2-acetyl-
3-methylcyclopentene (XXXIII) (128). That some ant species
utilize aromatic compounds as alarm pheromones is demonstrated by
the identification of methyl 6-methylsalicylate (XXXIV) in the

ponerine <u>Gnamptogenys</u> <u>pleurodon</u> (<u>129</u>).

XXXI   XXXII   XXXIII   XXXIV

Among bees, citral (<u>130</u>), 2-heptanone (<u>131</u>), and isopentyl acetate (<u>132</u>) have been shown to possess among other functions, that of alarm releasers.

2. Trail Pheromones. Tumlinson <u>et al</u>. (<u>133</u>) identified methyl 4-methylpyrrole-2-carboxylate (XXXV) as the major trail pheromone of the ant, <u>Atta texana</u>. Another poison gland product, 3-butyl-5-methyloctahydroindolizine (XXXVI) has been reported to be the dominant releaser of trail following for workers of <u>Monomorium</u> <u>pharaonis</u> (<u>134</u>).In contrast to these cyclic releasers

XXXV   XXXVI

of trail following, Huwyler <u>et al</u>. (<u>135</u>) demonstrated that heptanoic, octanoic, nonanoic, decanoic, and dodecanoic acids were components of the trail pheromone of <u>Lasius fuliginosus</u>.

Stingless bees lay chemical trails with mandibular gland constituents which have been identified as normal aliphatic alcohols or monoterpene aldehydes. <u>Trigona spinipes</u> generates a trail with a mixture of 2-heptanol, 2-undecanol, and 2-tridecanol, and it has been possible to successfully lay artificial trails with these alcohols (<u>136</u>). Trail following in workers of <u>Trigona subterranea</u> is released by citral (<u>130</u>), the stereoisomers of which are also utilized as alarm pheromones and defensive compounds. Such pheromonal parsimony appears to be especially typical of eusocial bees and ants.

3. Sex Pheromones. Gary (<u>137</u>) demonstrated that (<u>E</u>)-9-oxo-2-decenoic acid, a mandibular gland product of the queen honey

bee, Apis mellifera, was a powerful attractant for airborne
drones. This compound also possesses additional functions as a
queen substance for workers in the milieu of the hive.

Species of pine sawflies in the genera Neodiprion and
Diprion secrete a sex pheromone dominated by either the acetate
or propionate esters of 3,7-dimethylpentadecan-2-ol (138).
Reproductive isolation of these sawflies appears to be partly
related to the utilization of one or the other of these
diasteriomeric esters.

4. Queen Substance. The queens of many hymenopterous
species release primer pheromones in the colonial milieu and
these compounds strongly influence the reproductive or endocrine
systems of the workers. Butler et al. (139) identified (E)-9-
oxo-2-decenoic as the compound that inhibits both ovarian
development in workers (140) and queen cell construction (141).
The queen substance of the Oriental hornet has been identified
as δ-hexadecalactone (XXXVII) (142).

XXXVII

5. Disarming Pheromones. Certain species of both bees and
ants raid colonies of other species of social insects in order
to appropriate either food or foreign workers which eventually
function as slaves. In the American tropics, the stingless bee
Lestrimelitta limao disarms colonies of other stingless bees
with citral (143), the stereoisomers of which serve to effectively
destroy the colonial cohesion of the raided species (140). Citral
also functions as an attractant, alarm releaser, and defensive
substance for workers of L. limao.

Formicine ants effectively disarm workers of species whose
nests they are raiding with alkyl acetates, which originate in
the well developed Dufour's glands of the raiders (144).

6. Territorial Pheromones. Males of many species of bumble-
bees mark selected sites with labial gland products that attract
both males and females. These territorial mating spots are
"perfumed" with a wide variety of acyclic compounds that appear
to constitute species-specific blends that may promote reproductive isolation among the species of Bombus and Psithyrus (145).
Geranylgeraniol, geranylcitronellol, geranylgeranyl acetate,
2,3-dihydrofarnesyl acetate, and (E)-farnesyl acetate are among
the distinctive sesqui- and diterpenes utilized by these bees to
transform the branches of trees into potential love nests.

Males of the carpenter bee, Xylocopa hirutissima, establish and defend territories that are located proximate to projecting trees on mountain tops (146). These territories are maintained by a mandibular gland secretion that contains, as a major constituent, the cis-lactone of 2-methyl-5-hydroxyhexanoic acid (XXXVIII) (147).

XXXVIII

7. Flight Initiation Pheromones. The mating flights of many species of carpenter ants are initiated by male mandibular gland secretions (148). These chemical stimulators of female flight appear to constitute relatively species-specific blends of compounds that are dominated by compounds such as 2,4-dimethyl-2-hexenoic acid, methyl 6-methyl salicylate (XXXIV), methyl anthranilate (XXXIX), 10-methyldodecanoic acid, and the lactone mellein (XL) (149, 150). Recently, the sex-specific blend of

XXXIX   XL

pheromones secreted by males of Camponotus clarithorax was characterized as a mixture of alcohols and esters, several of which constitute unique arthropod natural products (151). In addition to 2,6-dimethyl-5-hepten-1-ol and 2-phenylethanol, this secretion contains the octanoate and the nonanoate esters of these alcohols, as well as citronellic and geranic acids. The significance of this unusual Camponotus secretion has not been determined, although it certainly must act as a reproductive isolating agent.

8. Chemical Releasers of Digging Behavior. The mandibular gland secretions of several species of ants have been demonstrated to be releasers of digging behavior in highly stimulated workers. Crewe and Fletcher (152) reported that the alkyl sulfides pro-duced by the ant Paltothyreus tarsatus--dimethyl disulfide and dimethyl trisulfide (153)--function to release highly oriented digging behavior. This behavior is highly adaptive since ant workers buried in soil can signal their imprisonment to their sister workers and be subsequently excavated. Wilson (154)

demonstrated that the mandibular gland products of Pogonomyrmex badius released digging behavior in workers, and Blum and Warter (155) reported that 2-heptanone, the alarm pheromone of Conomyrma pyramicus, was also capable of causing workers to excavate soil particles.

The Chiral World of Insects

Many of the compounds that constitute chemical signals in the world of insects contain chiral centers, and it now seems evident that a variety of insects can discriminate these enantiomers with great olfactory precision. Insects are exposed to a multitude of enantiomeric plant natural products, but in addition, these animals synthesize a variety of pheromones with centers of chirality. Obviously, it would be highly adaptive for these arthropods to both exhibit great olfactory acuity in the presence of floral enantiomers and great sensitivity to their own optically active pheromones. It appears that this is precisely the case.

Honeybee workers can be trained to easily discriminate between enantiomeric pairs which are both congruous and incongruous odorants for human beings (156). Significantly, these insects can "memorize" the information encoded in these specific signals and thus respond rapidly to them if later encountered.

Riley et al. (157) identified S-(+)-4-methyl-3-heptanone as the alarm pheromone of Atta texana and reported that it was 100X more active as an alarm releaser than the unnatural (-)-enantiomer. Similarly, Benthuysen and Blum (158) demonstrated that workers of Pogonomyrmex badius were more sensitive to the S(+) enantiomer than to the R-(-) enantiomer of this compound, which is the primary alarm pheromone of this species.

Iwaki et al. (159) synthesized the enantiomers of the gypsy moth sex pheromone, cis-7,8-epoxy-2-methyloctadecane (disparlure), and observed that the (7R,8S)-(+)-isomer was far more active as a sex pheromone than the (7S,8R)-isomer. EAG measurements indicated that the male moths were about 1000X more sensitive to the (+)-isomer than the (-) enantiomer of disparlure. A racemic mixture exhibited the expected activity of the active enantiomer. In contrast, Tumlinson et al. (52) noted that the attractant activity of (R,Z)-5-(1-decenyl)dihydro-2(3H)-furanone, (X), the sex pheromone of the Japanese beetle, was almost completely destroyed by as little as 10% of (S,Z) enantiomer.

Some of the aggregation pheromones of scolytid beetles also appear to be synthesized with great chiral specificity. The flight response of both sexes of the western pine beetle Dendroctonus brevicomis to (1R,5S,7R)-(+)-exo-brevicomin (XX), host terpenes, and racemic frontalin (XXI) was much greater than the response when the antipode of brevicomin was substituted (160). Similarly, (1S,5R)-(-)-frontalin was a much more powerful attractant than its antipode when tested in admixture with

racemic brevicomin and monoterpenes from the pine tree. In contrast, the ambrosia beetle, Gnathotrichus sulcatus, which
utilizes a 65:35 ratio of the S-(+) and R-(-) enantiomers of
6-methyl-5-hepten-2-ol as an attractant (69), exhibits a synergistic response to enantiomeric mixtures and is only weakly
attracted to the single isomers (161).

These results clearly demonstrate that insects possess
chiral chemoreceptors which have enabled them to exploit chemical
signals with maximum acuity and sensitivity. It is probable
that the olfactory world of insects will be found to be characterized by a diversity of chiral specificities which have
maximized their responsiveness as targets for enantiomeric signal
molecules.

Pheromones as Pest Control Agents: A Brave New World

The effective utilization of pheromones for pest management
will require a detailed comprehension of the biology of the
target species. Shorey et al. (2) have provided real optimism
for anticipating that an effective program for control of the
pink bollworm will be realized in the forseeable future. This
imaginative undertaking was made possible by exhaustive studies on
the biology of the pink bollworm and the concept of control by
air-permeation with gossyplure is an outgrowth of these biological
investigations. Although there has been great impatience with
the slow progress in this field, necessary studies on the bio-
ecology of insects such as the cabbage looper, boll weevil, bark
beetles, gypsy moth, redbanded leafroller, and the European corn
borer promise to provide the background information required to
make it possible to manipulate pest populations with identified
pheromones. Insects are remarkably adaptive animals, but there
are good grounds for concluding that enlightened control programs
utilizing pheromones or their analogs will eventually succeed in
reducing selected pest populations to manageable levels. Ultimately, insect pheromones may provide man with the seeds of
destruction for his chief competitors by bringing death to
arthropods instead of sex.

Acknowledgements

I am grateful to Drs. W. S. Bowers and J. H. Tumlinson for
providing me with their unpublished data on insect pheromones.

Literature Cited

(1) Butenandt, A., Beckmann, R., Stamm, D., Hoppe-Seyler's Z.
        Physiol. Chem. (1961), 324, 84.
(2) Shorey, H. H., Gaston, L. K., Kaae, R. S., in "Pest Manage-
        ment with Insect Sex Attractants", ACS Symp. Ser., No.
        23, Beroza, M., Ed., pp. 67-74, Washington, D.C., 1976.

(3) Jacobson, M., "Insect Pheromones", Academic Press, New York, 1972.
(4) Birch, M. C., Ed., "Pheromones", American Elsevier Publ. Co., New York, 1974.
(5) Blum, M. S., Brand, J. M., Amer. Zool. (1972), 12, 553.
(6) MacConnell, J. G., Silverstein, R. M., Ang. Chemie, Int. Ed. (1973), 12, 644.
(7) Beroza, M., Ed. "Chemicals Controlling Insect Behavior", Academic Press, New York, 1970.
(8) Wood, D. L., Silverstein, R. M., Nakajima, M., Eds., "Control of Insect Behavior by Natural Products", Academic Press, New York, 1970.
(9) Tahori, A., Ed., "Chemical Releasers in Insects", Gordon and Breach, New York, 1971.
(10) Roelofs, W. L., Comeau, A., in "Chemical Releasers in Insects), Tahori, A., Ed., pp. 91-114, Gordon and Breach New York, 1971.
(11) Silverstein, R. M., Rodin, J. O., Wood, D. L., Science (1966), 154, 509.
(12) Wood, D. L., Browne, L. E., Bedard, W. D., Tilden, P. E., Silverstein, R. M., Rodin, J. O., Science (1968), 159, 1373.
(13) Wood, D. L., Stark, R. W., Silverstein, R. M., Rodin, J. O., Nature (1967), 215, 206.
(14) Blum, M. S., Bull. Ent. Soc. Am. (1974), 20, 30.
(15) Roelofs, W. L., Comeau, A., J. Insect Physiol. (1971), 17, 1969.
(16) Roelofs, W. L., Comeau, A., Hill, A., Milicevic, G., Science (1971), 174, 297.
(17) McDonough, L. M., George, D. A., Butt, B. A., Ruth, J. M., Hill, K. R., Science (1972), 177, 177.
(18) McDonough, L. M., Moffitt, H. R., Science (1974), 183, 978.
(19) Beroza, M., Bierl, B. A., Moffitt, H. R., Science (1974), 183, 89.
(20) Klun, J. A., Robinson, J. F., Ann. Ent. Soc. Am. (1972), 65, 1337.
(21) Klun, J. A., Chapman, O. L., Mattes, K. C., Wojtkowski, P. W., Beroza, M., Sonnet, P. E., Science (1973), 181, 661.
(22) Beroza, M.. Muschik, G. M., Gentry, C. R., Nature, New Biol. (1973), 244, 149.
(23) Roelofs, W. L., Cardé, R. T., Tette, J., Environ. Ent. (1973), 2, 252.
(24) Shorey, H., in "Control of Insect Behavior by Natural Products", Wood, D. L., Silverstein, R. M., Nakajima, M., Eds., pp. 249-284, Academic Press, New York, 1970.
(25) Matsumura, F., Coppel, H. C., Tai, A., Nature (1968), 219, 963.
(26) Howard, R., Matsumura, F., Coppel, H. C., J. Chem. Ecol. (1976), 2, 147.
(27) Birch, A. J., Brown, W. V., Corrie, J. E. T., Moore, B. P., J. Chem. Soc. Perkin Trans. I (1972), 1972, 2653.

(28) Patil, V. D., Nayak, V. R., Dev., S., Tetrahedron (1973),
     29, 341.
(29) Moore, B. P., J. Insect Physiol. (1968), 14, 33.
(30) Nishida, R., Fukami, H., Ishii, S., Appl. Ent. Zool. (1975),
     10, 10.
(31) Persoons, C. J., Ritter, F. J., Lichtendonk, W. J., Proc.
     Kon. Ned. Akad. v. Wetensch., Amsterdam-C (1974), 77,
     201.
(32) Persoons, C. J., Verwiel, P. E. J., Ritter, F. J., Talman, E.,
     Nooijen, P. J. F., Nooijen, W. J., Tetrahedron Lett.
     (1976), 24, 2055.
(33) Tahara, S., Yoshida, M., Muzitani, J., Kitamura, C., Taka-
     hashi, S., Agr. Biol. Chem. (1975), 39, 1517.
(34) Nolte, D. J., Eggers, S. H., May, I. R., J. Insect Physiol.
     (1973), 19, 1547.
(35) Bowers, W. S., Nault, L. R., Webb, R. E., Dutky, S. R.,
     Science (1972), 177, 1121.
(36) Wientjens, W. H. J. M., Lakwijk, A. C., van der Marel, T.,
     Experientia (1973), 29, 658.
(37) Nault, L. R., Montgomery, M. E., Bowers, W. S., Science
     (1976), 192, 1349.
(38) Nishino, C., Bowers, W. S., Nault, L. R., personal communi-
     cation (1976).
(39) Calam, D. H., Youdeowei, A., J. Insect Physiol. (1968),
     14, 1147.
(40) Levinson, H. Z., Bar Ilan, A. R., Experientia (1971), 27,
     102.
(41) Aldrich, J. R., Blum, M. S., Duffey, S. S., Fales, H. M.,
     J. Insect Physiol. (1976), in press.
(42) Carlson, D. A., Mayer, M. S., Silhacek, D. L., James, J. D.,
     Beroza, M., Bierl, B. A., Science (1971), 174, 76.
(43) Mansingh, A., Steele, R. W., Smallman, B. N., Meresz, O.,
     Mozogai, C., Can. Ent. (1972), 104, 1963.
(44) Richter, I., Naturwissen. (1974), 61, 365.
(45) Richter, I., Krain, H., Mangold, H. K., Experientia (1976),
     32, 186.
(46) Uebel, E. C., Sonnet, P. E., Miller, R. W., Beroza, M., J.
     Chem. Ecol. (1975), 1, 195.
(47) Uebel, E. C., Sonnet, P. E., Bierl, B. A., Miller, R. W.,
     J. Chem. Ecol. (1975), 1, 377.
(48) Jacobson, M., Lilly, C. E., Harding, C., Science (1968),
     159, 208.
(49) Horler, D. F., J. Chem. Soc. C (1970), 1970, 859.
(50) Henzell, R. F., Lowe, M. D., Science (1970), 168, 1005.
(51) Hoyt, C. P., Osborne, G. O., Mulcock, A. P., Nature (1971),
     230, 472.
(52) Tumlinson, J. H., Klein, M. G., Doolittle, R. E., Ladd,
     Jr., T. L., personal communication (1976).
(53) Klein, M. G., Ladd, Jr., T. L., Lawrence, K. O., Environ.
     Ent. (1972), 1, 397.

(54) Tumlinson, J. H., Hardee, D. D., Gueldner, R. C., Science
        (1969), 166, 1010.
(55) Silverstein, R. M., Rodin, J. B., Burkholder, W. E., Gorman,
        J. E., Science (1967), 157, 85.
(56) Fukui, H., Matsumura, F., Ma, M. C., Burkholder, W. E.,
        Tetrahedron Lett. (1974), 40, 3563.
(57) Rodin, J. O., Silverstein, R. M., Burkholder, W. E., Gorman,
        J. E., Science (1969), 165, 904.
(58) Yarger, R. G., Silverstein, R. M., Burkholder, W. E., J. Chem.
        Ecol. (1975), 1, 323.
(59) Vité, J. P., Renwick, J. A. A., J. Insect Physiol. (1971),
        17, 1699.
(60) Renwick, J. A. A., Vité, J. P., J. Insect Physiol. (1972),
        18, 1215.
(61) Silverstein, R. M., Brownlee, R. G., Bellas, T. E., Wood,
        D. L., Browne, L. E., Science (1968), 159, 889.
(62) Kinzer, G. W., Fentiman, Jr., A. F., Page, Jr., T. F.,
        Foltz, R. L., Vité, J. P., Pitman, G. B., Nature (1969),
        221, 477.
(63) Wood, D. L., in van Emden, H. F., Ed., "Insect Plant Rela-
        tionships", pp. 101-117, Symp. Roy. Ent. Soc. (London)
        6, 1972.
(64) Renwick, J. A. A., Vité, J. P., Nature (1969), 224, 1222.
(65) Pitman, G. B., Vité, J. P., Ann. Ent. Soc. Am. (1970),
        63, 661.
(66) Kinzer, G. W., Fentiman, Jr., A. F., Foltz, R. L., Rudinsky,
        J. A., J. Econ. Ent. (1971), 64, 970.
(67) Vité, J. P., Pitman, G. B., Fentiman, Jr., A. F., Kinzer, G.
        W., Naturwissen. (1972), 59, 469.
(68) Borden, J. H., in Birch, M. C., Ed., "Pheromones", pp. 135-
        160, American Elsevier Publ. Co., New York, 1974.
(69) Byrne, K. J., Swigar, A. A., Silverstein, R. M., Borden, J. H.,
        Stokkink, E., J. Insect Physiol. (1974), 20, 1895.
(70) Pearce, G. T., Gore, W. E., Silverstein, R. M., Peacock,
        J. W., Cuthbert, R. A., Lanier, G. N., Simeone, J. B.,
        J. Chem. Ecol. (1975), 1, 115.
(71) Roelofs, W. L., Cardé, R. T., in Birch, M. C., Ed., "Phero-
        mones", pp. 96-114, American Elsevier Publ. Co., New
        York, 1974.
(72) Kennedy, J. S., J. Aust. Ent. Soc. (1972), 11,168.
(73) Weatherston, J., Roelofs, W., Comeau, A., Sanders, C. J.,
        Can. Ent. (1971), 103, 1741.
(74) Weatherston, J., MacLean, W., Can. Ent. (1974), 106, 281.
(75) Roelofs, W. L., Hill, A. S., Cardé, R. T., Baker, T. C.,
        Life Sci. (1974), 14, 1555.
(76) Tumlinson, J. H., Hendricks, D. E., Mitchell, E. R.,
        Doolittle, R. E., Brennan, M. M., J. Chem. Ecol. (1975),
        1, 203.
(77) Nesbitt, B. F., Beevor, P. S., Hall, D. R., Lester, R.,
        Dyck, V. A., J. Insect Physiol. (1975), 21, 1883.

(78) Bierl, B. A., Beroza, M., Collier, C. W., Science (1970),
        170, 87.
(79) Kasang, G., Schneider, D., Beroza, M., Naturwissen.
        (1974), 61, 130.
(80) Kasang, G., Knauer, B., Beroza, M., Experientia (1974),
        30, 147.
(81) Roelofs, W. L., Cardé, R. T., Science (1971), 171, 684.
(82) Smith, R. G., Daterman, G. E., Daves, Jr., G. D., Science
        (1975), 188, 63.
(83) Henderson, H. E., Warren, F. L. Augustyn, O. P. H., Burger,
        B. V., Schneider, D. F., Boshoff, P. R., Spies, H. S. C.
        Geertsema, H., Chem. Comm. (1972), 1972, 686.
(84) Kochansky, J., Tette, J., Taschenberg, E. F., Cardé, R. T.,
        Kaissling, K.-E., Roelofs, W. L., J. Insect Physiol.
        (1975), 21, 1977.
(85) Hummel, H. E., Gaston, L. K., Shorey, H. H., Kaae, R. S.,
        Byrne, K. J., Silverstein, R. M., Science (1973), 181,
        873.
(86) Tamaki, Y., Noguchi, H., Yushima, T., Hirano, C., Appl.
        Ent. Zool. (1971), 6, 139.
(87) Tamaki, Y., Noguchi, H., Yushima, T., Hirano, C., Honma, K.,
        Sugawara, H., Kontyû (1971), 39, 338.
(88) Meijer, G. M., Ritter, F. J., Persoons, C. J., Minks, A. K.,
        Voerman, S., Science (1972), 175, 1469.
(89) Nesbitt, B. F., Beevor. P. S., Cole, R. A., Lester, R., Poppi,
        R. G., Nature , New Biol. (1973), 244, 208.
(90) Tamaki, Y., Yushima, T., J. Insect Physiol. (1974), 20, 1005.
(91) Tamaki, Y., Noguchi, H., Yushima, T., Appl. Ent. Zool. (1973),
        8, 200.
(92) Brady, U. E., Tumlimson, J. H., Brownlee, R. G., Silverstein,
        R. M., Science (1971), 171, 802.
(93) Kuwahara, Y., Kitamura, C., Takahashi, S., Hara, H., Ishii,
        S., Fukami, H., Science (1971), 171, 801.
(94) Brady, U. E., Life Sci. (1973), 13, 227.
(95) Ganyard, Jr., M. C., Brady, U. E., Nature (1971), 234, 415.
(96) Tumlinson, J. H., Yonce, C. E., Doolittle, R. E., Heath, R.
        R., Gentry, C. R., Mitchell, E. R., Science (1974), 185,
        614.
(97) Roelofs, W., Hill, A., Cardé, R., Tette, J., Madsen, H.,
        Vakenti, J., Environ. Ent. (1974), 3, 747.
(98) Dahm, K. H., Meyer, D., Finn, W. E., Reinhold, V., Röller, H.,
        Naturwissen. (1971), 58, 265.
(99) Röller, H., Biemann, K., Bjerke, J. S., Norgard, D. W.,
        McShan, W. H., Acta Ent. Bohem. (1968), 65, 208.
(100) Leyrer, R. L., Monroe, R. E., J. Insect Physiol. (1973),
        19, 2267.
(101) Birch, M. C., in Birch, M. C., "Pheromones", pp. 115-134,
        American Elsevier Publ. Co., New York, 1974.
(102) Aplin, R. T., Birch, M. C., Experientia (1970), 26, 1193.

(103) Meinwald, J., Meinwald, Y. C., J. Am. Chem. Soc. (1966),
        88, 1305.
(104) Meinwald, J., Meinwald, Y. C., Mazzocchi, P. H., Science
        (1969), 164, 1174.
(105) Schneider, D., Seibt, U., Science (1969), 164, 1173.
(106) Pliske, T. E., Eisner, T., Science (1969), 164, 1170.
(107) Meinwald, J., Chalmers, A. M., Pliske, T. E., Eisner, T.,
        Tetrahedron Lett. (1968), 1968, 4893.
(108) Meinwald, J., Chalmers, A. M., Pliske, T. E., Eisner, T.,
        Chem. Comm. (1969), 1969, 86.
(109) Meinwald, J., Thompson, W. R., Eisner, T., Owen, D. F.,
        Tetrahedron Lett. (1971), (38), 3485.
(110) Edgar, J. A., Culvenor, C. C. J., Robinson, G. S., J. Aust.
        Ent. Soc. (1973), 12, 144.
(111) Edgar, J. A., Culvenor, C. C. J., Nature (1974), 248, 614.
(112) Culvenor, C. C. J., Edgar, J. A., Experientia (1972), 28, 627.
(113) Lundgren, L., Bergström,. G., J. Chem. Ecol. (1975), 1, 399.
(114) Pavan, M., Ronchetti, G., Atti Soc. Ital. Sci. Nat. Mus. Stor.
        Nat. Milano (1955), 94, 379.
(115) Blum, M. S., in Beroza, M., Ed., "Chemicals Controlling
        Insect Behavior", pp. 61-94, Academic Press, New York,
        1970.
(116) Ayre, G. L., Blum, M. S., Physiol. Zool. (1971), 44, 77.
(117) Blum, M. S., Warter, S. L., Monroe, R. S., Chidester, J. C.,
        J. Insect Physiol. (1963), 9, 881.
(118) Trave, R., Pavan, M., Chim. Ind., Milano (1956), 38, 1015.
(119) Cavill, G. W. K., Hinterberger, H., Proc. 11th Int. Congr.
        Ent. (1960), 3, 53.
(120) Crewe, R. M., Blum, M. S., J. Insect Physiol. (1972), 18,
        31.
(121) McGurk, D. J., Frost, J., Eisenbraun, E. J., Vick, K.,
        Drew, W. A., Young, J., J. Insect Physiol. (1966), 12,
        1435.
(122) Fales, H. M., Blum, M. S., Crewe, R. M., Brand, J. M.,
        J. Insect Physiol. (1972), 18, 1077.
(123) Ghent, R. L., "Adaptive Refinements in the Chemical Defen-
        sive Mechanisms of Certain Formicinae", Ph.D. Thesis,
        Cornell Univ., 1961.
(124) Maschwitz, U., Z. Vergl. Physiol. (1964), 47, 596.
(125) Regnier, F. E., Wilson, E. O., J. Insect Physiol. (1968),
        14, 955.
(126) Wheeler, J. W., Blum, M. S., Science (1973), 182, 501.
(127) Duffield, R. M., Blum, M. S., Wheeler, J. W., Comp.
        Biochem. Physiol. (1976), 54B, 439.
(128) Wheeler, J. W., Evans, S. L., Blum, M. S., Torgerson, R. L.,
        Science (1975), 187, 254.
(129) Duffield, R. M., Blum., M. S., Experientia (1975), 31, 466.
(130) Blum, M. S., Crewe R. M., Kerr, W. E., Keith, L. H.,
        Garrison, A. W., Walker, M. M., J. Insect Physiol.
        (1970), 16, 1637.

(131) Shearer, D. A., Boch, R., Nature (1965), 206, 530.
(132) Boch, R., Shearer, D. A., Stone, B. C., Nature (1962), 195, 1018.
(133) Tumlinson, J. H., Silverstein, R. M., Moser, J. C., Brownlee, R. G., Ruth, J. M., Nature (1971), 234, 348.
(134) Ritter, F. J., Rotgans, I. E. M., Talman, E., Verwiel, P. E. J., Stein, F., Experientia (1973), 29, 530.
(135) Huwyler, S., Grob, K., Viscontini, M., J. Insect Physiol. (1975), 21, 299.
(136) Kerr, W. E., Blum, M. S., Fales, H. M., unpublished data.
(137) Gary, N. E., Science (1962), 136, 773.
(138) Jewett, D. M., Matsumura, F., Coppel, H. C., Science (1976), 192, 51.
(139) Butler, C. G., Callow, R. K., Johnston, N. C., Proc. Roy. Soc. Lond. B (1961), 155, 417.
(140) Butler, C. G., Fairey, E. M., J. Apic. Res. (1963), 2, 14.
(141) Butler, C. G., Gibbons, D. A., J. Insect Physiol. (1958), 2, 61.
(142) Ikan, R., Gottlieb, R., Bergmann, E. D., Ishay, J., J. Insect Physiol. (1969), 15, 1709.
(143) Blum, M. S., Ann. Ent. Soc. Am. (1966), 59, 962.
(144) Regnier, F. E., Wilson, E. O., Science (1971), 172, 267.
(145) Kullenberg, B., Bergström, G., Stallberg-Stenhagen, S., Acta Chem. Scand. (1970), 24, 1481.
(146) Velthuis, H. H. W., de Camargo, J. M. F., Z. Tierpsychol. (1975), 38, 409.
(147) Wheeler, J. W., Evans, S. L., Blum, M. S., Velthuis, H. H. W., de Camargo, J. M. F., unpublished data.
(148) Hölldobler, B., Maschwitz, U., Z. Vergl. Physiol. (1965), 50, 551.
(149) Brand, J. M., Duffield, R. M., MacConnell, J. G., Blum, M. S., Fales, H. M., Science (1973), 179, 388.
(150) Brand, J. M., Fales, H. M., Sokoloski, E. A., MacConnell, J. G., Blum, M. S., Duffield, R. M., Life Sci (1973), 13, 201.
(151) Lloyd, H. A., Blum, M. S., Duffield, R. M., Insect Biochem. (1975), 5, 489.
(152) Crewe, R. M., Fletcher, D. J. C., J. Ent. Soc. South Afr. (1974), 37, 291.
(153) Casnati, G., Ricca, A., Pavan, M., Chim. Ind., Milano (1967), 49, 57.
(154) Wilson, E. O., Psyche (1958), 65, 41.
(155) Blum, M. S., Warter, Ann. Ent. Soc. Am. (1966), 59, 774.
(156) Lensky, Y., Blum., M. S., Life Sci. (1974), 14, 2045.
(157) Riley, R. G., Silverstein, R. M., Moser, J. C., Science (1974), 183, 760.
(158) Benthuysen, J. L., Blum, M. S., J. Ga. Ent. Soc. (1974), 9, 235.
(159) Iwaki, S., Marumo, S., Saito, T., Yamada, M., Katagiri, K., J. Am. Chem. Soc. (1974), 96, 7842.

(160) Wood, D. L., Browne, L. E., Ewing, B., Lindahl, K., Bedard,
       W. D., Tilden, P. E., Mori, K., Pitman, G. B., Hughes,
       P. R., Science (1976), 192, 896.
(161) Borden, J. H., Chong, L., McLean, J. A., Slessor, K. N.,
       Mori, K., Science (1976), 192, 894.

Benzoylphenyl Ureas—A New Group of Larvicides Interfering with Chitin Deposition

A. VERLOOP

Research Laboratories, Philips-Duphar B.V., The Netherlands

C. D. FERRELL

Thompson-Hayward Chemical Co., Kansas City, Kan. 66110

The development of selective crop protection compounds based on the interference with chitin deposition in fungi and insects has been one of the aims in pesticide design for several decades. A major development in this area was the discovery of the mode of action of the fungicidal antibiotic polyoxin D by Misato et al. in the period of 1968-1970 (1). In these and subsequent studies the Japanese group clearly demonstrated that polyoxin D and related compounds interfered with chitin synthesis in several fungi by inhibiting chitin synthetase, the ultimate enzyme in the biosynthetic pathway. This is illustrated in Figure 1 where the last part of this pathway is given. Other Japanese workers (2) found that the synthetic phosphorus-containing compound kitazin also prevented the incorporation of UDP-N-acetylglucosamine in chitin. However their further studies revealed that in this case the primary action was probably not on chitin synthetase itself but that kitazin prevented the permeation of the substrate through the cyto-plasmic membrane so that it was unable to reach the target enzyme (Figure 1).

In contrast to the situation mentioned in respect to fungicidal activity, no insecticides were described in the literature prior to 1970, the activity of which was based on interference with chitin formation. Now, in the course of investigations centered on the Philips-Duphar herbicide dichlobenil the derivative Du 19111 (I) was prepared.

FUNGICIDES INTERFERING WITH CHITIN FORMATION

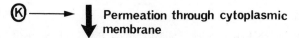

UDP - N - acetylglucosamine

Ⓚ ⟶ **Permeation through cytoplasmic membrane**

UDP - N - acetylglucosamine

Ⓟ ⟶ **Chitin synthetase**

Chitin

- -

Ⓟ   **POLYOXIN D**

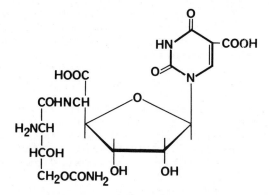

- -

Ⓚ   **KITAZIN**

$$(C_2H_5O)_2 - \underset{\underset{O}{\|}}{P} - S - CH_2 - \langle \bigcirc \rangle$$

Figure 1.

(I)

During the screening program no herbicidal or
phytotoxic effects were found, but it was observed
that larvae of several insects, including Pieris
brassicae, showed abnormal symptoms some 5 or 6 days
after ingestion of the compound. The larvae stopped
feeding and hung from the leaves, suggesting that
they were starting to moult. But instead of shedding
their exuviae they turned black and died. Closer
examination revealed that the apolysed larvae were
moving within their intact exuviae but that they
were totally or partly unable to shed these exuviae
and to wriggle out (3). Histological examination
of affected larvae revealed severe lesions in the
endocuticular tissue. Hence the newly formed cuticle
had to be a very delicate one, unable to resist the
muscular traction and the increased turgor during
moulting, so that affected larvae would not succeed
in casting their exuviae (3). Soft larval endocuticle
consists mainly of chitin and protein, integrated
as a complicated network, so that there are different
ways in which Du 19111 might affect its formation,
including an influence on chitin formation. Further
studies, to be discussed later, soon revealed that
an effect on chitin was the most probable mode of
action.

The high insecticidal activity of Du 19111
against the larval stages of several lepidopterous,
coleopterous and dipterous insects and its unique
mode of action prompted us to synthetise several
hundreds of benzoylphenyl ureas and to evaluate
their insecticidal potency in laboratory tests
and small scale field trials (4, 5, 6). These and
other studies led to the ultimate choice of
diflubenzuron (II) as the optimal derivative for
further development.

(II)

After the introduction of diflubenzuron ($\underline{7}$)
many authors published laboratory and field studies
on its insecticidal spectrum. These studies cannot
be discussed in the context of the present paper.
They have been summarized elsewhere ($\underline{8}$, $\underline{9}$, $\underline{10}$, $\underline{11}$).
However, it is relevant to mention that in several
studies, additionally to the larvicidal effect of
diflubenzuron, activities on the eggs of various
insect species have been found ($\underline{12}$, $\underline{13}$, $\underline{14}$, $\underline{15}$, $\underline{16}$, $\underline{17}$,
$\underline{18}$).These ovicidal effects can either be obtained
by topical application to the eggs or by feeding to
gravid female insects. In either case the phenomena
are similar: normal development of the primary stages
of the larvae in the eggs takes place but the
organisms are unable to leave the eggs by rupturing
them, because again the formation of the endocuticle
is disturbed. This very interesting "broadening" of
the insecticidal spectrum of diflubenzuron has been
discussed in details elsewhere ($\underline{19}$).
    A survey of the state of development of diflu-
benzuron in the USA has been given by Ferrell and
Verloop at the A.C.S. Meeting, August 1975 ($\underline{20}$):
diflubenzuron can be applied at very low rates in
agriculture (soybeans, cotton, apple orchards),in
forestry, for mosquito and fly control and probably
in stored grain. The same paper has summarised also
its low toxicity to mammals and to nontarget organisms.
In the meantime its commercial introduction has begun
in some European countries and in Egypt. Registration
in the U.S.A. and commercial introduction by the
Thompson-Hayward Chemical Company is expected at short
notice. However, it is not our intention to discuss
further these fascinating practical possibilities
of the benzoylphenyl ureas for insect control. In the
following part of this paper we would rather discuss
the scientific background of the discovery of
diflubenzuron, concentrating on the following aspects:

- its selection from the benzoylphenyl urea series,
- its fate in the environment,
- its mode of action.

Selection of diflubenzuron

After the discovery of Du 19111, many hundreds
of related benzoylphenyl ureas were synthetized
and screened with respect to larvicidal activity.
These efforts were guided by the study of quantitative structure-activity relationships (QSAR)
following the Hansch approach. In this method linear
free-energy related and other electronic, hydrophobic,
and steric substituent constants are used for a
quantitative analysis of the possible ways in which
substituents may modulate bioactivity in a congeneric
series. In the QSAR studies of benzoylphenyl ureas
the electronic Hammett σ-constants and the hydrophobic Hansch π-constants were used. To measure the
steric influences,   steric substituent constants
of a new type (B_1, B_2, B_3, B_4, and L) were applied
which had recently been introduced by us and which
give improved correlations in comparison with the
steric E_s constants used in the literature hitherto
($\underline{21}$, $\underline{22}$). The constants B_1toB_4 are measures of the
widths of substituents in four rectangular directions.
The L-constant accounts for the length of a substituent.
QSAR for the larvicidal effects of benzoylphenyl
ureas on <u>Pieris brassicae</u> and <u>Aëdes aegypti</u> larvae
were studied for the following subseries:
1. benzoylphenyl ureas substituted in the aniline
   ring,
2. benzoylphenyl ureas substituted in the benzoyl
   ring,
3. benzoylphenyl ureas substituted in the "bridge".
The present discussion will be confined mainly to
subseries 1 above and to the results with <u>Pieris
brassicae.</u> The other studies and a more complete
study of substituents of the aniline ring will be
published elsewhere ($\underline{23}$, $\underline{24}$). The most significant
equations for the larvicidal activities of
2,6-dichlorobenzoylphenyl ureas as functions of
para- and meta-substitution in the aniline ring
were:
For para-substituents
$$-\text{Log ED}_{50} = + 1.10 \ \pi + 2.37 \ \sigma - 0.40\text{L} - 0.27\text{B}_4 + 0.87$$
$$n = 31, \ r = 0.843, \ s = 0.499, \ F = 15.94$$

For para- and meta-substituents

$$-\text{Log ED}_{50} = + 0.93 \ \pi + 1.89 \ \sigma - 0.34 \text{L}^{para}$$
$$- 1.28 \text{L}^{meta} + 3.36$$
$$n = 48, \ r = 0.796, \ s = 0.564, \ F = 14.59$$

In these analyses ED_{50} is the concentration required
for a 50% reduction of the development of Pieris
brassicae L., n is the number of compounds in the
series, r is the correlation coefficient, s is the
standard deviation, and F is the F-value which
indicates the significance of the correlation found.
From the results given it can be concluded that the
inclusion of meta-substituents leads to essentially
the same regression equation as the one with only
para-substituents. Evidently all types of substituent
influences play a role. The sign of the σ-term means
that electron-withdrawing groups enhance the larvicidal activity, which was also concluded by Yu and
Kuhr in a recent paper on QSAR of the larvicidal
effect of a series of seven 2,6-dichlorobenzoylphenyl
ureas on Hylemya platura (25). These authors concluded from their analysis that hydrophobic effects
were negligible. However, it is quite evident from
the present results with the much larger series that
also hydrophobic and steric influences manifest
themselves. An analysis of all these effects leads
to the conclusion that the substituents should be
electron attracting, lipophilic, "short", and "thick",
in order to contribute maximally to the activity of
the molecule (23). In fact the experimental activities
of the p-Cl- and p-I- derivatives were found to be
about 100 times less than predicted but in repeated
tests the predictions were found to be correct.
Further studies revealed that in the first tests
very coarse particles of these two derivatives had
been used, while the testing of the other derivatives
had been performed with fine particles. This focused
attention for the first time on the great importance
of particle size in the evaluation of the benzoylphenyl ureas. The series discussed included Du 19111,
the first compound found, but the analyses indicated
that other derivatives were more active. From two
or three of the most active compounds PH 60-38 (III)
was chosen because it was found to be the one which
could be synthetized most economically on an
industrial scale. Consequently PH 60-38 was taken
for preliminary development both in the USA and in
Europe. It is interesting to note that PH 60-38 was
one of the compounds retested after the QSAR studies.

(III)

However, at this stage the results of another
area of our research of the benzoylphenyl ureas, i.e.
the environmental studies, were going to have a
vital influence on the further selection of the best
compound. A preliminary study with a radioactive
preparation of the "parent" compound Du 19111,
labeled with ^{14}C at the carbonyl group of the benzoyl
ring, revealed that this compound was very stable
in agricultural soils: a halflife of more than six
months was found. A more extensive study was
carried out with the first candidate for development,
PH 60-38, labeled (with ^{14}C) at the same position, A halflife in soils of 6-12 months was again obtained.
It was also found that 2,6-dichlorobenzamide was the
principal labeled metabolite. Now there are several
possible routes for the hydrolysis of the benzoylphenyl ureas, as is illustrated in Figure 2, where
route A would lead to ortho-substituted benzoic
acids and p-chloro-phenyl urea while routes 2 and
3 would both result in ortho-substituted benzamides
and p-Cl-aniline as the primary conversion products.
Evidently routes 2 or 3 were the preferred ones in
the case of PH 60-38 with X = Cl (28).
        The fact that route 1 was of minor importance
in the case of X = Cl was familiar to us because
or our earlier work on the fate of our herbicide
dichlobenil, or 2,6-dichlorobenzonitrile, in soils.
Dichlobenil is degraded quite easily into 2,6-
dichlorobenzamide, but this compound, BAM, is very
stable in soils with a halflife of at least two
years, as is illustrated in Figure 3 (26, 27).
We knew that a shift of at least one chlorine atom
from the ortho-position to the meta- or para-
position resulted in much more soil-degradable
benzamides but this could not be applied here,
because we had learned from other QSAR studies with
the benzoylphenyl ureas mentioned earlier that the
2,6-position of the (chlorine) substituents was
essential for a high larvicidal activity.
However, we also knew that the smaller fluorine
atoms would still permit of a high rate of hydro -

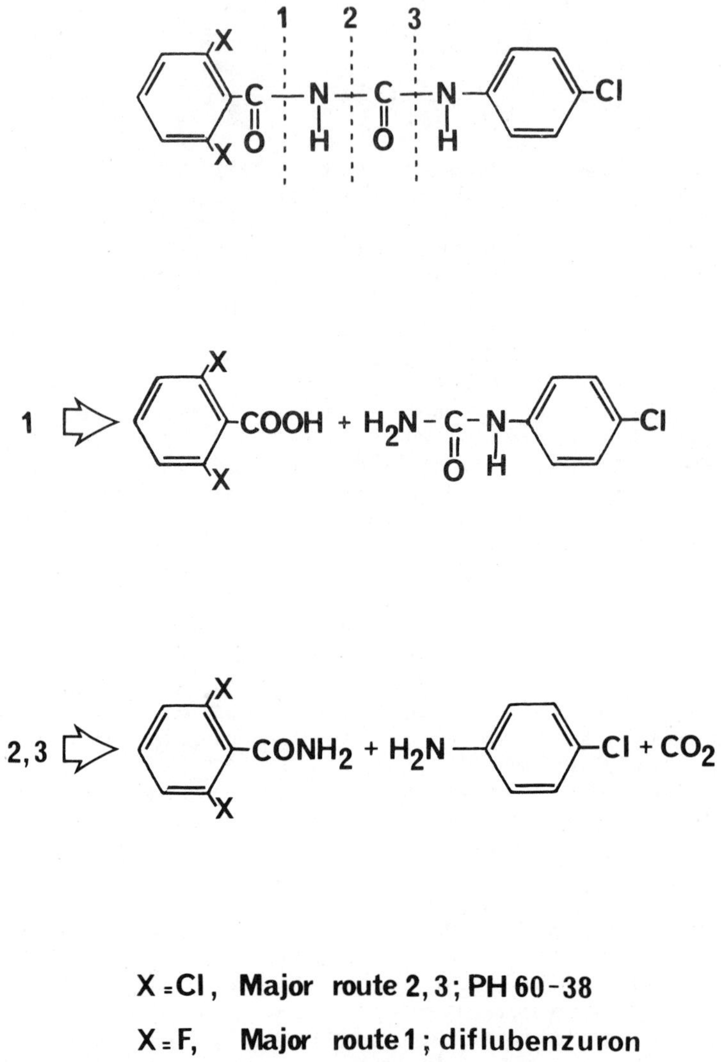

X = Cl, Major route 2, 3; PH 60-38

X = F, Major route 1; diflubenzuron

Figure 2. Possibilities of the hydrolytic cleavage of 2,6-substituted benzoyl-phenyl urea

lysis of 2,6-difluorobenzamide in soils, with a
halflife of 2-3 weeks, as is illustrated in Figure 3.

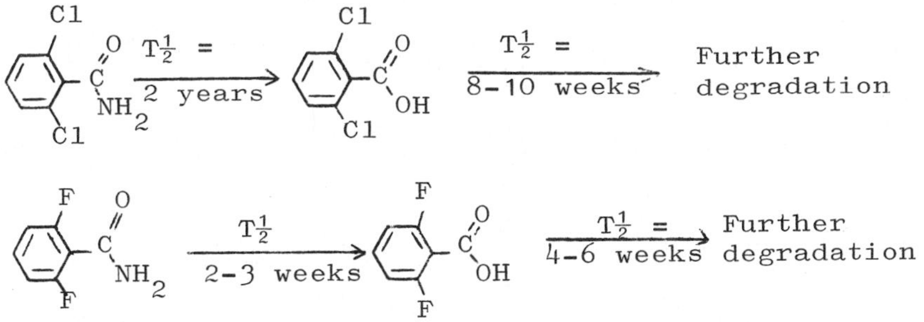

*Figure 3.   Degradation of 2,6-dichlorobenzamide (BAM) and 2,6-difluorobenzamide
in the soil*

On putting one and one together the synthesis of
the fluorine analogue of PH 60-38 suggested itself
as a possible means of obtaining a higher rate of
degradation in soils via route 1. This idea proved
very fruitful: the predictions of a faster degradability and of the primary metabolic pathway
of the fluorine analogue, PH 60-40 or diflubenzuron
(II), in soils were both found to be correct.
Moreover, the larvicidal activity of the new
derivative was appreciably higher than that of
PH 60-38, which was a complete and pleasant surprise for us at that time.
    Of course this new finding initiated the
synthesis of a large number of 2,6-difluorobenzoyl-
phenyl ureas and again QSAR was used for the
optimisation of the series. A combined analysis
of the 2,6-difluorobenzoyl and 2,6-dichlorobenzoyl
subseries (IV) was performed both as a function
of variation of the substitution pattern in the
aniline ring.

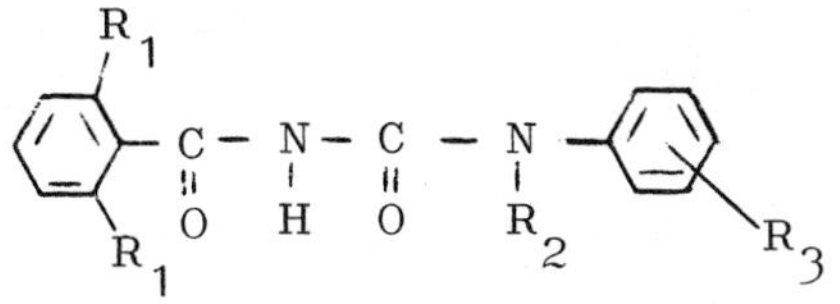

(IV)

The differences in the two subseries are accounted
for with the aid of the dummy parameter D_1 which was
made zero in the 2,6-dichlorobenzoyl subseries
(R_1 = Cl) and unity in the 2,6-difluorobenzoyl
subseries (R_1 = F). In this analysis also a number
of compounds were included in which the aniline
nitrogen was substituted with a methylgroup; here
the dummy parameter D_2 was used, with D_2 = 0 if
R_2 = H, and D_2 = 1 if R_2 = CH_3. The resulting
regression equations were:
For R_3 = para-substituents

$$-\text{Log ED}_{50} = + 1.10 \ \pi + 2.35 \ \sigma - 0.40L - 0.27B_4$$
$$+ 1.40D_1 - 0.70D_2 + 0.84$$
$$n = 48, \ r = 0.909, \ s = 0.408, \ F = 32.63$$

For R_3 = meta- and para-substituents
$$-\text{Log ED}_{50} = + 0.95 \ \pi + 1.99 \ \sigma - 0.34L^{para}$$
$$- 0.24B_4^{para} - 1.30L^{meta} + 1.40D_1$$
$$- 0.61D_2 + 3.38$$
$$n = 70, \ r = 0.892, \ s = 0.535, \ F = 34.37$$

It can be concluded that these equations are very
similar to the equations discussed earlier for the
2,6-dichlorobenzoyl subseries as far as the electronic, hydrophobic, and steric influences are
concerned. The coefficients of the dummy parameters
lead to the conclusion that the 2,6-difluorobenzoyl
subseries is about 25 times more active on Pieris
brassicae than the 2,6-dichlorobenzoyl series,
whereas methyl substitution at the aniline nitrogen
systematically decreases the activity by a factor
of about five (23).
     The similarities in the influences of the
different parameters in the two subseries suggested
that the optimum compound for development should
still contain the p-Cl-aniline moiety, so that
diflubenzuron was ultimately selected as the final
benzoylphenyl urea derivative to be developed as
a new selective insecticide.

Fate of diflubenzuron in the environment.

     Soils (28, 29). Let us first discuss the rate
of degradation of diflubenzuron in agricultural soils.
The halflife found initially was 8 - 16 weeks,

depending on the type of soil (Table 1). This was
still rather high in comparison with the halflife
of 2 - 3 weeks found for the model compound 2,6-
difluorobenzamide. Further studies revealed the
probable explanation of this discrepancy. It was
found that the halflife of diflubenzuron was largely
dependent on the form in which it was brought into
the soil, as is illustrated in Table 1.

Table 1. Influence of particle size on apparent
rate of degradation of diflubenzuron (28, 29).

$T\frac{1}{2}$ in weeks in several soils		Formulation
PH 60-38	Diflubenzuron	
25 - 50	8 - 16	Suspension, mean particle size 10µ
8 - 25	0.5 - 1	Suspension, mean particle size 2µ
-	Approx.1	Aqueous solution

$$\text{Pestic. suspension} \xrightarrow{k_1} \text{pestic.solution} \xrightarrow{k_2} \text{metabolites}$$

In the initial experiments particles with an average
size of 10µ had been used, but a halflife of 0.5 -
1 week was found when particles with an average size
of 2µ were applied. This interesting phenomenon
might be caused by the specific physical properties
of diflubenzuron: owing to its very low aqueous
solubility of about 0.2 ppm this insecticide, like
other pesticides with a low solubility, will be
present in the soil as a dispersion in the concentration applied. Thus in the equation given in Table
one the apparent halflife may be governed by the
rate of dissolution, k_1, or by the true rate of
degradation, k_2. On using particles with an average
size of 2u, k_2 is apparently rate determing because
in that case the halflife of 0.5 - 1 week is similar
to that found when a true solution is applied. The
rate of dissolution of particles is generally correlated linearly with their surface

area, so that k_1 will decrease if larger particles are applied. With crystals like those of difluben-zuron - having a high melting point and consequently a high energy of crystallisation - the rate of dissolution of larger particles might be so low that k_1 becomes rate determining, i. e. $k_1 < k_2$. With the related compound PH 60-38, (III), a comparable but smaller effect of the particle size on the apparent rate of degradation in soils was observed as is illustrated in Table 1. The influence of the type of soil on the rate of degradation of diflubenzuron is much less important, because with five agricultural soils and three hydrosoils, including the soil types recommended by the EPA and the German BBA, the variation in the halflife was only a factor of approximately two.

    The rate of degradation of diflubenzuron in a terrestrial soil was also studied by Metcalf et al. (30), who found practically no degradation 4 weeks after application of an acetonic solution of diflubenzuron to air-dried soil. We, however, obser-ved that diflubenzuron crystallized from acetonic solution "on" soil with a particle size of largely >10 μ. The commercial WP formulation of diflubenzuron has a standardized particle size of 1 - 5 μ with an average value of 2 μ, so that these higher halflife values obtained with larger particles are of no practical significance. This standardisation of the particle size is also necessary because of its great influence on the insecticidal activity of benzoylphenyl ureas. This was already mentioned in the discussion of the QSAR studies. The influence of particle size on the larvicidal activity of diflubenzuron was further illustrated elsewhere (3). These influences might have the same explanation as that of the effect of particle size on the rate of degradation in soils.

    More detailed studies of the metabolic pathways of diflubenzuron in soils have been carried out with radioactive preparations labeled in four different positions of the molecule for a study of the ulti-mate fate of the primary degradation products.

    These studies will be merely summarized in this paper. A more extensive discussion is pub-lished elsewhere (29). In all experiments discussed here, diflubenzuron was applied to the soil as an aqueous suspension of 2-μ particles at a concen-tration of 1 μg/gram soil, roughly corresponding to a dose of 300 grams a.i. per hectare. The first

aspect studied was the nature of the primary degradation process of diflubenzuron, by comparing the
degradation in normal soils and in steam-sterilized
soils. A representative example of the results with
a preparation labeled with ^{14}C in the aniline ring
and with a sandy loam soil is illustrated in Table 2.
It can be seen that in the nonsterile soil only 2%
of diflubenzuron was left after four weeks. But in
the sterile soil some 94% of the applied diflubenzuron was still present after this period. It can
be concluded that the degradation is of a microbiological nature.

Table 2. Fate of diflubenzuron-ring-U-^{14}C in
sterile and non-sterile sandy loam soil after 4 weeks
(Percentage of initial amount of diflubenzuron)
(28, 29)

	Sterile	Nonsterile
Extractable [14]C	96	43
Extractable PH 60-40	94	2
Non-extractable [14]C	4	27

A general survey of the metabolic pathways of
diflubenzuron in soils is given in Figure 4. It was
already mentioned that the main primary degradation
process was a micro biological hydrolysis of the
"bridge" of the molecule in such a way (route A)
that p-chlorophenyl urea and 2,6-difluorobenzoic
acid were formed. Let us first discuss the "urea"
part of the diflubenzuron molecule. p-Chlorophenyl
urea was identified by thin-layer chromatography
(tlc), reversed isotope dilution analysis (rid), and
mass spectrometry (ms). Up to 70% of the ^{14}C-aniline
label applied to the soil was recovered as p-chlorophenyl urea, depending on the type of soil, which
clearly illustrates that this pathway is of primary
importance. The rate of the degradation processes
is illustrated in the upper half of Figure 5, with
respect to an agricultural sandy loam soil. It can
be seen that between 2 and 28 weeks the amount of
extractable radioactivity is practically identical
with the amount of p-chlorophenyl urea found.

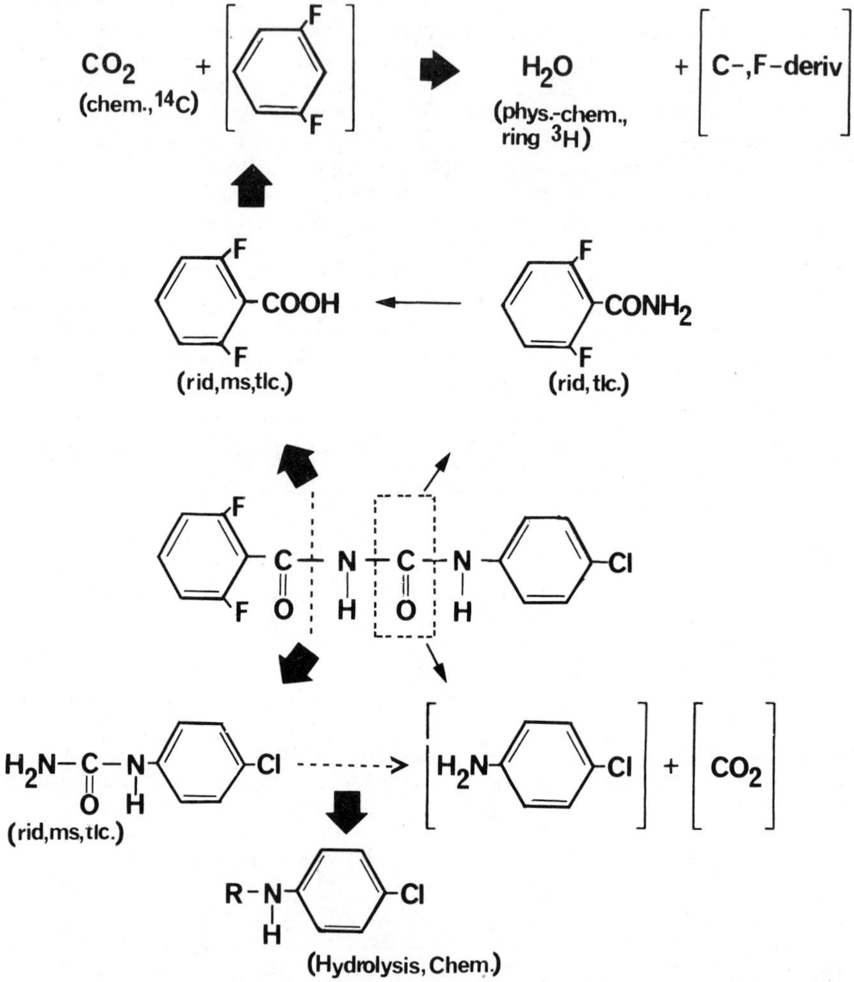

Figure 4. Proposed pathways of the degradation of diflubenzuron in agricultural soils and hydrosoils. Abbreviations: rid = reversed isotope-dilution; ms = mass spectrometry; tlc = thin layer chromatography.

The fate of this primary metabolite is further
illustrated in the lower half of Figure 5 where
the degradation of p-chlorophenyl urea is given
when this ^{14}C- aniline ring-labeled compound was
applied to the same type of soil in a separate
experiment. In both studies a halflife of about
10 weeks was found for this metabolite. The decrease
of p-chlorophenyl urea can rather quantitatively
be explained by the gradual formation of bound
residues. We are currently studying the nature of
the bound residues, for instance by means of extraction procedures which avoid the formation of
artefacts. This method has revealed that the bound
residues contain p-chlorophenyl urea as well as
small amounts of p-chloroaniline. Free p-chloroaniline or its further possible degradation products,
e.g. chlorinated azo- and azoxybenzenes, were not
present in the extractable residues.

The main degradation pathway of diflubenzuron
in soils would lead to the formation also of 2,6-
difluorobenzoic acid as a primary metabolite.
Starting with diflubenzuron preparations labeled
with ^{14}C and ^{3}H in the benzoyl ring, 2,6-difluoro-
benzoic acid has indeed been identified by thin-
layer chromatography (tlc), gas chromatography (glc),
reversed isotope dilution analysis (rid), and mass
spectrometry (ms). Because of its rapid further
degradation in agricultural soils with a halflife
of less than 4 weeks, the maximum amount of 2,6-
difluorobenzoic acid found was 20% of the diflubenzuron applied. The fate of the acid was studied
further with a diflubenzuron preparation labeled
with ^{14}C in the carbonyl group of the benzoyl
moiety. The major part of this labeled material
was identified by chemical analysis after about 12
weeks as CO_2, proving that decarboxylation is the
first step in the degradation of 2,6-difluorobenzoic
acid. Further information was obtained with diflubenzuron labeled with ^{3}H in the benzoyl ring. In this
study, up to 50% of the tritium label added to a
clay hydro-soil was identified as tritiated water.

As mentioned earlier, hydrolysis according to
route 2 or 3 leading to p-chloroaniline and 2,6-
difluorobenzamide is the main pathway in the slow
degradation of the "sister" compound PH 60-38.
As expected this pathway was demonstrated also in
the case of diflubenzuron, though as a minor
process: 2,6-difluorobenzamide has been identified
in amounts of at the most 2% of the applied dose by
means of thin layer chromatography (tlc) and rever-

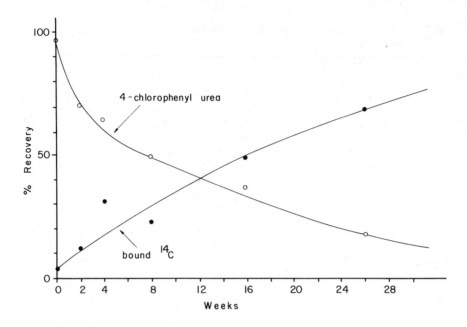

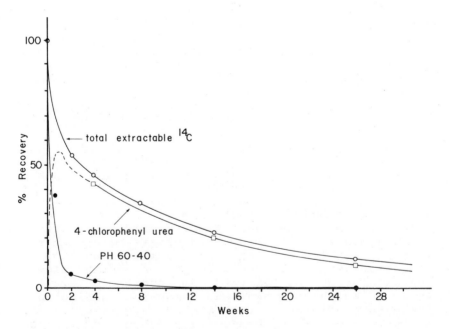

Figure 5.   Rate of degradation of diflubenzuron (upper half) and of p-chlorophenyl urea (lower half) in an agricultural sandy loam soil. Percent recovery of applied dose.

sed isotope dilution analysis (rid). In separate
experiments with ^{3}H-difluorobenzamide it was found
to be degraded rapidly into 2,6-difluorobenzoic
acid with a halflife of about two weeks in a clay
hydrosoil (Figure 6). In this experiment the halflife of the 2,6-difluorobenzoic acid formed was
again about 4 weeks (29).

    Plants. In contrast to the fast and complicated
degradation of diflubenzuron in soils, the fate of
the insecticide in plants after leaf application is
rather simple.

    Table 3. Persistence of diflubenzuron on plant
leaves two months after topical application in a
greenhouse study (31).

| Fraction | percentage of applied dose | | | |
	soybean	apple	maize	cabbage
TER	93	86	94	100
Diflubenzuron	96	89	95	100
TBR	4	2	5	5
TR	97	88	99	105

TER = Total extractable residue.
TBR = Total bound residue.
TR = Total residue.

Labels:

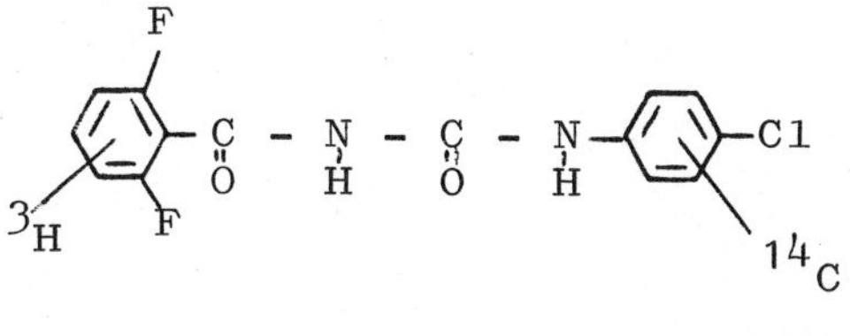

This is illustrated in Table 3, where an analysis
is presented of plant leaves two months after application of labeled diflubenzuron as an aqueous
suspension of 2 μ particles on soybean, apple, maize
and cabbage plants in a greenhouse study. It can be

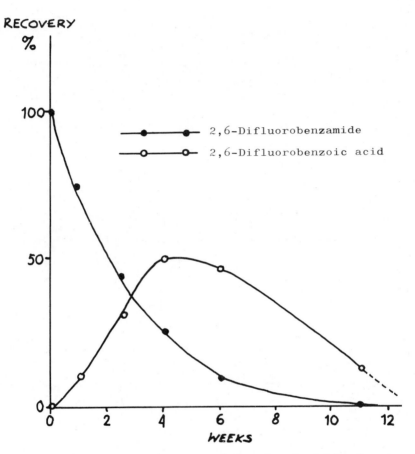

Figure 6. Degradation curves of 2,6-difluorobenzamide and 2,6-difluorobenzoic acid after incubation of clay hydrosoil with ^{3}H-2,6-difluorobenzamide. Recovery in percentage of applied dose.

observed that $\geqslant$ 95% of the analysed radioactivity
was found in the extractable fraction and that it
consisted completely of unaltered diflubenzuron.
At harvest, 4 - 5 months after application, the
crops were analyzed (Table 4).

Table 4. Residues in crops , 4 - 5 months
after leaf application of ^{3}H-^{14}C-labeled diflubenzuron (calculated as ppm diflubenzuron) (31)

	Total ^{3}H	Total ^{14}C
Soybean, milled beans	< 0.02	< 0.02
Maize, milled grains	< 0.001	< 0.001
Apples	< 0.002	< 0.005

Labels:

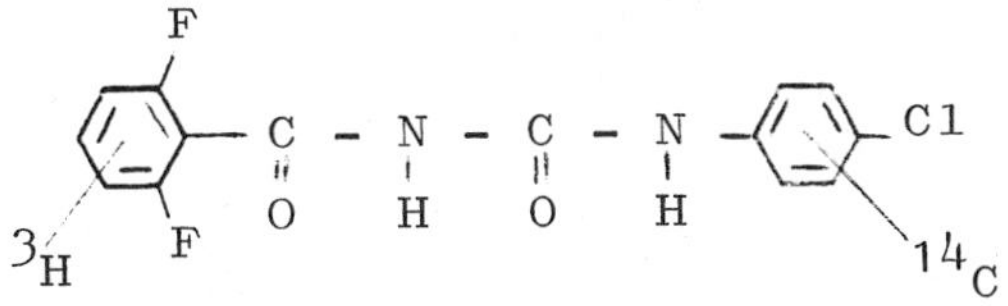

From the results it is clear that no residues were
found up to the sensitivity limit of the analytical
methods used. Furthermore untreated leaves were
found to contain practically no radioactive material.
It can be concluded that diflubenzuron after application on plants is very persistent and has no systemic properties. In other studies it was found that
diflubenzuron does not permeate through the cuticular
barrier into the leaves of broad bean. These studies
on the fate of diflubenzuron on and in plants will
be published more extensively elsewhere (31). Essentially the same results were obtained by Still in a
study on the metabolic fate of diflubenzuron on
cotton plants (32). In addition to metabolism, other
factors might influence the fate of diflubenzuron
on plants, i.e. washing off and photochemical degradation. Ruzo et al. (33) and Metcalf et al. (30)
studied the photodegradation of diflubenzuron at
respectively >285 nm and 254 nm, for example in
methanol, under rather drastic conditions and found
essentially the same degradation pathways.

However, under more natural conditions, e.g. according to the methods recommended in the EPA Guidelines the rate of the photochemical degradation was
found to be very low (34). In other experiments
washing off of diflubenzuron from plant leaves with
high amounts of simulated rainfall was found to be
negligible (34). All these results point to a high
residual activity of diflubenzuron after application
to the crops and to the absence of any metabolites
formed by direct degradation on or in the plants.

Insects and ecosystems. A high stability of
diflubenzuron was also found after uptake by insects.
In Table 5 some studies are summarized of the fate
of diflubenzuron and the parent compound Du 19111.

Table 5. Fate of benzoylphenyl ureas in insects.

Insect	Application	Clearance[a]	Absorption[b]
Diflubenzuron			
P.brassicae larvae (36)	Suspension on leaves	0.5	30-35
A. grandis $\overset{\circ}{+}/\overset{\text{\textbardbl}}{\circ}$ (37)	Topical and injection	1-2	100
E. acrea larvae (30)	Suspension in medium	-	25-40
Du 19111			
P.brassicae larvae (35)	Suspension on leaves	1	> 35

a) $T\frac{1}{2}$ in days; b) Percentage of applied dose.

In all cases, metabolism was found to be completely
absent. The amount of absorption by the insects
depends on the method of application; especially
after oral uptake of suspensions, about 2/3 of the
labeled material remains in the gut and is excreted
in the faeces. However, the absorbed material is
also readily excreted: for the clearance an average
$T\frac{1}{2}$ of about one day was found. This phenomenon
explains the reversible character of the insecticidal
activity of diflubenzuron. The high stability in

insects was also apparent in a study of the behaviour
of diflubenzuron in the Metcalf model ecosystem (30).
Some of the results obtained are presented in Table
6. The so-called ecological magnification, defined
in Table 6, was determined for three different radiolabeled preparations A, B, and C. It can be seen that
mosquito larvae, which are in the middle of the
Metcalf food chain, show a rather high magnification.
But the magnification found in fish was more than
an order of magnitude lower, so that the authors concluded that diflubenzuron did not bioconcentrate in
the fish through food-chain transfer. The magnification found in snails is also reassuring especially
in comparison with the concentrations found in algae.
In respect to DDT, Metcalf et al. have reported ecological magnifications of 10,000 for fish and of
5000 for snail in their model ecosystem (38).

Table 6. Bioaccumulation of diflubenzuron in
Metcalf model ecosystem (30)

Biological Object	Ecological magnification (E.M.) with labeled preparation		
	A	B	C
Snail (Physa sp.)	86	95	221
Fish (Gambusa affinis)	19	14	80
Mosquito larvae (Culex sp.)	779	596	1099

Labels:

$$E.M. = \frac{\text{Concentration in biological object}}{\text{Concentration in water}} \text{ after 33 days}$$

Animals. Finally another important aspect to be
discussed, e.g. in relation to mammalian toxicology,
is the fate of diflubenzuron in animals. Post,
Willems and co-workers have studied the fate of the
insecticide in the rat after oral administration of
[3]H-benzoyl and ^{14}C-anilino ring-labeled preparations.
Consistent recoveries of radioactivity were obtained
in all studies, most of it being retrieved in urine
and faeces. The radioactivity in the carcasses was
only a few per cent of each label, so that there is
no accumulation of diflubenzuron or metabolites in
the rat body. From the amounts of label found in the
urine and bile it was concluded that at least 50%
of a dose was absorbed by the intestines. The resorbed diflubenzuron was (almost) completely metabolized. The proposed metabolic pathways are given
in Figure 7. It can be observed that about 20% is
degraded in the same way as found in the soil studies,
i.e. a hydrolysis of the "bridge" of the molecule
leading to 2,6-difluorobenzoic acid and p-chlorophenyl
urea as primary metabolites. Most of the p-chlorophenyl urea is further degraded, which was also found
in separate studies in which ^{14}C-labeled-p-chloro-
phenyl urea itself was administered orally to rats.
In the rat studies a major additional metabolic
pathway was discovered, which had not been found in
soils, i.e. the hydroxylation of the intact diflubenzuron molecule leading to the three different
metabolites indicated in the Figure, which were found
partly as conjugates. These hydroxy derivatives accounted for almost all the metabolites in the bile and
for about half the metabolites in the urine. The rat
metabolism studies will be published more extensively
elsewhere (39).

Mode of action of diflubenzuron.

In the introduction it was stated that the
disturbances of the endocuticular matrix of Pieris
brassicae larvae by the parent benzoylphenyl urea
compound Du 19111 were caused by an influence on
chitin formation, thus assigning to the benzoylphenyl
ureas an insecticidal position equivalent to that of the
fungicidal polyoxins. In the last part of this paper
we shall try to adduce arguments supporting that
statement.
The first argument was supplied by Post and
Vincent (40) in their study of the incorporation of
radiolabeled glucose in tissue fractions of normal

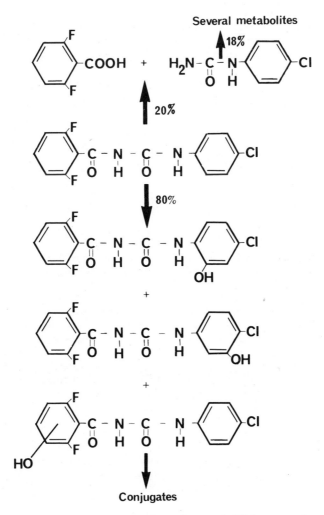

Figure 7.   Proposed metabolic pathway of diflubenzuron in rats (percentages of resorbed material)

and Du 19111 treated <u>Pieris brassicae</u> larvae (Table 7)

Table 7.   Incorporation of radioactivity from $(6-^{14}C)$-D-glucose in tissue fractions of normal and Du 19111-treated <u>Pieris</u> larvae, expressed as μg glucose, with standard deviations (<u>40</u>).

	Haemolymph plus gut contents	KOH hydrolysate and washings	Glycogen fraction (pellets)	Chitin fraction (cuticles)	Total
Control	0.69 ±0.21	1.74 ±0.34	0.38 ±0.11	1.25 ±0.34	4.03 ±0.54
Treated	0.96 ±0.25	2.48 ±0.51	0.59 ±0.16	0.02 ±0.01	4.05 ±0.59

From this Table it is clear, on the one hand, the total radioactivities incorporated in the tissues of normal and treated larvae are identical. On the other hand, however, practically no labeled glucose has been incorporated in the chitin fraction from the cuticles. The other tissue fractions show a slightly increased amount of radioactivity. The localisation of the inhibition of glucose incorporation was studied further by Post and co-workers by means of micro-autoradiography (<u>41</u>). It was found that in endocuticle of <u>Pieris</u> larvae a narrow zone of radioactivity is formed after injection of $(^{3}H-)$-D-glucose. By contrast, in the larvae treated with Du 19111 via leaf feeding, this zone was completely absent. In the incorporation study by Post and Vincent (<u>40</u>), Du 19111 had been administered by feeding of treated cabbage leaves to fifth instar <u>Pieris</u> larvae during 24 hours prior to injection of labeled glucose, while the analysis was carried out 24 hours after injection. This study was repeated with diflubenzuron by Deul et al. (<u>42</u>) and essentially the same results were obtained.
     However, Deul et al. also studied the rapidity of inhibition by diflubenzuron: they injected ^{14}C-labeled glucose into control larvae and ^{14}C-labeled glucose + diflubenzuron into test larvae and analysed the incorporation as a function of time after injection (<u>42</u>). The results are summarized in Figure 8. It can be concluded that most of the incorporation in the controls had already taken place <u>15 minutes</u> after injection and that diflubenzuron is capable of

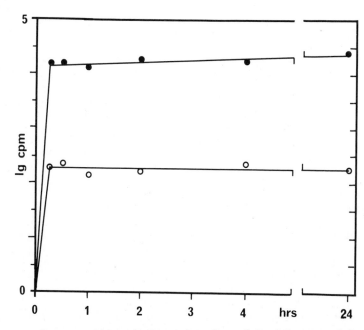

Ig cpm = incorporation of radioactivity from injected
[6-^{14}C]-D-glucose.
1,2 ... hours = time after (simultaneous) injection of
radioactive glucose.

● = controls.
o = treated with 1 µg/larva

Figure 8. *Rate of inhibition of chitin synthesis after injection of diflubenzuron in fifth instar* Pieris brassicae *larvae 24 hr after ecdysis*

inhibiting this incorporation to the extent of >95%
even after such a short period. Indications of the
rapidity of action of diflubenzuron on the chitin
deposition were also obtained by Ker (43) in his
studies of the effect of the insecticide on adult
locusts. In one study, adult locusts were starved
prior to being given diflubenzuron-treated barley
for six hours, after which they returned to untreated
barley. In microphotographs of the pre alar arm and
of the hind tibia of locusts in polarized light a
band of   non-birefringent   material, i.e. free of
chitin, can be observed which corresponds to not more
than a day's growth. In another study diflubenzuron
was injected and it was found that the production of
chitinless cuticle started in less than 80 minutes
(43).

From the results discussed so far it can be concluded that diflubenzuron interferes very rapidly
with chitin deposition. The possible effects on the
deposition of protein, the second important component
of the endocuticular matrix, were studied by Hunter
and Vincent with adult locusts (44). It was concluded
that protein deposition was completely unaffected as
regards the quantity of protein found. Another conclusion was that cross-linking of the protein - as
revealed by the differing solubilities of the protein
fractions - was also unaffected. Deul et al. (45)
furthermore found practically no effect of diflubenzuron on protein synthesis in cuticles of Pieris
brassicae larvae.

The mode of action of diflubenzuron in housefly
larvae (Musca domestica) was studied by Ishaaya and
Casida (46). These authors found that dietary diflubenzuron increased the cuticle chitinase and phenoloxidase activities when analyzed three days after
addition of two-day old larvae to the media. These
authors considered that the increased chitinase level,
possibly caused by hormone stimulation, might explain
the observed decreased chitin deposition. However, the
complete inhibition of glucose incorporation within
15 minutes in Pieris brassicae endocuticle might not
easily be explained by the chitinase theory. For that
reason Deul et al. (42) carried out a comparative
study with Pieris larvae of the influence of diflubenzuron on the inhibition of glucose incorporation, on
the one hand, and on its influence on the chitinase
activity, on the other. The results are presented in
Figure 9. It can be observed that one and three days
after ecdysis, when glucose inhibition is almost completely blocked, chitinase activity is practically

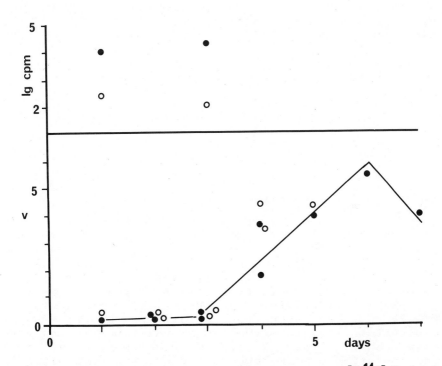

lg cpm = lg incorporation of radio activity from injected $[6\text{-}^{14}C]$-D-glucose

v   = chitinase activity in μmoles AGA/hr/grams larvae

● = controls

o = injected with 1 μg diflubenzuron/larva

*Figure 9.   Influence of diflubenzuron on chitin synthesis and braeakdown in fifth
instar* Pieris brassicae *larvae as a function of age after ecdysis*

zero both in treated and control larvae. After three
days chitinase activity starts to increase both in
treated and in untreated larvae until the next moult
about 6 days after ecdysis. The results of this
experiment definitely exclude the chitinase hypothesis to explain the primary mode of action of diflubenzuron, at least in Pieris brassicae.

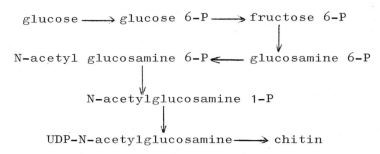

Figure 10. Biosynthetic pathway of chitin synthesis from glucose

        The alternative possibility to explain the mode
of action is the inhibition of one of the enzymes in
the pathway of chitin biosynthesis, illustrated in
Figure 10. Considering the rapidity of the process,
a direct inhibition without hormonal interference was
most probable. Post et al. compared the rates of
incorporation of ^{14}C-labeled glucose into the ultimate chitin precursor, uridine diphosphate N-acetylglucosamine or UDPAG, in both normal and Du 19111-
treated Pieris larvae and found that these rates did
not differ significantly (41). Hence the conclusion
seemed justified that the "parent" compound Du 19111
did not inhibit an intermediate step between glucose
and UDPAG. This led to the hypothesis that either
the ultimate enzyme of the pathway, chitin synthetase,
was blocked or that a closely related process was
affected by Du 19111. Deul et al. found in another
study that diflubenzuron inhibited the incorporation
of ^{14}C-labeled UDPAG in the chitin fraction of Pieris
brassica cuticles and thus they arrived at the same
conclusion with respect to that compound (42). Of
course the ultimate proof that diflubenzuron blocks
chitin synthetase in Pieris brassicae larvae can only
be obtained by inhibition experiments with the pure
isolated enzyme. But the isolation of chitin synthetase from insects is a notoriously difficult problem

and our efforts in that area have not as yet led to success.

In this context the comparison of the insecticide diflubenzuron with the fungicide polyoxin D is interesting in more than one respect. It not only closes the circle in our paper, so to speak, but it can also furnish strong circumstantial evidence to support our hypothesis of the mode of action of diflubenzuron. Marks and Sowa were the first to compare diflubenzuron and polyoxin D in their effects on the β-ecdyson-dependent in-vitro synthesis of chitin by the cockroach (Leucophaea maderae) leg regenerates (47). These authors found that both compounds almost completely inhibited the incorporation of ^{14}C-labeled D-glucosamine into the chitin fraction. In a later study with ^{14}C-labeled N-acetyl-D-glucosamine similar results were obtained, and the I_{50} value of inhibition of chitin synthesis was found to be 6.11×10^{-10}M for diflubenzuron and 7.53×10^{-7} M for polyoxin D (48). The difference in intrinsic activity can partly be explained by the roughly hundredfold accumulation of diflubenzuron in the insect tissue.

These interesting results prompted us to compare diflubenzuron and polyoxin D in their effects on Pieris brassicae larvae (49). In preliminary studies it had been found that polyoxin D did not affect the larvae via leaf feeding but that injection resulted in larvicidal effects. Histological examination revealed that both compounds gave similar effects, i.e. the disturbance of the regular endocuticular layers and the formation of globular coagulated particles as discussed earlier for Du 19111. Further information was obtained by incorporation studies as is illustrated in Table 8. After leaf feeding of polyoxin D no effect on the incorporation of radiolabeled glucose could be observed, even at a tenfold higher dose. But quite comparable effects were obtained with the two compounds after incubation with a preliminary "in vitro" system. After injection, when part of the permeability barriers in the larvae is absent, polyoxin D inhibits the glucose incorporation, but less so than diflubenzuron. The conclusion seems obvious that the intrinsic effects of both compounds are practically identical but that polyoxin D is much more hindered by the permeability barriers present in the Pieris brassicae larvae. On the strength of the evidence presented by Misato and co-workers that polyoxin D is a competitive inhibitor of chitin synthetase, a

similar conclusion for the mode of action of diflubenzuron seems justified (49)

Table 8. Inhibition of incorporation of $(6-^{14}C)$
-D-glucose into chitin fractions of <u>Pieris brassicae</u>
larvae by diflubenzuron and polyoxin D, as percentage
of controls.

Method	Diflubenzuron		Polyoxin D	
	Dose (nmoles)	Inhibi- tion (%)	Dose (nmoles)	Inhibi- tion(%)
Oral uptake by larvae via leaf feeding	10-20	95	200	0
Injection into larvae, simultaneous with glucose	3	90	50	45
Injection into larvae, 3 hours prior to glucose	-	-	50	95
Incubation with skin + adhering tissue	30	80	80	80

In addition to the effects of diflubenzuron on
the chitinase and phenoloxidase levels, observed by
Ishaaya and Casida (46), other biochemical influences
of diflubenzuron and Du 19111 have been described in
the literature (Table 9). A common feature of all
these effects is their analysis one or more days
after treatment. As any effects of these benzoylphenyl ureas become visible on the living insects
only at the time of the next moult, when susceptible
larvae die, investigators are prompted to search for
defects up to a considerable time after application.
In comparison with the very fast inhibition of
chitin synthesis discussed above, in our opinion
these studies can at the most indicate "secondary"
effects. A considerable number of effects of this
type can be **expected** to be found and published in
the future.

Table 9. "Secondary" effects of benzoylphenyl ureas in insects.

Compound	Insect larvae	Analysis (days after treatment)	Effect
Du 19111 (50)	Pieris brassicae L. Thaumetopoae pityo campa S.	1,2 3,12	Increase followed by decrease of respiratory metabolism and of pentose-cycle.
Du 19111 (40)	Pieris brassicae L.	2	Slightly increased biosynthesis of non-chitinous materials.
Diflubenz- uron (46)	Musca domestica L.	3	Increase of chitinase and phenoloxidase activity.
Diflubenz- uron (51)	Musca domestica L.	2	Increased activity of β-ecdyson-metabolizing enzymes and increase of microsomal oxidase activity.
Diflubenz- uron (42)	Pieris brassicae L.	2	Slightly increased biosynthesis of nonchitinous material.

Summarizing, diflubenzuron features mentioned in the introduction of this paper can be completed as follows: The new insecticide has favourable environmental properties because it is non-persistent in soils and it has a low biological magnification. It is stable on plants and in insects, hence it has a long residual activity. It represents the best choice from the series of the benzoylphenyl ureas. It is a reversible inhibitor of chitin synthesis in insects, probably by blocking chitin synthetase.

Abstract.

    The development of selective crop protection
compounds based on the interference with chitin
deposition in fungi and insects is one of the aims
in pesticide design. Polyoxin D and kitazin have
been successfully developed along these lines in the
field of fungicides some years ago. The benzoylphenyl
ureas, which exhibit activity against the larval stages of several insect species by interfering with
chitin deposition in the endocuticle and thus with
the moulting process, were first introduced in 1972.
The study of this new series ultimately led to the
development of 1-(4-chlorophenyl)-3-(2,6-difluoro-
benzoyl) urea (common name diflubenzuron) as a new
selective larvicide with favourable environmental
properties. In the present paper this development
has been discussed, based on the literature as well
as on new results from our laboratories, with main
emphasis on: 1) The optimisation of the series by
chemical synthesis guided by the study of quantitative structure-activity relationships; 2) The rational development of the soil degradable diflubenzuron
from its more persistent predecessors and its metabolic pathways in soil, plants, animals and model
ecosystems. 3) The mode of action of diflubenzuron
at the histological and molecular biological level.

Literature cited

1. Endo, A., Kakiki, K., and Misato, T., J. Bacteri-
    ol. (1970), 104, 189 and preceding papers.
2. Maeda, T., Abe, H., Kakiki, K., and Misato, T.,
    Agr. Biol. Chem. (1970), 34, 700.
3. Mulder, R., and Gijswijt, M. J., Pestic. Sci.
    (1973), 4, 737.
4. Wellinga, K., Mulder, R., and van Daalen, J. J.,
    J. Agr. Food Chem. (1973), 21, 348.
5. Wellinga, K., Mulder, R., and van Daalen, J. J.,
    J. Agr. Food Chem. (1973), 21, 993.
6. Van Daalen, J. J., Meltzer, J., Mulder, R., and
    Wellinga K., Naturwissenschaften (1972), 59, 312.
7. Mulder, R., and Swennen, A. A., Proc. 7th British
    Insecticide and Fungicide Conf. (1973), 729
8. Elings, H., and Dieperink, J. G., Mededelingen
    van de Faculteit Landbouwwetenschappen, Gent
    (1974), 39, 833.
9. Bijloo, J. D., Phytiatrie phytopharmacie (1975),
    24, 147,

10. Van Busschbach, E. J., Phytiatrie phytopharmacie (1975), 24, 159.
11. Nölle, H. H., Van Busschbach, E. J., and Verloop, A., Mitteilungen aus der Biol. Bundesanstalt f. Land- und Forstwirtschaft Berlin - Dahlem (1975) 165, 161.
12. Ascher, K. R. S., and Nemny, N. E., Phytoparasitica (1974), 2, 131.
13. Taft, H. M., and Hopkins, A. R., J. Econ. Entomol., (1975), 68, 551.
14. Moore, Jr., R. F., and Taft, H. M., J. Econ. Entomol. (1975), 68, 96.
15. Carter, S. W., J. Stored Prod. Res. (1975), 11, 187.
16. Holst, H., Z. f. Pfl. Krankh. (1975), 82, 1.
17. Wright, J. E., and Spates, G. E., J. Econ. Entomol. (1976), 69, 365.
18. Grosscurt, A. C., Mededelingen van de Faculteit Landbouwwetenschappen, Gent (1976), 41, (in press).
19. Grosscurt, A. C., paper in preparation.
20. Ferrell, C. D., and Verloop, A., Abstr. Pap., 170th Meet., Amer. Chem. Soc. (1975), PEST 35.
21. Verloop, A., Hoogenstraaten, W., and Tipker, J., Abstr. Pap., 167th Meet., Amer. Chem. Soc. (1974), CHLT 011.
22. Verloop, A., in "Drug Design" (E. J. Ariëns, ed.), Vol. 7 (1976), pp 255 - 311. Academic Press, New York.
23. Verloop, A., and Tipker, J., submitted to Pestic. Sci.
24. Tipker, J., Wellinga K., and Verloop, A., Symposium Pesticides Group, S.C.I. (London, Feb. 1977).
25. Yu, C.-C., and Kuhr, R. J., J. Agr. Food Chem. (1976), 24, 134.
26. Verloop, A., Residue Reviews (1972), 43, 55.
27. Nimmo, W. B., and Verloop, A., Z. f. Pfl. Krankh. (1975), VII, 147.
28. Verloop, A., Nimmo, W. B., and De Wilde, P. C., Abstr. Pap., 8th Int. Plant Protection Congress, Moscow (1975).
29. Verloop, A., Nimmo, W. B., and De Wilde, P.C., submitted to Pestic. Sci.
30. Metcalf, R. L., Lu, P.-Y., and Bowlus, S., J. Agr. Food Chem. (1975), 23, 359.
31. Nimmo, W. B., Verloop, A., and De Wilde, P. C., submitted to Pestic. Sci.
32. Still, G. G., personal communication.

33.   Ruzo, L. O., Zabik, M. J., and Schuetz, R. D.,
      J. Agr. Food Chem. (1974), 22, 1106.
34.   De Wilde, P. C., unpublished results, Philips-
      Duphar.
35.   Meltzer, J., Houtman, A. C., and Van der Kolk,
      B. J., unpublished results, Philips-Duphar.
36.   Deul, D. H., and Vos, C., paper in preparation.
37.   Still, G. G., and Leopold, R. A., Abstr. Pap.,
      170th. Meet.,   Amer. Chem. Soc. (1975), PEST 5.
38.   Metcalf, R. L., Sanga, G. K., and Kapoor, I. P.,
      Environm. Sci. Technol. (1971), 5, 709.
39.   Post, L. C., and Willems, A. G. M., paper in
      preparation.
40.   Post, L. C., and Vincent, W. R., Naturwissen-
      schaften (1973), 60, 431.
41.   Post, L. C., De Jong, B. J., and Vincent, W. R.,
      Pest. Biochem. Physiol. (1974), 4, 473.
42.   Deul, D. H., De Jong, B. J., and Kortenbach, J.
      A. M., submitted to Pest. Biochem. Physiol.
43.   Ker, R. F., J. Insect. Physiol., in press.
44.   Hunter, E., and Vincent, J. F., Experientia
      (1974), 30, 1432.
45.   Deul, D. H. et al., unpublished.
46.   Ishaaya, I., and Casida, J. E., Pest. Biochem.
      Physiol. (1974), 4, 484.
47.   Marks, E. P., and Sowa, B. A., in "Mechanism of
      Pesticide Action" (G. K. Kohn, ed.), ACS Sympo-
      sium Series, Vol. 2 (1974), pp. 144 - 155,
      Amer. Chem. Soc., Washington, D.C.
48.   Sowa, B. A., and Marks, E. P., Insect Biochem.
      (1975), 5, 855.
49.   Gijswijt, M. J., Deul, D. H., and De Jong, B. J.,
      submitted to Pest. Biochem. Physiol.
50.   Moreau, R., Castex, C., and Lamy, M., Ann. Zool.-
      Écol. anim. (1975), 7, 161.
51.   Yu, S. J., and Terriere, L. C., Life Sci. (1975),
      17, 619.

Fourth Generation Insecticides

W. S. BOWERS

New York State Agricultural Experiment Station, Geneva, N. Y.

Following discovery of the insect juvenile hormones and their importance to insect development, agricultural scientists became excited about the possibility of using these hormones for insect control. The presence of the juvenile hormones (JH) throughout immature development and during adult life was readily demonstrated by classical endocrinological techniques. It was soon shown that these hormones prevent precocious development during the larval and nymphal stages and that adult insects required JH in order to permit development of the ovaries. C. M. Williams (1) prepared the first active extract from the cecropia moth and showed that this extract prevented adult development when applied to insect pupae. Treated pupae molted into morphogenetic monsters and died. Treatment of other stages produced no ill effects. From these studies it became clear that during the transformation of the immature insect into the adult (during the pupal stage) the juvenile hormones must be absent. This short developmental period is completely deranged when supplied with JH.

Three juvenile hormones in Figure 1 were identified by Bowers et al. (2), Roller et al. (3), Meyer et al. (4), Judy et al. (5). Although the natural juvenile hormones soon proved to be too labile under field conditions, many analogs were prepared which in addition to increased stability were much more active than the natural hormones, Bowers (6), Pallos et al. (7), Slama et al. (8). Zoecon has registered one analog (9) for control of floodwater mosquitos and manure-breeding flies. The overall utility of control of insects with JH, however, is limited to those insects which can be brought into contact with the hormones during their brief period of sensitivity (i.e. pupal or last-stage nymph). Under most field conditions insects exist in all stages of development and all but the last developmental stages are unaffected by excess JH since these are stages which require JH.

Taking a somewhat different view, we reasoned that since juvenile hormones are required throughout most of an insect's

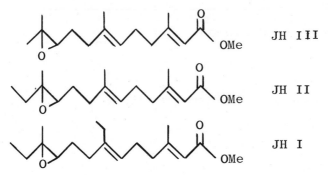

JH III

JH II

JH I

Figure 1.   Natural juvenile hormones

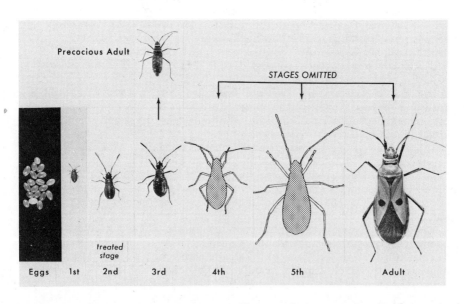

Figure 2.   Induction of precocious metamorphosis in the cotton stainer Dysdercus cingulatus with Precocene II

life, a more generally useful method of insect control would be
by preventing the secretion of these hormones. Thus, a hormone
antagonist should stop immature development and cause the insect
to molt prematurely to an adult. Likewise, an adult insect without juvenile hormone could not develop its ovaries and would be
sterile. Certain adult insects require JH for the production of
sex pheromones and might be rendered unattractive by a hormone
antagonist. Insect diapause in certain larvae (10) is caused by
an excess of JH, while adult diapause results from a lack of JH
(11, 12). Interfering with the presence or absence of JH during
these stages could be disastrous for insects.

   Our strategy for an endocrinologic approach to insect control
therefore was based upon the search for anti-juvenile hormones.

   JH analogs have been found in plants (13, 14) so it seemed
possible that anti-hormones might also exist in plants.

   We began to extract plants with apolar solvents and tested
these extracts by contact and fumigation against the cotton
stainer, Dysdercus cingulatus, and the milkweed bug, Oncopeltus
fasciatus. Eventually we found that the extract of the bedding
plant, Ageratum houstonianum, contained two potent anti-juvenile
hormones.

   By contact and fumigation the extract induced milkweed bug
and cotton stainer nymphs to molt to tiny adults, skipping one or
more of their immature stages. These miniature adults did not
reproduce and quickly died (Figure 2).

   Treatment of adult females prevented ovarian development or,
if developed ovaries were present at the time of treatment, the
ovaries were caused to regress to the undeveloped state.

   We were unable to induce precocious metamorphosis in other
insect Orders, but could sterilize many of the adult stages by
treatment with the extract.

   Isolation and identification of the two natural anti-
juvenile hormones revealed two simple chromenes; 7-methoxy-2,2-
dimethyl chromene and 6,7-dimethoxy-2,2-dimethyl chromene (Figure
3). Since these compounds induced precocious metamorphosis, we
called them Precocene I and II respectively. Subsequently we
found that both compounds had been previously identified and
synthesized (15, 16, 17). We developed an efficient synthesis for
these compounds, shown in Figure 4.

   In additional biological work we found that virgin female
American cockroaches, Periplaneta americana, stopped producing
their sex attractant following treatment with Precocene II, while
milkweed bug and Mexican bean beetle eggs treated with Precocene
II were unable to hatch. Normal non-diapausing Colorado potato
beetles treated with Precocene II promptly left their food plants,
burrowed into the soil and entered diapause.

   All of these biological effects of the precocenes indicated
that the secretion of the juvenile hormones had been prevented.
We tested this hypothesis by treating insects with both Precocene
II and juvenile hormone. We found that, when these compounds

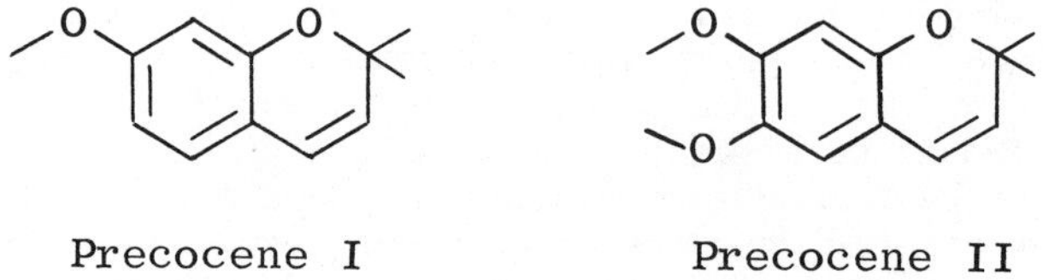

Precocene I   Precocene II

Figure 3. Anti-juvenile hormones from Ageratum houstonianum

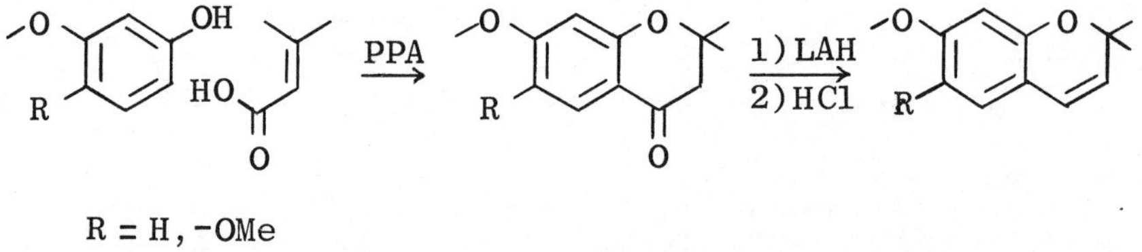

R = H, -OMe

Figure 4. Synthesis of precocene. Reaction of an appropriate phenol with dimethyl
acrylic acid and polyphosphoric acid (PPA) on the steam bath gives the chromanone
in quantitative yield. Reduction with lithium aluminum hydride (LAH) and brief
treatment with 4N hydrochloriic acid gives the chromene.

were combined, milkweed bug nymphs developed normally, adult insects developed their ovaries successfully and produced viable eggs. Thus, the effects of the precocenes are fully reversible and confirm our hypothesis that they are acting to prevent the secretion of the juvenile hormones.

As previously stated, these compounds do not show anti-juvenile hormone activity against all insects, but open the door to a new mode of insect control which affects most insect stages and provides a broader dimension to the endocrinologic strategy of insect control.

If the juvenile hormones and their analogs are representative of third-generation pesticides (18), the anti-juvenile hormones may be considered in a fourth-generation concept.

Literature Cited

(1) Williams, C. M., Nature (1956) 178, 212.
(2) Bowers, W. S., Thompson, M. J., Uebel, E. C., Life Science (1965) 4, 2323.
(3) Roller, H. K., Dahm, H., Sweeley, C. C., Trost, B. M., Angew. Chem. (1967) 79, 190.
(4) Meyer, A. S., Schneiderman, H. A., Hanzman, E., Ko, J. H., Proc. Natl. Acad. Sci. U. S. (1968) 60, 853.
(5) Judy, K. J., Schooley, D. A., Dunham, L. L., Hall, M. S., Bergot, B. J., Siddall, J. B., Proc. Natl. Acad. Sci. U. S. (1973) 70, 1509.
(6) Bowers, W. S., Science (1969) 164, 323.
(7) Pallos, F. M., Menn, J. J., Letchworth, P. E., Miaullis,J.B., Nature (1971) 232, 486.
(8) Slama, K., Romanuk, M., Sorm, F., "Insect Hormones and Bio-analogues" 477 pp., Springer Verlag, New York, 1974.
(9) Hendrick, C. A., Staal, G. B., Siddall, J. B., J. Agr. Food Chem. (1973) 21, 354.
(10) Chippendale, G. M., Yin, C. M., Nature (1973) 246, 511.
(11) de Wilde, J., De Boer, J. A., J. Insect Physiol. (1961) 6, 152.
(12) Bowers, W. S., Blickenstaff, C. C., Science (1966) 154, 1673.
(13) Bowers, W. S., Fales, H. M., Thompson, M. J., Uebel, E. C., Science (1966) 154, 1020.
(14) Cerny, V., Dilejs, L., Labler, L., Sorm, F., Slama, K., Collect. Czech. Chem. Commun. (1967) 32, 3926.
(15) Alertson, A. R., Acta. Chem. Scand. (1955) 9, 1725.
(16) Huls, R., Bull. Soc. Chim. Belg. (1958) 67, 22.
(17) Livingstone, R., Watson, R. B., J. Chem. Soc. (1957) 1509.
(18) Williams, C. M., Sci. Amer. (1967) 217, (1) 13.

Plant Regulators

Introduction

STANLEY RIES

Pesticide Research Center, Michigan State University, East Lansing, Mich. 48824

Since Charles Darwin first observed tropistic responses in 1880 and Professor F. W. Went explained these responses as due to auxin in 1928, plant physiologists have dreamed of chemically regulating the growth of our major economic crops. The general working hypothesis was and is clear and testable. Isolate growth substances, identify them, synthesize similar compounds and apply these to control vegetative growth, flowering, senescence, cold hardiness and post harvest quality. It should also be possible to control specific growth processes such as respiration, protein synthesis, nitrogen fixation and photo-respiration.

In general, we have not been too successful. This is particularly true when we are compared with plant breeders and geneticists, who have proven that given time they can successfully develop cultivars which yield more high quality food per hectare under different environmental conditions.

Now we are entering a new era in the study of plant regulation with a better understanding of naturally occurring plant regulators and more emphasis on empirically looking for substances which favorably effect plant growth processes.

This symposium is devoted to reviewing what has been accomplished in plant regulation, and to delineating recent successes in this dynamic area of plant science.

15

Post Harvest Responses and Plant Growth Regulators

MORRIS LIEBERMAN

Post Harvest Plant Physiology Laboratory, Beltsville Agricultural Research Center, Agricultural Research Service, U.S.D.A., Beltsville, Md. 20705

Regulation and control of post harvest metabolism with respect to ripening, aging, and senescence, has for many years been associated with degradation and the action of ethylene (1). Recent concepts and interpretations however, suggest that aging and senescence in plant tissues are not only deteriorative processes but also developmental processes in which other growth regulators play important roles (2). Thus, although ethylene is still considered a major influence on post harvest metabolism, the other plant hormones, the auxins, gibberellins, cytokinins, and abscisic acid, are also thought to significantly influence the aging process. Most likely, ethylene action results from interactions with these hormones.

In this report I briefly review classical observations on the effect of ethylene on post harvest tissues, especially those of fruit, and point out why ethylene was considered the ripening hormone. Secondly, I call attention to reasons for questioning ethylene as the exclusive ripening hormone and review recent data linking ethylene action to the action of other hormones and vice versa. Finally, I briefly discuss ethylene production and inhibition in plant tissue. These considerations may give rise to new concepts of controlling aging and senescence of plant tissues and of preserving crops after harvest.

Physiological Responses to Ethylene. Classically, two types of fruit have been recognized with respect to their response to ethylene (1): (a) climacteric fruit, such as apples or avocado, which show an immediate rise in respiration and an accelerated ripening rate when exposed to a few parts per million of ethylene; and (b) non-climacteric fruit, such as citrus, which show a rise in respiration during exposure to much higher concentrations of ethylene (100 ppm or more) then a return to the normal rate when ethylene is removed (Figure 1). Continuous application of such high levels of ethylene nevertheless accelerates ripening in non-climacteric fruit, which appear to resist reaction to ethylene (3). In contrast climacteric fruit

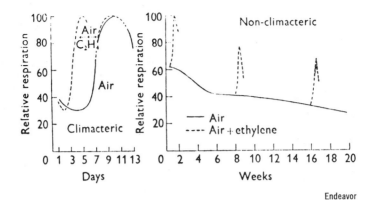

Figure 1. Effect of ethylene on respiration of climacteric and non-climacteric fruit. Ethylene causes greatest response in climacteric fruit when applied to mature fruit prior to the climacteric rise. In nonclimacteric fruit high concentrations of ethylene stimulate respiration for short time periods. This stimulation is observed at any time upon application of ethylene (3).

usually require only a few ppm of ethylene to trigger the ripening process.

Ethylene was believed to be the ripening hormone, because it is a natural metabolite, is virtually absent in mature but non-ripening fruit, and is produced in increasing amounts just prior to the onset of ripening. Furthermore, ethylene applied at relatively low concentrations can induce ripening and aging in green mature fruit, accelerating, but not altering, the natural processes. Compared to related compounds, ethylene is unique in its effectiveness in inducing ripening and aging (Table I).

Table I. Comparative Effectiveness of Ethylene and Related Analogues in Pea Stem-Section Assay (From Burg and Burg (4)

Compound	Relative Activity: Moles/unit effectiveness
Ethylene	1
Propylene	130
Vinyl chloride	2,370
Carbon Monoxide	2,900
Acetylene	12,500
1-Butene	140,000

The climacteric rise in respiration is considered a portend
of the shift in metabolism from anabolism to catabolism. This
transition from the fully mature state to the ripening state
occurs more sharply in faster growing fruit, such as the apple,
in which there is hydrolytic conversion of starch to sugars and
of insoluble pectins to soluble pectins. There is also a loss
of chlorophyll, and a synthesis of anthocyanins, carotenoids and
xanthophylls, as well as occurrence of other such reactions
associated with ripening. In non-climacteric fruit, such as
citrus, which show no comparable rise in respiration or ethylene
production, growth and development are prolonged and ripening
occurs only on the tree. An orange requires 8-11 months from
full bloom to maturity, in contrast to an apple, which may
require only 4-5 months (5).

    Resistance to Ethylene as a Ripening Agent. The classical
concept of ripening, especially of climacteric fruit, is that
ethylene triggers a cascade of reactions leading to ripening and
aging. This concept has been questioned because such a triggering phenomenon is absent in non-climacteric fruit. Also,
under some conditions ethylene does not trigger fruit ripening,
even in climacteric fruit (6). Thus, for example, avocados do
not ripen on the tree, despite their internal atmosphere of
about 0.1 ppm ethylene, a concentration which can induce ripening
in the harvested fruit. Even treatment of the unharvested fruit
with 50 ppm ethylene for 48 hours does not cause ripening. The
resistance to ripening by ethylene extends to newly harvested
avocado fruit. Application of 100 ppm ethylene 1 hour after
harvest had no effect on ripening (7). However 24 hours after
harvest, ethylene treatment considerably accelerated ripening,
much as expected. Such data gave rise to the idea of an "anti-
ripening" inhibitor, which, presumably, is most active in the
unharvested fruit and dissipated after harvest.
    Grapes also do not respond to ethylene as expected. In
development of the grape 3 stages of growth can be distinguished.
An early rapid enlargement is followed by a slow stage of
growth which is again followed by a rapid growth stage. The
grape ripens during the third stage but without increase in
ethylene production (Figure 2). However, a sharp increase in
abscisic acid (ABA) does occur and is correlated with ripening
of the berry. While the sensitivity to ethylene increased during
ripening of this fruit (9) it is also possible that ethylene is
not the major ripening factor.
    Such examples of "anomalous" ripening behavior data suggest
that other factors in addition to ethylene significantly affect
ripening and senescence. The experiments with citrus and avocado
suggest anti-ripening substances and the studies with the
developing grape suggest that ABA may play a role in these
processes. However, ABA appears to be a substitute or supplement
to ethylene and not a triggering agent (10).

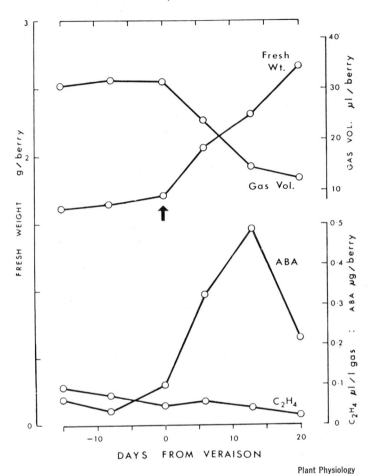

Figure 2.   Ethylene concentration in extracted gas, weight of abscisic acid (ABA), fresh weight and volume per berry in "Doradillo" grapes during the stationary and ripening stages of growth (pre and post veraison) (8)

Other Factors Influencing Ripening and Aging. Tradition-
ally, plant hormones are associated with growth and development
of young vigorous tissues. It is now evident, however, that
these hormones (auxins, cytokinins, gibberellins and ABA) may
also be important to ripening, aging and senescence, and to many
other aspects of post harvest metabolism. Conversely, ethylene,
which was associated with ripening in aging cells and tissues,
appears also to play an important role in young vigorously
growing tissues (11).
    Without in any way diminishing the importance of ethylene
in the control and regulation of ripening and aging, I emphasize
the critical supplemental importance of auxins, gibberellins, and

cytokinins, along with ABA, in the ripening and aging processes
in post harvest tissues. Ripening, aging, and senescence of
plant tissues and organs are developmental stages in the life
cycle and, like any other stage in growth and development, are
regulated and controlled, at the organizational level, by interaction between ethylene and other plant hormones.

Evidence for Hormonal Interactions with Ethylene. There
is evidence of antagonism between auxins, gibberellins and
cytokinins on one hand and ethylene and ABA on the other (12).
The control of fruit growth, development, ripening and aging
may depend on the relative importance of a specific hormone in
the total hormonal balance. Various hormones may tend to be
dominant or latent depending probably on their levels or concentrations at a given stage of the life cycle.
    Figure 3 shows the hypothetical kinetics of growth,
respiration and relative hormone levels in a climacteric fruit
at different stages of its life cycle. Hypothetical hormone
levels during development and ripening have been speculated on
before (13). The rationale for this outline is based on the
known influences of the various hormones on cell division,

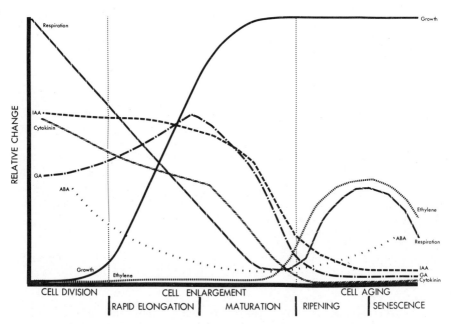

Figure 3. Theoretical kinetic curves for growth, respiration, and hormonal levels in climacteric fruit during growth, development, maturation, and ripening

elongation, and senescence.   In very young fruit, cell division
is the major activity, and, auxins, gibberellins and cytokinins
are at their highest levels, ethylene is virtually absent, and
ABA content is relatively high (14).   The levels of hormones
reflect their activities which are presumably high during cell
division.   ABA may operate as a brake during this stage by
opposing the possible excessive growth effects of high concentrations of some of these hormones.   Also, ABA is somehow
also related to water uptake which is important in young tissues
(15).   During rapid cell elongation gibberellins may tend to
increase somewhat in keeping with their importance in elongation
processes.   During maturation, the auxins, gibberellins, and
cytokinins decline, reaching very low levels toward the end of
the maturation period.   It is during this time that the levels
of ethylene and ABA begin to rise, preceding somewhat the
increase in respiration associated with climacteric fruit.

Although only limited data are available on endogenous
hormone levels during different stages of fruit growth and
development, some data do support this simplistic model.   For
example stem growth appears to result from a rise in auxin
levels (16) and rate of tomato fruit ripening is inversely related to cytokinin content (17).   Evidence for the interrelationships of hormonal levels and ripening and aging is also
obtained from experiments in which various hormones are added to
ripening or aging fruit tissues.   For example, the auxin,
β-naphthylacetic acid, has little effect on color development
in ripening banana peel disks, whereas the cytokinin benzyladenine
considerably retards coloring and, therefore, ripening in these
disks (18).   The tendency of exogenous auxin to retard ripening
may be counterbalanced by the ability of auxins to stimulate
ethylene production.   Gibberellins also retard ripening (color
formation) in banana peel disks, whereas applied ABA at 10^{-5} to
10^{-3}M accelerates ripening, as might be expected from the known
antagonism between ABA and gibberellins (18).

The influence of growth hormones (auxins, cytokinins, and
gibberellins) and ABA on ethylene production in apple tissue
slices of various stages of maturity before, during, and after
the climacteric rise in respiration is shown in Figure 4.   Preclimacteric tissue slices, which evolve virtually no ethylene,
are strongly inhibited by the cytokinin, isopentenyl adenosine
(IPA), indole acetic acid (IAA), and to a lesser extent by
gibberellic acid (GA).   The effect of all three hormones is even
more inhibiting to ethylene production by these tissues. However,
ABA stimulates ethylene production in preclimacteric tissue
slices.   At later stages in the ripening process, IAA and GA do
not inhibit ethylene production and IAA may actually stimulate.
On the other hand, IPA consistently inhibits ethylene production
at all stages of ripening throughout the climacteric and post-
climacteric periods.   No greater retardation is achieved by
addition of GA and IAA to IPA at this stage.

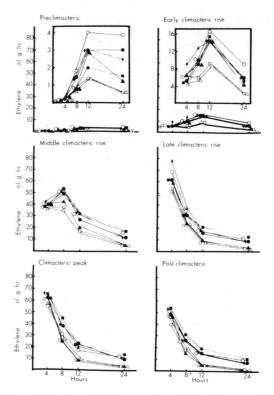

*Figure 4. Influence of IAA, GA, cytokinin (IPA),
and ABA, alone and in combinations, on ethylene
production of pre-climateric, climacteric, and
post-climateric apple tissue slices*

ABA stimulates ethylene production in preclimacteric and
early climacteric tissue slices but subsequently has little
effect on ethylene production in aging tissue slices from apples.
These data also show that the influence of a hormone may be
considerably altered by combinations with other hormones. Thus,
IAA, which stimulates ethylene production in climacteric and
post climacteric tissue does not stimulate but inhibits when
combined with IPA and GA.

Feedback Relationship Between Ethylene and Other Plant
Hormones. If ethylene production in ripening fruit is an index
of aging and senescence, then its suppression should result in
retardation, or antagonism to ripening, aging, and senescence.

At the preclimacteric stage of development, just prior to the
rise in ethylene production, the concentrations of auxins,
gibberellins, and cytokinins are assumed to be very low.
Addition of large amounts of these growth hormones tend to
suppress ethylene production. However, after ethylene production
starts and accelerates, only cytokinin consistently suppresses
ethylene production. This suggests a special antagonism between cytokinins and ethylene production. This antagonism is
consistent with the well known retardation effect of cytokinins
on loss of chlorophyll and protein in aging leaves (19).

The relative large scale production of ethylene by aging
tissues, after the ripening reactions are fully in motion, raises
the question as to whether or not continuous presence of
ethylene is necessary for the progress of aging and senescence.
Fairly large amounts of ethylene are produced even from fully
senescent tissues. This might suggest a loss of control over
ethylene production. Such an interpretation would mean that ethylene produced by post climacteric tissue is a by-product of aging metabolism wherein control of hormonal synthesis is lost.
However, the fact that ethylene production in post-climacteric
tissues can be suppressed by a cytokinin suggests that it is
always under physiological control and hormonally regulated.

Scheme for Interrelationship between Ethylene and Other
Hormones. From these data and others presented below, one can
arrive at a simple scheme for the antagonistic and supportive
relationships of these hormones in metabolism. Figure 5 shows
hypothetical interconnections between the various hormones
as they relate to cell division, growth, development and
senescence during the life cycle of a plant or organ.

Two categories of hormones may be distinguished: (1) the
auxins, gibberellins, and cytokinins, which are mainly associated
with growth and development by regulating cell division, enlargement and maturation, and (2) ethylene and ABA, which generally
tend to oppose or antagonize the activities of category 1 hormones and to function mainly in senescence and aging. During
growth and development category 2 hormones may oppose the
excessive actions of category 1 hormones, which may otherwise
cause distorted and abnormal growth effects. These hormones
may exist in feedback loops. Auxins are known to stimulate
ethylene production (20) and, conversely, ethylene is known to
reduce auxin levels (21) (22). Gibberellins and ABA are known
to oppose each other in their influence on induction of α-amylase
synthesis in the barley aleurone layer (23). Cytokinins and ABA
are known to oppose each other in transpiration phenomena with
respect to regulating opening and closing of stomata (24).
Cytokinin is known to both stimulate (25) and depress (26)
ethylene production in plants. I do not know of an opposing
action of ethylene on cytokinin synthesis or activity but such
may very likely exist.

INTERACTIONS BETWEEN PLANT HORMONES

FEEDBACK LOOPS

CATEGORY 1   CATEGORY 2

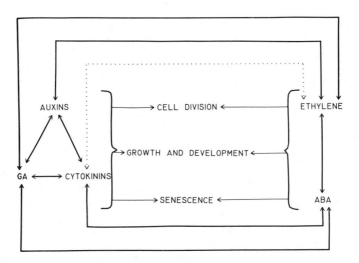

Figure 5. Hypothetical scheme of linkages and feedback relationships between category 1 and category 2 plant hormones related to their overall influences on growth, development, maturation, and senescence

The antagonism between gibberellins and ethylene has been well documented. For example, they are antagonistic in regulating the growth of cells in the subhook region of epicotyls of etiolated seedlings (27). Whereas GA at 10^{-5}M causes excessive cell elongation and ethylene at 0.5 ppm which causes the formation of isodiametric, short, squat cells, the combination of both hormones results in the formation of almost normal shaped cells.

Another type of hormonal interaction is illustrated by the complementary or supplementary effects of two category-1 hormones on apple shape and size. The treatment of North Carolina Red Delicious apples (grown in warm Spring weather) with gibberellins A_4 and A_7 and a cytokinin (about 25 ppm each) just after full bloom, causes them to develop morphologically like Northwest Red Delicious apples (grown in cool Spring weather). The excess cytokinins increases cell division in the calyx lobes, and the gibberellins accentuate elongation of the fruit. The final product is an elongated fruit with well developed calyx lobes, in contrast to the shorter and flatter fruit obtained without hormonal treatment (28).

The specific mode of action of these hormones at the molecular level is unknown. However, a science of Plant Pharmacology is developing based on a conceptional understanding of the known effects of plant hormones and their interactions. An example of plant pharmacology is shown in Table II, wherein a combination of commercial growth regulators was used to reinforce and antagonize each other's action, and thereby produce a desired effect.

Table II   Effect of Ethephon, Alone and in Combinations with Daminozide and Auxin, on Abscission, Firmness and color of McIntosh Apples (From Edgerton and Blanpied (29))

Treatment[1]	Harvest Date	Drop %	Firm (lb)	Red Color %
Daminozide	Sept.24,1968	2	16.3	56
Daminozide + Ethephon	Sept.24,1968	77	15.5	67
Daminozide + Ethephon+TP	Sept.24,1968	3	14.7	91
Control	Sept.24,1968	29	14.5	51

[1] Daminozide applied at 2000 ppm on Aug. 9, 1968.
Ethephon applied at 250 ppm on Sept. 15, 1968
TP applied at 20 ppm on Sept. 15, 1968

Daminozide (succinic acid 2,2-dimethyl hydrazide) is a growth retardant which antagonizes ethylene in some reactions but also tends to reinforce other ethylene effects. Applied to mature apples on the tree, daminozide reduces fruit drop and increases firmness. These effects indicate retardation of ripening. However, red color formation is also increased, which is an effect associated with accelerated ripening. When daminozide is applied with ethephon, an ethylene-forming compound[(2-chloroethyl)phosphonic acid], red color formation is further enhanced, but fruit drop is considerably increased. By addition of an auxin, TP[(2,4,5-trichlorophenoxy)propionic acid] to the spray, fruit drop is almost completely eliminated and red color is enhanced even more (29). Thus, these plant growth regulators, which may be considered to represent ethylene, auxin, and a compound that appears to have characteristics of both hormones, the desired measure of retardation and acceleration of ripening was obtained.

Production and Inhibition of Ethylene. Now I would like to illustrate how knowledge about a plant hormone can be used to control and regulate its action. Methionine is the precursor of ethylene in plant tissues (30). Therefore, any compound which blocks methionine metabolism might be expected to inhibit ethylene biosynthesis. Rhizobitoxine was recognized as an inhibitor of methionine biosynthesis (31), as were its analogues shown in Figure 6 (32).

(1) CH_2-CH-CH_2-O-$\overset{H}{\underset{|}{C}}$=C-CH-COOH
      | | | |
      OH NH_2 H NH_2

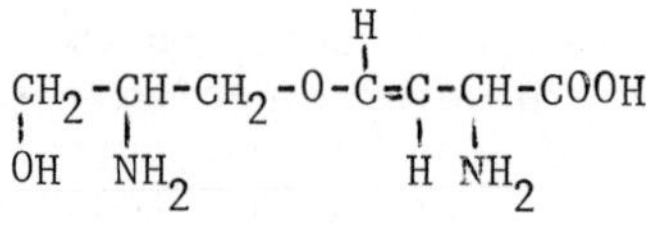

L-2-amino-4-(2-amino-3-hydroxypropoxy)-<u>trans</u>-3-butenoic acid
(Rhizobitoxine)

---

(2) CH_2-CH_2-O-$\overset{H}{\underset{|}{C}}$=C-CH-COOH
      | | |
      NH_2 **H** NH_2

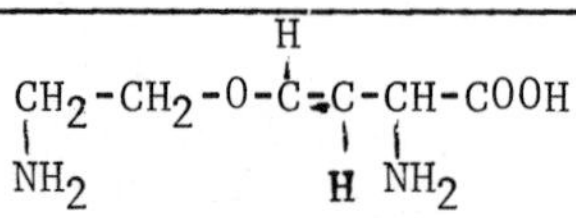

L-2-amino-4-(2-aminoethoxy)-<u>trans</u>-3-butenoic acid

---

(3) CH_3-O-$\overset{H}{\underset{|}{C}}$=C-CH-COOH
                 H NH_2

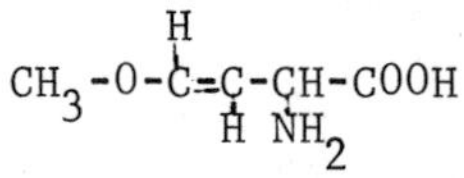

L-2-amino-4-methoxy-<u>trans</u>-3-butenoic acid

---

(4) CH_3S-$CH_2$$CH_2$-CH-COOH
                          |
                         NH_2

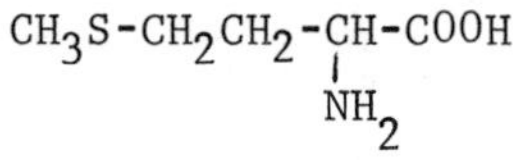

L-Methionine

Figure 6.   Enol ether substituted amino acid analogues of methionine which are inhibitors of ethylene production in plants

These enol ether-substituted amino acids are natural products isolated from the fermentation broths of <u>Rhizobium japonicum</u> (rhizobitoxine) (<u>31</u>), <u>Pseudomonas aeruginosa</u> (methoxy analogue) (<u>33</u>) and a species of <u>Streptomyces</u> (ethoxy analogue) (<u>34</u>).

  Apple fruit, infiltrated with rhizobitoxine and stored at 0° for 11 weeks, exhibited much reduced ethylene production and respiration (<u>35</u>). This strongly suggests that ripening and aging of the fruit was retarded by the inhibition of ethylene production. Aging was also retarded in orchids held in solutions of the ethoxy and methoxy analogues. These experiments suggest that metabolic blocks of the biosynthesis of ethylene can retard the aging process. However, in some tissues, such as tomatoes, rhizobitoxine does not block all ethylene production. There is an indication of a second pathway of ethylene production or a means of circumventing the rhizobitoxine block. Therefore, there is the necessity for an additional chemical to block either the second pathway or the route around the ethylene block. Perhaps a combination of rhizobitoxine, cytokinin, and a free radical quencher can act to retard the aging process in plants.

I believe agricultural chemistry in the next century will enter a new era in which the science of Plant Pharmacology will be developed. From knowledge of the mode of action of the plant hormones a series of compounds and combinations of these will be formulated to control and regulate plant growth and development, for human needs.

Literature Cited

1. Biale, J.B., Advances in Food Research (1960) 10, 293-354.
2. Lieberman, M., Physiol. Vegetale (1975) 13, 489-499.
3. Biale, J.B. and Young, R.E., Endeavour (1962) 21, 164-174.
4. Burg, S.P. and Burg, E.A., Science (1965) 148, 1190-1196.
5. Monselise, S.P., "Colloque Intern. C.N.R.S. No. 238, Facteurs et Regulation De La Maturation Des Fruits 97-103, Paris (1975).
6. Coombe, B.G., Annual Review of Plant Physiol. (1976) 27, 507-528.
7. Gazit, S., Jour. Amer. Soc. Hort. Science (1970) 95, 229-231.
8. Coombe, B.G. and Hale, C.R., Plant Physiol. (1973) 51, 629-634.
9. Hale, C.R., Coombe, B.G., and Hawker, J.S., Plant Physiol. (1970) 45,620-623.
10. Tingua, P.O. and Young, R.E., Plant Physiol. (1975) 55, 937-940.
11. Zimmerman, R.H., Lieberman, M., and Broome, O.C., Plant Physiol. (1976) (in press).
12. Lieberman, M. and Kunishi, A.T. in "Plant Growth Substances 1970" edited by D.J. Carr, 549-560, Springer-Verlag, Berlin, 1971.
13. Dilley, D.R., HortScience (1969) 4, 111-114.

14. Powell, L.E. HortScience (1970) 5, 326.
15. Hiron, R.W.P. and Wright, S.T.C.,Jour. Expt. Botany (1973) 24,769-781.
16. Hatcher, E.S.J., Ann. Botany (1959) 23,409-423.
17. Varga, A. and Bruinsma, J., Jour. Hort. Science (1974) 49, 135-142.
18. Bruinsma, J., Knegt, E., and Varga, A. in Colloque Intern. C.N.R.S. No. 238, Facteurs et Regulation De La Maturation Des Fruits, 193-198, Paris (1975).
19. Richmond, A.E. and Lang, A. Science (1957) 125, 650-651.
20. Lieberman, M., and Kunishi, A.T. Plant Physiol.(1975) 55, 1074-1078.
21. Michener, H.D., Amer. Jour. Botany (1938) 25 711-720.
22. Valdovinos, J.G., Ernest, L.C. and Henry, E.W. Plant Physiol. (1967) 42, 1803-1806.
23. Chrispeels, M.J. and J.E. Varner. Nature (1966) 212, 1066-1067.

24. Mizrahi, Y., Blumenfeld, A., Richmond, A.E. Plant Physiology (1970) 46, 169-171.

25. Fuchs, Y. and Lieberman, M. Plant Physiol. (1968) 43, 2029-2036.

26. Lieberman, M. and Sloger, M. Plant Physiol. (1975) 56, 56 (Supplement).

27. Stewart, R.N., Lieberman, M. and Kunishi, A.T., Plant Physiol. (1974) 54, 1-5.

28. Williams, M.W. and Stahly, E.A., Jour. Amer. Soc. Hort. Sci. (1969) 94, 17-18.

29. Edgerton, L.J. and Blanpied, G.D., Jour. Amer. Soc. Hort. Science (1970) 95, 664-666.

30. Lieberman, M., Kunishi, A.T. Mapson, L.W. and Wardale, D.A., Plant Physiol. (1966) 41, 376-382.

31. Owens, L.D., Science (1969) 165, 18-25.

32. Owens, L.D., Lieberman, M. and Kunishi, A.T. Plant Physiol. (1971) 48, 1-4.

33. Scannell, J.P., Pruess, D.L., Denny, T.C., Sells, L.H., Williams, T. and Stempel, A., The Jour. of Antibiotics (1972) 25, 122-127.

34. Pruess, D.L., Scannell, J.P., Kellett, M., Ax, H.A., Jancek, J., Williams, T.H. and Stempel, A., The Jour. of Antibiotics (1974) 27, 229-233.

35. Lieberman, M., Kunishi, A.T. and Owens, L.D., Colloque Internation. C.N.R.S. No. 238 "Facteurs et Regulation De La Maturation Des Fruits" 161-170, Paris (1975).

Growth Regulators in Flowering and Fruit Development

L. C. LUCKWILL

Long Ashton Research Station, University of Bristol, England

Some of the earliest practical applications of growth regulators related to flowering and fruit development and many of the pioneers were American. Prominent amongst them were Felix Gustafson of Ann Arbor, Michigan, who in 1936 was the first to induce parthenocarpic fruits with auxins; Gardner, Marth and Batjer of the USDA who in 1939 pioneered the use of 1-naphthalene-acetic acid for pre-harvest drop control in apples - a method still in regular use today; and Clark and Kerns in Hawaii who used the same substance in 1942 to induce synchronous flowering in pineapples.

In general, plant growth regulators mimic the action of genes and their special value and significance in the perennial fruit crops is that they enable us to do today what might take decades or even centuries to accomplish by conventional breeding techniques. Most pomologists would agree that it would be highly desirable, and technically feasible, to breed an apple variety that would set fruit without pollination, that would not be sub-ject to biennial bearing or need thinning, whose fruits would not drop from the tree before harvest, which could be readily propa-gated from cuttings and, above all, one that would partition a greater proportion of its assimilates into fruit, as opposed to vegetative growth. No one, however, is likely to embark on such an ambitious project because of the enormous time scale involved and the impossibility of predicting the needs of the industry that far ahead. So we are left with the alternative of using growth regulators to overcome the present genotype deficiencies of the crop - a subject which forms the central theme of this review.

Flower Initiation

The most obvious genotypic deficiency of the apple is the tendency to produce light and heavy crops in alternate years.

This phenomenon, which varies in intensity in different varieties, is characteristic of many other perennial fruit crops in which flower initials are laid down in the summer of the year before flowering. The sparse flower induction which accompanies a heavy crop was formerly attributed to depletion of the carbohydrate and nitrogenous reserves of the tree: but, whilst alternate bearing may have developed as a means by which the tree could conserve its food reserves, the control mechanisms are clearly hormonal in nature.

Leaves promote flower induction. As in so many biological processes a balance of a promoter and an inhibitor seems to be involved. In the pome fruits the flower promoting influence comes from the rosette of leaves subtending the terminal bud in which initiation occurs. The greater the total area of the subtending leaves, the greater the chance of the bud becoming floral. In plants where flowering is induced by the photoperiod there is strong evidence that, after induction by the critical dark period the leaves produce a flowering hormone (1) which, however, has never been unequivocally isolated and identified. Although flowering is not induced by photoperiod in the apple, it is possible that the same or a similar type of substance is produced. Another possibility, yet to be explored, is that leaves function only indirectly in flower induction by aiding the movement into the spur of hormones carried in the transpiration stream. The most likely type of hormones to be involved here would be the group of substituted aminopurines known as cytokinins, particularly zeatin (6-(4-hydroxy-3-methylbut-2-enyl)-aminopurine) and its ribotide, which are believed to originate in the root and are found in relatively high concentrations in the xylem sap, particularly in the early part of the season (2). There is, as yet, no direct evidence that flower initiation in apple can be promoted by applied cytokinins, though it is of interest to note that in Perilla Beever and Woolhouse (3) found increases in cytokinin produced in the roots at the time of floral induction. Rather stronger evidence of cytokinin involvement came from Mullins (4) who showed that, in the absence of roots, inflorescence development in grape vines can be stimulated by the application of 6-benzylaminopurine (BAP) and 6-(benzylamino)-9-(2-tetrahydropyranyl)-9H-purine (PBA), and from Skene (5) who found that chlormequat, which promotes flower initiation in the vine, also increases the concentration of endogenous cytokinin in the bleeding sap. Monselise and Halevy (6) have shown that benzothiazole-2-oxyacetate, a compound with cytokinin-like properties, though different in chemical structure, will promote flowering in Citrus. However, the present evidence for the involvement of cytokinins in flower initiation in pome fruits, like that for the existence of a specific flowering hormone, remains circumstantial and further experimental evidence is needed.

<u>Seeds inhibit flower induction</u>. The data of Huet (7)
illustrate the effect of leaves in promoting flower initiation in
the seedless Williams (Bartlett) pear. Although normally seedless
in warm climates this pear will produce seeds if cross-pollinated,
and the same experiment illustrates the dramatic effect which
these seeds have in inhibiting flower initiation. This effect of
seeds was first noted by Tumanov and Gareev (8), and confirmed
by the work of Chan and Cain (9). Luckwill (10) suggested that
the effect was due to endogenous gibberellins which are present
in very high concentrations in seeds at certain stages of
development.

Evidence that gibberellins are the operative hormones
involved is partly indirect and partly direct. Indirect evidence
comes from the observation that young fruitlets only become
inhibitory to floral initiation at 5 to 6 weeks after full bloom,
which is also the time they start to produce large amounts of
GA_4 and GA_7 (10): (11), an observation, incidentally, which
explains why fruit thinning needs to be done within this time
limit if return bloom for the following year is to be increased
(Table I). The direct evidence is the fact that in apple and
many other species (strawberry, plum, cherry, pear, almond,
apricot, orange, <u>Fuchsia</u>) sprays of gibberellic acid applied
shortly after bloom will reduce or completely inhibit flowering
the following year. This inhibiting effect of GA on flower

TABLE I

Apple cv. Emneth Early. Effect of fruit removal at
different times on flower initiation in bourse buds

No. of weeks after full bloom when trees were de-fruited	No. of fruit buds formed as % of those the previous year	Gibberellin content of seeds μg GA_3/1000 seeds
0	123	–
2	146	< 1.0
4	150	< 1.0
6	59	3.2
8	11	19.2
10	8	27.1
Not de-fruited	6	–

initiation appears in direct contrast to its role in long day
rosette type plants (e.g. cabbage, radish, lettuce, etc.) in
which GA will promote flowering under non-inductive conditions.
The general situation seems to be that gibberellin promotes
induction in those species which flower on long shoots, but
inhibits it in species which flower on short shoots, suggesting

that the action of the hormone is not on induction per se, but
rather on the vegetative phase which precedes it (12): (1).

If gibberellins produced in seeds are the main cause of
flower inhibition and hence of biennial bearing in fruit trees,
we might expect to find differences in gibberellin production
between strongly biennial and more regular cropping varieties.
In fact, although varieties differ in their gibberellin production, no correlation with biennial cropping tendencies exists
(10). An alternative and more likely explanation is suggested by
the work of G.V. Hoad at Long Ashton (13), which shows that in
the strongly biennial Laxton's Superb a much larger quantity of
gibberellin can be collected in an agar block placed on the cut
base of the pedicel than in the less biennial Cox's Orange
Pippin, suggesting that gibberellin transport is a key factor in
biennial cropping.

Chemical control of biennial flowering. On the basis of
these hypotheses we can suggest seven possible ways in which
growth regulators might be used to control biennial flowering
and cropping. Four of these are treatments which could be
applied in the 'on' (fruiting) year to increase flower induction,
and three are designed to decrease flower induction and would
therefore be applied in the 'off' (non-fruiting) year. To
increase flowering we might:-

1. Block GA synthesis. There are a number of anti-
gibberellin compounds which probably function in this way. On
apples the most effective is succinic acid-2,2-dimethylhydrazide
(daminozide, SADH, 'Alar'). This compound is widely used for
inducing early cropping, an extreme example of which is the
'meadow orchard', an experimental system of apple production in
which trees, planted 12 x 18 inches apart are sprayed with
daminozide to induce flower initiation in their first year of
growth (14). The effect of daminozide on flower induction
(Table II) can be enhanced by mixing it with 2-chloroethyl-

TABLE II

Additive effects of daminozide and ethephon on the induction of
flowers on one-year-old trees of apple cv. Cox's Orange Pippin.
Mean number of blossom clusters/tree as a result of a single
spray applied the previous summer

Ethephon (ppm)	Daminozide (ppm)			
	0	625	1250	2500
0	3	8	10	12
625	9	11	13	17
1250	10	12	15	22
2500	16	19	23	21

phosphonic acid (ethephon). While it is most effective on non-fruiting trees, daminozide will also increase flower induction on fruiting trees, but where the crop is very heavy, as it often is in 'on' years of strongly biennial varieties, its effect is quite small. It is therefore not very useful for the control of biennialism.

  2. Block GA transport. A number of growth regulators are known which will block the transport of gibberellin from seed to bourse, and compounds such as 2,3,5-tri-iodobenzoic acid (TIBA) are effective in permitting flower induction to take place even in the presence of a heavy crop. But the flowers so induced set poorly and no increase in crop is obtained, probably because the food reserves of the tree have been depleted (Table III). So again, this is not a practical method.

TABLE III

Effect of TIBA 150 ppm applied as a spray to heavy cropping trees of apple cv. George Cave in 1969

	Control	TIBA	Significance
Blossom clusters per tree in 1970	253	611	Significant at < 1.0%
Crop per tree (kg)	27.6	35.4	Not significant

  3. Induce seedless fruit. As we have seen, seedless fruits do not inhibit flower initiation. In many varieties of apple and pear seedless fruits can be induced by applying growth regulators under conditions where natural pollination has failed or been prevented. But the most effective growth regulator is GA, particularly when mixed with the right proportion of an auxin, such as 2-naphthoxyacetic acid (2-NOA) and a cytokinin. Hence, the treatment which induces parthenocarpy is itself inhibitory to flower induction.

  4. Thin fruitlets. This is the most practical and widely used 'on' year treatment to even out cropping from year to year. Naphthalene compounds, particularly 1-naphthylacetic acid (NAA) and its amide (NAm) and the insecticide carbaryl (1-naphthyl methyl carbamate) have been widely used for many years to induce the abscission of fruitlets: but timing is critical and effects can vary widely from season to season depending, amongst other factors, on rate of uptake and metabolism. Recently there has been much interest in the possibility of using ethephon for fruit thinning but, here again, attention to time of application is required to avoid complete de-fruiting of the tree as fruitlets abscind much more readily in June, when natural auxin production is low, than in May or July (Table IV).

TABLE IV

The varying sensitivity of apple cv. Cox's Orange Pippin to
ethephon applied at different times as a fruit thinning agent.
% fruit drop during the 11 days following spraying

| | Ethephon conc. (ppm) | | |
	0	200	1000
May	2.5	2.8	41.5
June	11.5	32.0	92.5
July	2.5	15.0	15.0
August	2.7	10.0	46.0
September	5.0	12.8	49.5

'Off' year treatments which have been tried in order to
decrease flower initiation include:-

5. Reduce leaf area. Application of 1% NaDNOC early in the
season to scorch the young foliage is a possible way of reducing
flower induction; however, an unacceptable amount of leaf
damage must be inflicted to get a worth-while reduction in bloom
the following year, and this leaf area is needed to build up the
food reserves of the tree.

6. Apply GA. An attractive possibility is to spray the tree
with GA in the 'off' year to prevent excessive flower initiation,
particularly as this does not affect the photosynthetic
efficiency of the foliage. Unfortunately, even at high concentrations, GA has proved ineffective on completely 'off' year
or deblossomed trees, although it will inhibit flowering when
applied to fruiting trees. The explanation of this paradox is
not clear but it may be that the gibberellin has to combine with
some second factor from the fruit itself before it can become
inhibitory to flower induction (15).

7. Apply other flower inhibitors. Besides gibberellin, a
number of other compounds are known which will reduce fruit bud
formation in apple. They include meta-tolylphthalamic acid and
xanthine (10) and the herbicides bromouracil and thiouracil used
in low (50 ppm) concentration (16), but none of these have yet
found commercial application.

To sum up - it would seem that reduction of the 'on year'
crop by blossom or fruit thinning with growth regulators remains
the most practical way of controlling biennial bearing in apples:
but we still need more reliable and consistent fruit thinning
agents.

Fruit Development

'Direct action' hypothesis. In the wild, the fruit is
simply the packaging for the all-important seeds on which the
future of the species depends, so it is not surprising in
cultivated fruits to find that seed and fruit development are
closely linked. Although amongst cultivated fruits there are
notable exceptions, the general rule is - no seed development,
no fruit. Moreover, the number and disposition of seeds in the
fruit determine its size and shape, its liability to drop before
it is fully grown and often its biochemistry and storage properties. These facts have long been known. Later it was discovered that by applying growth regulators of the auxin or
gibberellin type, seedless fruits of many species could be
induced to develop without the usual preliminaries of pollination
and fertilization. The next discovery was that developing
(though not mature) seeds were themselves rich sources of
hormones such as cytokinins, auxins and gibberellins. These
hormones are produced in the seed, not at a steady rate, but in
strong flushes in well marked succession corresponding with the
development of successive tissues within the seed - first the
nucellus, then the free nuclear endosperm, the cellular endosperm
and finally the embryo itself. At this point it seemed
reasonable to propose the hypothesis that the fruit tissues grew
in direct response to hormonal stimuli emanating from the seeds.
In particular, it seemed logical to assume that cytokinins, in
which the free-nuclear endosperm is rich, were associated with
the early phases of fruit growth in which cell division is dominant, whilst gibberellins, which appear later, were responsible
for stimulating cell enlargement. Unfortunately, this simple
hypothesis was not substantiated by more detailed investigations
which, with few exceptions, showed no close correlation between
the peaks of hormone production in the seed and the various
phases of fruit growth. In the apple, for instance, there is no
apparent correlation between the percentage increase in volume
of the fruit each week and the concentration of gibberellin in
the seeds (Fig.2).

'Competing sinks' hypothesis. Although a few adherents of
the 'direct action hypothesis' (including most text books!) still
fight a rearguard action, most workers in this field have now
transferred their allegiance to the hypothesis of 'competing
sinks'. This supposes that the factor normally limiting the
growth of an ovary into a fruit is not the minute quantities of
hormone required for cell division and cell expansion, but rather
the carbohydrates and amino acids needed for building new tissues
which are required in large quantities. These have to be
attracted from the general pool against the competing demands of
the vegetative growing points. Although the mechanism is obscure
there is strong evidence that metabolites and mineral elements

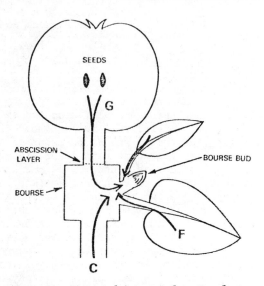

Figure 1. Hormonal factors influencing flower initiation in bourse bud of apple. G = gibberellins, C = cytokinins, F = florigin?

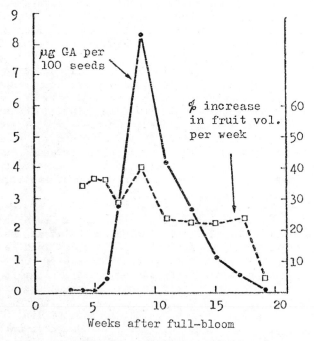

Figure 2. Gibberellin production in seeds of apple compared with rate of increase in fruit volume (cv. Cox's Orange Pippin)

move preferentially toward sites of high hormone concentration.
Of the three major groups of growth promoters auxins are of
prime importance in stimulating this hormone-directed transport,
but combination with gibberellins or cytokinins, or both, results
in strong synergistic action (17). On this hypothesis the high
concentrations of hormones found in the seeds are necessary in
order to create a strong physiological sink capable of competing
with the stem and root apices. The main experimental evidence
for this hypothesis comes from experiments in which the competition between vegetative and fruit growth is partially
relieved by removing all the shoot tips quite early in the
season. If the suppression of shoot growth is very severe it
is possible to induce parthenocarpic or seedless development of
the fruit by this method (18). In other situations fruit set
can be greatly enhanced through an increased retention of fruitlets which otherwise would have dropped off because their seed
content was too low to enable them to compete. The data of
Quinlan and Preston (19) confirm the earlier findings of Abbott
and suggest that we have here a potentially valuable technique
for improving the cropping of apples at the expense of shoot
growth, much of which is not required and will, in any event, be
removed in winter pruning. But manual removal of shoot tips is
hardly practical on an orchard scale; what we need is a growth
regulator which will arrest shoot growth without causing un-
desirable side effects on the fruit. Daminozide has proved
quite effective on young trees, when applied shortly after petal
fall and is now used as a routine spray in the 'meadow orchard'
to increase fruit set (Table V). Dramatic increases in yield are

TABLE V

Promotion of fruit-set in apple by suppressing shoot growth
with daminozide 2500 ppm applied at petal-fall stage.
Mean of 100 trees

Variety	Fruits per 100 blossom clusters Control	Daminozide
Lord Lambourne	10	23
Egremont Russet	17	58

obtained on these small trees, but the method is not so effective
on the more conventional type of tree. Other growth regulators
which have been tested include (2-chloroethyl) trimethylammonium
chloride (CCC, Chlormequat, Cycocel), Ancymidol, maleic hydrazide, morphactins and fatty acid esters, but all produce un-
desirable side effects on leaf or fruit growth or skin finish:
nevertheless the principle is established as a sound one - all

we need is the right growth regulator!

Induction of parthenocarpy. An alternative method of
improving fruit set, or of completely circumventing the need for
pollination, is by hormone spraying to induce parthenocarpy, a
method which has found commercial application in the production
of seedless grapes, in figs and tomatoes, and also in pears,
where GA sprays have been used to save the crop after the flowers
or fruitlets have been damaged by spring frosts (20). In species
which respond to hormone sprays it is often found that synthetic
auxins, gibberellins and sometimes cytokinins, are equally
effective in stimulating fruit growth, and that the three
different types of hormones, when applied in mixtures, show
synergistic activity, an observation which suggests that the
mechanism of action is similar to that suggested for the
endogenous hormones, viz. creating mobilization centres for
metabolites rather than direct stimulation of tissue growth.
The apple has proved one of the most difficult subjects for the
chemical induction of parthenocarpy, and for this reason the work
of Schwabe and his co-workers at Wye College in England is of
great interest and potential value to the fruit industry. They
have developed a triple hormone fruit-setting spray containing
gibberellic acid (600 ppm), the synthetic auxin 2-naphthoxyacetic
acid (40 ppm) and the cytokinin benzyladenine (300 ppm) - more
recently replaced by diphenylurea (21). Trials on Cox's Orange
Pippin over eight years have given consistent increases in yield
on both pollinated and unpollinated flowers. On sweet cherry
(cvs Early Rivers and Merton Glory) very spectacular yield
increases have been achieved and the same mixture has given
promising results on European plum (cv. Victoria). Apart from
the possible side effects of this spray on flower production for
the following year, the high cost of gibberellic acid would
probably make the treatment uneconomic at the present time.

Control of fruit ripening and abscission. The ripening of
fruits such as the apple which show a respiration climacteric
has long been known to be associated with ethylene, and the
advent of compounds such as ethephon, which release ethylene
within the tissues of the plant, has given us an unprecedented
degree of control over the ripening process. It enables fruit
growers to harvest high quality apples earlier in the season
than would otherwise be possible and to spread their labour
requirements for harvest over a longer period than would otherwise be possible. Ethephon alone will induce abscission and to
counteract this it needs to be applied in combination with an
auxin, such as 2,4,5-TP, or with daminozide. A combination of
750 ppm a.i. ethephon and 15 ppm 2,4,5-TP applied about 10 days
before the desired harvest date has proved highly effective on
early varieties such as Worcester Pearmain (Table VI) and Early

Macintosh, whereas main crop varieties tend to react more slowly. The rate of reaction is a function, not only of variety, but also of temperature and degree of water stress and, in practice,

TABLE VI

Effect of ethephon in combination with daminozide or 2,4,5-TP on the quality of Worcester Pearmain apples harvested on Aug. 25th

	Control	Ethephon + daminozide	Ethephon + 2,4,5-TP
% of fruits with ¾ or more surface colour	0	68	60
Relative amount of anthocyanin	170	270	220
Starch content (on a 1-6 scale)	1.4	1.9	4.4
Pressure resistance (lb)	18.7	18.7	17.0
% pre-harvest drop	8.3	1.6	8.6

growers are recommended to follow the progress of ripening by a simple starch/iodine test (22).

Other compounds, such as benzyl-isothiocyanate (23), act as antiethylene agents - probably by blocking natural biosynthesis - and these may find applications for delaying ripening of fruits and perhaps prolonging their storage life.

Conclusions

Growth regulators clearly have many uses and potential uses in fruit growing. Although I have concentrated on the apple, on which most work has been done, a similar story could have been told for almost any other cultivated fruit in which growth regulators can modify cropping behaviour through effects on flower induction and fruit set. I have stressed how local concentrations of endogenous hormones, such as occur in shoot tips and young seeds, regulate the distribution of photosynthates by creating physiological 'sinks', the relative strengths of which determine the proportion of the tree's resources which it devotes to fruit production as opposed to vegetative growth, much of which is unwanted and is destined to be pruned away the following winter.

Some progress toward the control of assimilate partitioning by means of growth regulators has been made, and one practical outcome is the novel system of apple production known as the 'meadow orchard'. It is probably in this field of assimilate partitioning that the greatest potential for the future use of growth regulators lies.

Literature Cited

1. Chailakhyan, M. Kh. Fiziologiya Rast. (1971) 18(2), 348–357.
2. Luckwill, L.C. and Whyte, P. S.C.I. Monogr. (1968) No.31, 87–101.
3. Beever, J.E. and Woolhouse, H.W. Nature (New Biology) Lond. (1973) 246, 31–32.
4. Mullins, M.G. J. exp. Bot. (1967) 18, 206–214.
5. Skene, K.G.M. Science (1968) 159, 1477–1478.
6. Monselise, S.P. and Halevy, A.H. Proc. Amer. Soc. hort. Sci. (1964) 84, 141–146.
7. Huet, J. Physiologie Végétale (1972) 10(3), 529–545.
8. Tumanov, I.I. and Gareev, E.Z. Trudy. Inst. Fiziol. Rast. Timirjazeva 7, 22–108.
9. Chan, B.G. and Cain, J.C. Proc. Amer. Soc. hort. Sci. (1967) 91, 63–67.
10. Luckwill, L.C. "Physiology of Tree Crops" 237–253. Academic Press, London and New York (1970).
11. Luckwill, L.C., Weaver, P. and MacMillan, J. J. hort. Sci. (1969) 44, 413–424.
12. Luckwill, L.C. Proc. XIX Int. Hort. Congr. Warsaw (1975) III, 235–245.
13. Hoad, G.V. Rep. Long Ashton Res. Stn for 1975 (1976) 43.
14. Luckwill, L.C. and Child, R.D. Acta Horticulturae (1973) 34(1), 213–220.
15. Fulford, R.M. Rep. East Malling Res. Stn for 1972 (1973) 93.
16. Buban, T. Bot. Közl. (1969) 56(4), 251–256.
17. Seth, A.K. and Wareing, P.F. J. Exp. Bot. (1967) 18, 65–77.
18. Abbott, D.L. Ann. appl. Biol. (1960) 48, 434–438.
19. Quinlan, J.D. and Preston, A.P. J. hort. Sci. (1971) 46 525–534.
20. Luckwill, L.C. Rep. Long Ashton Res. Stn for 1961 (1962) 61–66.
21. Goldwin, G.K. and Schwabe, W.W. Proc. 12th British Weed Control Conf. (1974) 131–136.
22. Luckwill, L.C. and Child, R.D. Expl Hort. (1973) 25, 1–6.
23. Patil, S.S. and Tang, Chung-Shih, Plant Physiol. (1974) 53, 585–588.

INDEX

P

Q

R

S

T